£7.95

CU00687186

Published 1984
by Scarthin Books, Cromford, Derbyshire DE4 3QF
Reprinted 2008

© Cliff Williams 1984

www.scarthinbooks.com

e-mail: clare@scarthinbooks.com

Typesetting and layout by CJWT Solutions, St Helens WA9 4TX

ISBN 978-0-90775-807-5

Printed by Lightning Source

Clay Cross Tunnel : The North Portal

Acknowledgements

I am indebted to the following people and institutions for their help and kindness in assisting me with my research :-

Miss Joan Sinar, County Archivist for Derbyshire; Mrs. Jean Radford, Local Studies Librarian, Matlock; John Lilly, Local Studies Librarian, Chesterfield; Mrs. Anne Mellors, Local Studies Librarian, Derby Central Library; and their respective staffs.

The Public Records Office, Kew;   The House of Lords Record Office;   Wakefield Library H.Q.

I am also indebted to Dick Childs, Clay Cross Company; to the late Michael Richard Hale for some photographs; and particularly to Trev Cave, who first encouraged me to undertake this work; and to the publishers for their interest and advice.

Finally, I should like to thank my wife Anne, and daughters Anne-Marie and Rachel for their patience during the time it has taken to complete this book.

Driving The
Clay Cross Tunnel

Navvies on the
Derby/Leeds Railway

Cliff Williams

Scarthin Books
Cromford, Derbyshire
2008

DRIVING THE CLAY CROSS TUNNEL

Contents

INTRODUCTION

Chapter One   *CONTRACTORS*
Planning the route
Opposition
The Act is passed
Winning contracts
The work begins
Sub-contractors and tommyshops

Chapter Two   *THE NAVVIES AT WORK*
Pay disputes
The work proceeds
Accidents and injuries
Operations and treatments
The workhouse and Sick Clubs

Chapter Three   *THE NAVVIES AT HOME*
Homes
Womenfolk
Pastimes
Booze
Fighting
Profaning the Sabbath

Chapter Four   *LAW AND ORDER*
Problems of peace-keeping
Anglo-Irish Rivalry and the Rotherham Riots
Navvy or Navy?
The locals fight back
Supplementing their diet
Railway policemen

Chapter Five   *THE WORK COMPLETED*
Celebrations
Effect on roads
Metamorphosis

INTRODUCTION

The turnpike road network that spread its web throughout Derbyshire during the eighteenth and nineteenth centuries, together with the canal systems, had a profound influence on the industrial and economic growth of the county. During this time an enormous geographical expansion of its markets had taken place, and an increasing demand for coal was being created by a rapidly rising industrial system. The final phase of this expansion, however, had to await the further development of the railways.

In May 1833, an Act was passed for the making of the Birmingham Company's railway and about the same time the Midland Counties Railway Company were to make a connecting line from Rugby to Derby. It was now considered imperative that a company should be incorporated to continue this line of communication from Derby to Leeds.

This North Midland Railway (N.M.R.) line ran a distance of 72 miles from Derby to Leeds, and had a tremendous impact on the county. Undoubtedly, the place most affected by this new line in Derbyshire was Clay Cross. This village was transformed virtually overnight from a peaceful agricultural village into a rumbustious, dynamic industrial town. Its metamorphosis was conceived early in 1837, with the driving of the N.M.R. line and the Clay Cross Tunnel that runs directly under the centre of the town; and the simultaneous establishment of George Stephenson's Colliery Company at Clay Cross.

A most decisive indication of this dramatic change can be immediately deduced from an analysis of the early census returns. These returns record 564 persons (262 male and 302 female) residing in the Clay Lane township in 1831; and by 1841, the population had dramatically risen by over 260% to 1,478 (828 male and 650 female). The bulk of this increase occured during the last five years of the decade between 1837 and 1841, and was almost entirely due to the large migratory influx into Clay Cross of people who first came to excavate the tunnel and work in George Stephenson's coal mines. According to the 'Derbyshire Courier' just after the census returns were published 'the number would have been considerably larger had it been taken on any other day as there are many workmen employed there who have lodgings in Clay Cross, but have families living elsewhere, where they go on Saturday night and return to Clay Cross on Monday morning, and who consequently were not included in the return it being taken for Sunday night'.

The story is frequently and emphatically told, ad nauseam, that it was George Stephenson who first discovered coal in Clay Cross whilst driving the Clay Cross Tunnel. This is simply not true and there is an abundance of evidence to prove conclusively that coal was mined in the Clay Cross area a considerable time before Stephenson arrived on the scene.

Clay Cross is situated on the ridge or escarpment which is approximately parallel with the strike of the outcropping coal measures, which being near to the surface, would be relatively easy to mine. Part of the Roman Road, Ryknield Street, runs along this exposed coalfield at Stretton and Clay Cross and during an archeological excavation of a section of this road at New Tupton, in May 1975, the presence of coal dust was found in some quantity, which suggests that coal was transported at some time along this Roman road. During opencast operations at Stretton in March 1969, a number of old bell-pits were uncovered together with some other old workings.

The earliest documentary evidence so far uncovered that records coal-mining in the area appears in a Stretton Survey of 1655/66 — 'The rent for the coal pits upon the Common of Stretton in the possession of Thomas Wragg ... £10 ...'. At one time the land Clay Cross is now situated on formed part of the medieval manor of Stretton and the manorial commons of Stretton extended from the manor of Shirland up to the area of the present Market Street in Clay Cross. From the 1650's onwards there is a substantial amount of documentary evidence showing the extent of coalmining activity in the Clay Cross and Stretton areas and also in the immediate surrounding areas of Morton, Shirland, Tibshelf, Pilsley, North Wingfield, Grassmoor, Alton, Wingerworth, South Normanton and Blackwell. Towards the end of the eighteenth century, however, coalmining appears to have been in decline in the Clay Cross area, possibly to the extent of only supplying local domestic needs. Indeed, in Farey's list of coalmines for Derbyshire in 1811, the '9th' coal at Clay Cross is recorded has having been 'worked formerly'.

Though there had been some diversification into an industrial economy during the eighteenth century, by the dawn of the nineteenth century, Clay Cross had reverted back to an agarian-based economy, with some domestic element of weaving and framework knitting. It was not until

1837, that we see the conception of a metamorphosis which rapidly transformed Clay Cross into an industrial town — a company town — the epitome of most mining villages; relatively small yet dynamic; not too rural but not totally urban; an introspective yet volatile community entirely dominated by one company.

Clay Cross Population

Date	Male	Female	Total	Houses
1801	193	160	353	65
1811	211	211	422	97
1821	230	235	465	105
1831	262	302	564	111
1841	828	650	1,478	305
1851	1,234	1,044	2,278	487
1861	2,284	1,812	4,096	730
1871	2,746	2,394	5,140	967
1881	3,402	2,945	6,347	1,246
1891	3,794	3,349	7,143	1,290
1901	4,105	3,596	7,701	1,466
1911	4,418	3,947	8,365	1,756
1921	4,483	4,203	8,686	1,776
1931	4,488	4,009	8,497	1,857
1941	*No census during the war period*			
1951	4,331	4,222	8,553	2,451
1961	4,618	4,545	9,163	2,965
1971	4,854	4,871	9,725	3,355

Frederick Swanwick

CHAPTER ONE

CONTRACTORS

Planning the route

On the 16th July 1836, George and Robert Stephenson were appointed engineers-in-chief for the construction of the North Midland Railway line at a joint salary of £2,000 per annum — 'including travelling expenses'. However, both George and Robert were immersed in so much other work at this period they appear to have had very little to do with either its planning or construction, and probably only acted as consultant engineers. Their status as engineers at this date was quite renowned and the North Midland Railway Company were eager to secure their services, as their professional influence would no doubt impress parliament. The engineer responsible for the bulk of the work on the 72 mile stretch between Derby and Leeds was Frederick Swanwick, and he was appointed assistant engineer on 23rd September 1836.

> ... that in sanctioning this appointment to be assistant engineer to this company when called upon to do so by George Stephenson it will be upon the express understanding that Mr. Swanwick will confine his attention solely to this work and the Sheffield and Rotherham Railway and before this appointment is finally concluded they wish to have his assurance to this effect.

The total cost of the engineers' salaries, clerks and Chesterfield office expenses up to December 1840 was £48,894.

Frederick Swanwick, was born October 1st 1810, in the city of Chester, and at the age of seventeen in 1826, he entered the University of Edinburgh to study maths, natural philosophy and geology. By 1827, he returned home to study maths privately, and in 1829, he was articled as a pupil with George Stephenson, who was then constructing the Liverpool and Manchester railway.

> Frederick Swanwick bound himself apprentice to George Stephenson for 4 years and 8 months from October 5th 1829, in the occupation of civil engineer.

Swanwick actually resided with Stephenson who quickly recognised his pupil's talents and after only a year Stephenson appointed him his private secretary.

In 1834, Stephenson then assigned to him the construction of the Whitby and Pickering line.

> ... and it is striking proof of his confidence in his pupil that George Stephenson gave him carte blanche as to the selection of the route and the formation of the line. But before this successful maiden effort of his professional career had reached completion Frederick Swanwick had been called upon to undertake the laying out of the North Midland Railway in the Autumn of 1835.

In January 1836, the boring along the line of the Clay Cross Tunnel was completed and the surveyor's findings were considered to be extremely favourable, the whole of the area found to be in strong bind interspersed with beds or seams of coal. The workmen then continued north to Leeds to complete their survey and the following September, another survey was carried out on the line between Chesterfield and Clay Cross. The cost of surveying and land valuing on the N.M.R. up to December 1840 was £7,538.

The plans of the strata for the tunnel section were prepared for the N.M.R. by Joseph Gratton, of Timberfield House (now Stretton House). Gratton also sank a number of pits along the line of the tunnel and at the two deep cuttings north and south of the proposed entrances.

> The pits are to be fenced round and be left open for the inspection and information of such persons as wish to become contractors.

Joseph's son, John Sterland Gratton, was also an estate agent for the Midland Railway company and is buried in the Stretton cemetery (24th October 1888) a few yards from Smithymoor or Stretton station and the southern entrance to the Clay Cross Tunnel.

After surveying the route, Swanwick no doubt conferred with George Stephenson and they both agreed to take the N.M.R. line through the lower valley route. Despite strong opposition, they argued that the various towns off the route would have to be satisfied with branch lines. The result was that, as we read in the 'Clay Cross Chronicle' 1908,

There is deception about Clay Cross which irritates the stranger.
You think that when you reach the railway station you are there —
but you are not. It seems like a touch of fraud to find when you land
at Clay Cross, that you are exactly two miles from Clay Cross and
that your railway ticket entitles you to walk free of charge, up the
long hill to the town.

Opposition

The engineers' recommendations for the line were not readily
acceptable and were vigorously contested both within and outside
Parliament. In Derbyshire the main problem was whether or not the line
could be taken from Chesterfield direct to Sheffield. After surveying the
line as far as Owler Bar, the N.M.R. engineers rejected the line to
Sheffield and concluded that a tunnel six miles long would be necessary.
During March 1836 a subscription of over £5,000 was raised in Sheffield
for the purpose of opposing the proposed N.M.R. line ...'which does
not embrace in its course the manufacturing districts of Sheffield'. Mr.
Leather, engineer, who supported the Sheffield opposition was
employed to give evidence to the Commons Select Committee, and
urged that it was quite possible to take the line direct to Sheffield. The
Sheffield opposition was eventually withdrawn in June 1836, and the
N.M.R. agreed to pay £3,000 towards the cost of this opposition.

The principal ironmasters in the neighbourhood of Chesterfield
welcomed the N.M.R. line despite it only cutting through the periphery
of the town and ...'were proceeding to London to give favourable
testimony to this important undertaking'.

The Cromford Canal Company, obviously, opposed the N.M.R. Bill,
but did not elect to put their case to either of the Select Committees.
Under the restraints of the Act, however, the N.M.R. had to pay the
Cromford Canal Company £100 compensation for every 24 hours the
railway works obstructed and stopped the canal. In March 1838, an iron
aqueduct 150 feet long, 9 feet wide and 6 feet deep, was made at the
Butterley Company's ironworks for the purpose of taking the canal over
the railway at Bull Bridge near Ambergate. It was transported from
Butterley in five separate sections and was assembled and riveted during
the night to lessen the penalties imposed on the N.M.R. This aqueduct
was demolished by the Derbyshire County Council in 1968 to
accomodate a road improvement scheme.

When questioned about the economic importance of the Chesterfield
area Swanwick stated that it ...'was not of any great trade; there are

markets and ironworks close by'. Two Derby witnesses, however, did expect the railway to affect the trade to Chesterfield, and Thomas Cox, who manufactured 1,500 tons of white lead yearly in Derby referred to the existing difficulties of transport into Yorkshire. By water it took three or four weeks to reach Leeds via Hull, and ten to fourteen days to Sheffield via Gainsborough, where the delay was such that he preferred to send his lead to Sheffield by the turnpike road through Chesterfield. Francis Saunders, an influential corn merchant of Derby was also concerned about the slow communications to the considerable markets of both Chesterfield and Sheffield. By land the mileage to Chesterfield was 28, and by water along the Trent and canal it was estimated at about 80 or 90 miles.

The N.M.R. Bill was opposed in both Houses of Parliament and nearly 3,000 pages of manuscript evidence was presented to the Commons Select Committee and a further 165 pages of printed evidence was presented to the Lords Select Committee.

Mr. Vignoles, engineer, argued for the high level route and preferred a continuation of the Erewash branch of the Midland Counties line, which proposed to cut through the ridge up to Clay Cross and down to Sheffield. Despite his arguments for the alternative route, the inveterate opposition of the Aire and Calder canal interests, and a somewhat precarious passage through Parliament, the North Midland Railway Bill finally received Royal Assent on the 4th July 1836.

The Act is passed

'Whereas the making of the railway from Leeds to Derby would be productive of great public advantage, by opening an additional, certain, expeditious communication between the towns aforesaid and intermediate towns and districts and also by facilitating the means of intercourse between the North of England, the Midland Counties, the Metropolis, and the West and South of England ... May it therefore please your Majesty that it may be enacted; and be it enacted by the King's most excellent Majesty, by and with the advice and consent of the Lords Spiritual and Temporal, and Commons in Parliament assembled, and by the authority of the same, that William Aldham (and 87 other Proprietors incorporated) ... shall be and they are hereby united into a company for making and maintaining the said railway and other works by this Act authorised ... and for that purpose shall be one body corporate by the name and style of the North Midland Railway Company' (Act of Parliament July 4th 1836).

On this news reaching Chesterfield the bells of the Parish Church commenced ringing a merry peal which was continued the whole of the afternoon and a subscription was entered into and liberally contributed to for the purpose of remunerating the ringers.

This particular Act enabled the N.M.R. Company to raise up to £1,500,000 for the making of the railway and it was divided into shares of £100 each. The list of subscribers show that the main backing came from the Yorkshire industrial area and the London and the Bristol region. There were ten subscribers from Derbyshire but none from the Clay Cross or Chesterfield area. George Carr Glynn, one of the original partners of the George Stephenson Company at Clay Cross, was a substantial shareholder and chairman of the N.M.R. Board.

In 1837, 1839 and 1841, respectively, three other Acts relating to the N.M.R. were sanctioned, which amongst other things, enabled them to make a branch line leading to certain coal fields in the parish of North Wingfield. There were seven tenders for this particular branch line, including one from Linacre and Chapman of Clay Cross, but it was awarded to Mr. Radford of Alfreton for the sum of £5,500 — Swanwick estimated this contract at £5,400. The George Stephenson Company also built an inclined plane to link up with the main trunk line, and it was known locally as the Zig Zag railway and communicated with Stephenson's No. 1 pit and Turnpike Colliery and is clearly marked on the 1841 Tithe map. The Wingerworth Colliery Company also connected up with the main trunk line from their Tupton Colliery; and their Lings Colliery connected up with the Duke's Incline (built by the N.M.R.) that ran to the Clay Cross Station.

Running from Derby northwards the N.M.R. line commenced . . .'at or near certain closes called or known by the name of Darwin's Close, in the Parish of St. Alkmund Derby' and in Derbyshire it cut through the following Parishes and Townships :- Little Chester, Breadsall, Little Eaton, Allestree, Makeney, Duffield, Belper, Heage, Wirksworth, Crich, Wessington, South Wingfield, Shirland, Brackenfield, Morton, Stretton, Clay Lane, Clay Cross, Woodthorpe, Tupton, North Wingfield, Pilsley, Wingerworth, Chesterfield, Staveley, Eckington, Killamarsh and Beighton and eventually terminated in Leeds — . . .'at or near certain gardens in the Parish and Township aforesaid now in the occupation of George Banks, adjoining to the eastside of a street or lane called Hunslett Lane'.

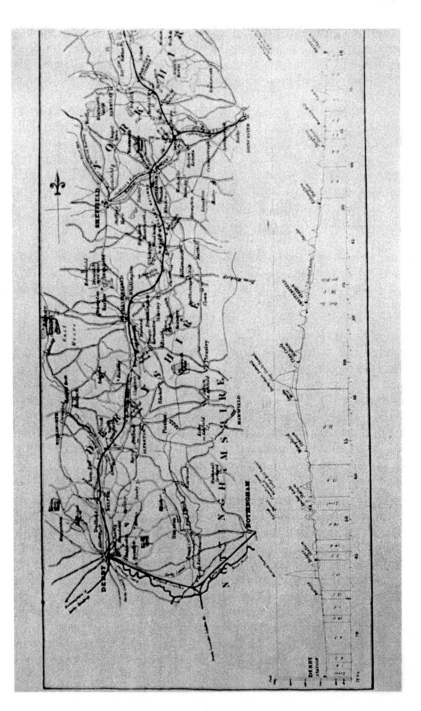

16

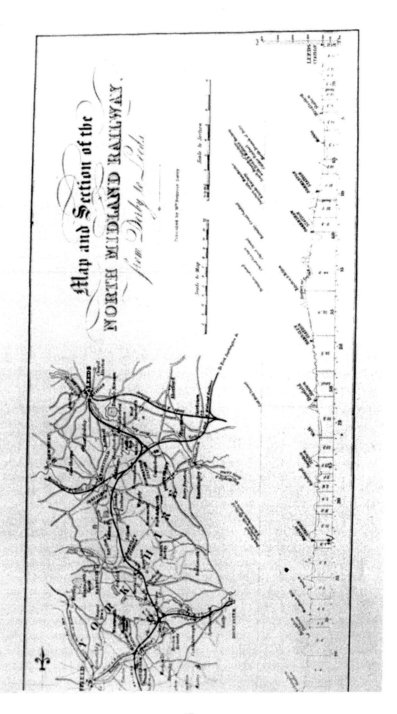

Tenders were then invited by the N.M.R. Company for the whole of the work to be done on the various section of the line. The construction work for the entire line was divided up into 30 contracts, and the Clay Cross Tunnel contract was number eight.

Winning Contracts

In November 1836, the plans and the specifications for the Clay Cross Tunnel were complete and in December, tenders for the work were invited. The first principal contractor to be employed on the tunnel was Messrs. Hardy, Copeland and Cropper of Watford, Herts. The original estimate for the tunnel excavations etc., was £96,000 but the above named contractors agreed to complete the work for the sum of £105,460, after their first tender of £126, 952, was turned down. The only other tender for the tunnel contract was from Henry Clark of Sheffield, who submitted a tender for £131,416. The N.M.R. reported in February 1837.

> The magnitude and importance of the works connected with the Clay Cross Tunnel necessarily attracted the attention of the Directors, and they have much satisfaction stating that under the judicious advice of Messrs. Stephenson and Mr. Swanwick, a contract has been concluded with competent parties, upon favourable terms, which the directors feel convinced will ensure the expeditious and certain execution of the work.

Some details of this contract were reported in the 'Derbyshire Courier'.

> The cutting, formation and excavating the tunnel at Clay Cross, has at length been contracted for by Messrs. Hardy, Copeland and Cropper of Watford, Herts; for the sum of £105,460. The tunnel is we understand, to be 29 feet in width, and 25 feet 11 inches in height when completed, exclusive of 4 feet in thickness of broken stones at the bottom on which the sleepers and rails are to be laid. This is we believe, 4 feet wider than tunnels on the London and Birmingham line. There are to be six fifteen-horse whimseys (steam winding engines of fifteen horsepower), and a pumping and working shaft at each end: this will enable the work to be proceeded with at twelve different places at the same time, exclusive of the two ends (ten shafts were actually sunk). The tunnel is to be arched completely round with bricks laid in Roman cement; and near to the middle is to be a ventilation shaft 60 feet in diameter. (This was obviously a printing error as no shaft on the tunnel exceeded ten feet in diameter). The total length of the tunnel will be 1,800 yards, and its greatest depth below the surface about 48 yards; and by the contract the whole is to be completed by the 1st May 1839; but it is generally

NORTH MIDLAND RAILWAY.

CONTRACTS FOR WORKS.

THE Directors of the North Midland Railway Company will meet at the Railway Office, No. 13, George Street, Mansion House, London, on Saturday, the 7th day of January, 1837, at One o'Clock precisely, to receive Tenders for a Contract,—

To make a Tunnel one mile in length at Clay Cross, in the parish of North Wingfield, in the county of Derby, and to keep the same in repair for one year after completion.

Drafts of the Contracts with Plans and Specifications of the Works, will be ready for inspection, at the Engineer's Office in Chesterfield, on and after Thursday the 15th December next.

Printed forms of Tender may be had, after the above date, at the Railway Offices in London, Leeds, and Chesterfield, *and no others will be attended to.*

The Tenders must be delivered at the Railway Office in London, on or before One o'Clock on the said 7th day of January, under a sealed cover, addressed to the Secretary, and indorsed, "Tender for Works," and the parties tendering, or persons duly authorized by them, must be in attendance at the time of Meeting.

The parties whose Tenders are accepted, will be required to enter into a Bond, with two sureties for the due performance of their Contract, in a penalty of not less than 10 per cent. on the gross sum contracted for, and the names of the proposed sureties are to be specified in the Tender.

The Directors will not bind themselves to accept the lowest offer.

The Contractor (if he require it) will be furnished by the Company with a Counterpart of the Contract, at his own expense.   By Order,

H. PATTESON,
Secretary.

London, 1st December, 1836.

thought to be impossible to complete in the time. The contractors are, however, using every possible exertion, and have already engaged several sets of workmen to commence immediately. We wish them success — they are experienced hands at tunnelling — the Liverpool tunnel, the Leicester tunnel and the Watford tunnel; as well as several other extensive works on the above and other lines of railway, have been completed by them and on all occasions we believe they have given satisfaction.

The whole of the North Wingfield contract commencing at the northern end of the tunnel and terminating at Hasland, a distance of three miles and thirty two chains, was contracted for by Mr. Waring of Sheffield for £39,500 — approximately 350,000 cubic yards of earth were excavated from this section. Mr. Trubshaw of Leighton Wood, Staffordshire, won the South Wingfield contract extending from South Wingfield to the southern entrance of the Clay Cross tunnel for £103,060 — approximately one million cubic yards of earth were removed from this section.

Time was of paramout importance to both the N.M.R. and the contractors, and fines were imposed for not completing contracts on time. The contractors' payments were usually paid in monthly instalments, but subject to the engineers' approval of the work completed. Ten per cent of the contract was usually kept back until twelve months after the completion of the work, during which time the contractor had to maintain the work completed. The engineers could also insist that more men should be taken on if the work was behind schedule, and they could dismiss the contractors for shoddy workmanship. In June 1839, the N.M.R preferred a charge of assault against Isaac Nelson (brother of main contractor) and Jesse Shaw when they evicted a workman off the Eckington contract. Apparently, the contractors had neglected to repair a section of the cutting and so the engineer instructed another gang of workmen to complete the work. Mr. Vickers, solicitor, for the N.M.R. stated

> ... that by agreement between the Company and the different contractors, powers were reserved, by which the engineer had authority when they considered it necessary, to set men to work if the contractor refused to do so.

All materials brought to the site became the property of the railway company and could not be removed without their permission.

The work begins

On the 2nd February 1837, the first sod was turned up in a field close to the toll-bar house and the tunnel excavations commenced with the sinking of the deep ventilation shaft which stands almost in the centre of the tunnel. It is 144 feet deep, and is situated on the highest point of the N.M.R. line, 360 feet above sea level.

Just after the work on the tunnel had commenced the 'Derby and Chesterfield Reporter' mentioned that the Company's inspector had arrived in the town to superintend the work on the tunnel. If this had been George Stephenson, his arrival would have been emblazoned across the local news section of the local press. At this date he was a much revered public figure and known as the 'Father of the Railways'. Indeed, George Stephenson did not arrive in the area until 1838, when he removed from Alton Grange in Leicestershire to Tapton House on Castle Hill overlooking Chesterfield. Stephenson's priorities at this date, however, were the establishment of his company at Clay Cross and the sinking of the No. 1 and Tupton pit complex, together with the building of the coke ovens and the planning and development of his lime works at Ambergate and Crich. The inspector refered to in the 'Reporter' was, undoubtedly, Frederick Swanwick and on February 1837,

> ... accordingly an office has been engaged at Chesterfield as the most convenient place on the line for the occupation of Mr. Swanwick, who has been appointed resident engineer with assistant engineers under his direction.

There is no doubt that George Stephenson would have frequently visited Clay Cross during the progress of the tunnel but more so to attend to his own investment in the coal mines. Indeed, the first newspaper report concerning a visit to Clay Cross does not appear until November 1841. On this occasion there was a massive landslip at the northern entrance of the tunnel which blocked the main line and

> ... Messrs. George Stephenson, Swanwick and other gentlemen were soon on the spot and all the hands that could be got were immediately set to work to clear the line.

Stephenson's coal could only be loaded economically on the northern side of the line and this blockage would be a serious threat to his business. By 1840, the company were sending coal to London partly by rail and partly by canal from Rugby onwards and in 1845, they had the distinction of being the first to send coal to London direct by rail.

21

Along the line of the tunnel and the rest of the line the N.M.R. purchased various plots of land and property to enable them to proceed with the excavations. According to the restraints of the Act, the N.M.R. company could not purchase lands exceeding 22 yards in width —

> except in those places where a greater breadth shall be judged necessary for carriages to wait, load, or unload and to turn or pass each other, or for raising embankments for crossing valleys, or low ground.

They were allowed to deviate from the original plan no more than 100 yards and

> in passing through a city or town such deviation shall not extend to a greater distance than ten yards from the line so deliniated upon the said plans.

The only local opposition to the N.M.R. with regards to the route came from Gladwin Turbutt of Ogston Hall and in May 1839, a notice was given to the Sheriff of Derbyshire to empanel a Jury for trials of issue at Derby 'relative to sundry purchases from Turbutt Esq'.

At about the same date that the tunnelling operations commenced, 'Hill House' came up for sale and was sold by auction at the George and Dragon.

> This house is calculated for the residence of a small genteel family; and it is likewise well adapted for a tradesman desirious of establishing a business in this populous and important neighbourhood.

This particular house, no doubt served as the 'site' office and accomodated the assistant engineers supervising the tunnelling operations. It was the most substantial building in the village at this date and was situated just a few yards from the deep ventilation shaft on the centre of the tunnel. The 1841 Tithe Award reveals that this particular property was owned by George Stephenson and Company and was purchased from the N.M.R. together with the East and West Tunnel Rows in 1840, after the tunnel was finally completed. According to the 1841 census returns, 'Hill House' was then occupied by James Campbell, who came to Clay Cross early in 1840, to supervise the sinking of Stephenson's pits and the installation of the inclined planes at Crich and Clay Cross. Campbell was previously employed at Stephenson's Snibston collieries in Leicestershire.

The engineers in charge of a particular stretch of line could bring in new contractors, as we have seen, if they considered that work was not

Robert Stephenson　　　　　　　　*George Stephenson*

progressing satisfactorily, and in August 1838, Swanwick brought in Edward Price to take over half of the tunnel contract. This 'spirited' new contractor had previously completed the famous Kilsby Tunnel in Northamptonshire on the Birmingham and London Line, and he was recommended to the N.M.R. by George Stephenson and Frederick Swanwick. On his arrival to the town he immediately commenced building new offices, stables and outbuildings of various description in order to facilitate the completion of the tunnel on time.

One of the stables erected by Edward Price was later converted into a school for George Stephenson and Company and was appropriately called the 'Stable School'. It was opened sometime in 1843, and Mr. Hudson was the schoolmaster until 1854, when the Company replaced him after they opened their new school — . . .'to teach the children their relative duties in life'. The Stable School was of a wooden construction and was still standing in 1910.

The first principal contractors employed on the tunnel together with contractors on other works on the line are listed on a framed testimonial printed on silk, which together with a candelabrum and dinner service of plate were presented to Robert Stephenson at a public dinner held at the Station Hotel, Aldersgate Street, London, on the anniversary of his birthday — 16th November 1839.

Sub-contractors and Tommyshops

Much of the work on the tunnel contract was let out by the main contractors to sub-contractors, and when work was organised in this way, the function of the principal contractor was that of overlooker, who made doubly sure that the sub-contractors worked as speedily and efficiently as possible. Although the principal contractor remained responsible to the N.M.R.'s engineers for the whole of the work undertaken, the N.M.R. and the principal contractors were not in most cases the employers of the navvies and other labourers. This system kept them free from any dispute with the workmen. In some cases the work on the line was even let out by the sub-contractors, thus creating sub-sub-contractors, removing further any responsibility of the N.M.R. and the principal contractors as direct employers.

Several of the Clay Cross sub-contractors were also beerhouse keepers and the owners of 'tommyshops' and they had a tremendous hold over many of their workmen with the power to hire and fire at random, and determine wages and prices, and to some extent regulate the quality of the goods sold at their tommyshops.

The N.M.R. line was driven during the 'golden age' of food adulteration and most of the goods offered at the tommyshops would be adulterated by the retailer. The 'truck' system of payments by ticket or in kind put the workmen at the mercy of the unscrupulous sub-contractor and the shopkeepers, who overcharged, gave short weight, adulterated food and drink; and more often than not the tickets were never worth their face value. The 1831 Truck Act did not extend to railway works, but on the Midland Counties line in September 1837, an overseer was summoned by a labourer for paying wages in truck and the tickets were produced as evidence. The overseer was ordered to pay wages in money, and the magistrate informed the contractor that he was liable to a penalty of £10 for the first offence, £50 for the second and £100 for every other time he should pay wages of labourers on the truck system.

Navvies were not given to saving and lived from day to day. More often than not, they had no money of their own until they were paid, and as they were not paid on a weekly basis they frequently had to live on credit. If, however, a workman wanted credit, he would ask the sub-contractor for a 'sub' up to the value of the money he was likely to earn. This 'sub' was generally given in the form of a ticket or tally which could be exchanged at the prescribed tommyshops. The contractor who had issued the tickets, would deduct their value from the wages due to the workman, and this usually kept him indebted to the contractor. Some tommyshops were let out to shopkeepers on the express understanding that a certain percentage of the profits went back to the contractors. S. Nelson, a contractor on the Eckington stretch of railway, kept such a tommyshop and George Weston, one of his employees, visited Nelson's tommyshop to obtain some provisions and demanded more than his employer thought proper to let him have.

> He (Weston) then took the liberty to help himself to sugar and
> different articles, and on Mr. Nelson endeavouring to prevent him
> the assault took place — Weston was ordered to pay 17/-.

In January 1838, several excavators attended court and attempted to obtain a summons against a sub-contractor under Mr. Waring, for the payment of their wages in money and not in truck. They complained of the disadvantage they laboured under in having the greater part of their earnings paid in goods and 'those of inferior quality' and also of the bad faith which their employer had showed in his engagement with them. Despite the complaints however, this case does not appear to have been heard in court.

Long intervals between pay were essential to a thriving truck system and on some of the lines the workmen had first to accept truck payments before they would be set on. Although the workmen at Clay Cross appear to have been paid fortnightly, they certainly would have had no alternative but to accept this system of payment if they were left penniless after their paymaster had absconded with their wages.

In November 1837, a Clay Cross sub-contractor by the name of Samuel Maw ('but in the consequence of having a sallow complexion was honoured with the cognomen of Yellow Sam') contrived to swindle the 40 men he employed, and absconded with £150 he owed them for work already completed. Yellow Sam also owed several hundred pounds to various tradesmen in the district.

> Our readers are no doubt aware that many, if not all the sub-
> contractors on the railroads, instead of paying wages in coin, issue
> provision tickets which the men take to certain shops (tommyshops)
> and give in exchange of goods. These tickets are collected
> fortnightly by the sub-contractor who give the required amount of
> cash for them. Yellow Sam acted on this principle but lately allowed
> his bills to remain in the hands of the tradesmen, continuing all the
> time to receive the usual amount of wages from the head contractor.
> The creditors, several of them brewers having a claim to a large
> amount, resolved to sell what remained in the house (Maw's beer
> house) for the benefit of the whole.

25

About one hundred excavators were also determined to have their share of the beer that remained.

> Several barrels of ale were immediately carried from the cellar to the room above; the ends were knocked out and a scene followed which is impossible to describe. The whole body of thirsty excavators rushed to the barrels armed with basins, kettles, cans and vessels of every conceivable description which they applied to their mouths and gulped down the contents — and caused such a scene of drunkeness in that hitherto peaceful and rural neighbourhood.

It appears that this was the third time that Yellow Sam had absconded with the wages due to the navvies on the line of the railway between London and Chesterfield. Enquiries were made at all the toll-gates in the district of Clay Cross, but it was found that the 'fugitive' had passed through none.

South portal of Clay Cross tunnel showing deep cutting

Another sub-contractor on the tunnel contract by the name of Tune, who kept a tommyshop and sold beer without a licence, also decamped suddenly and unexpectedly. His debts were quite extensive and

> in the event of packing up, he either had not time or forgot to pay the numerous debts which he had accumulated.

26

Mr. Tune knew exactly what he was doing and when he came to pay out the fortnight's reckonings, he sold any of his stock that could be easily turned into money and hit the road with his booty before daylight the following morning. He sold the workmen two kilderns of beer which he had not paid for, together with twenty empty barrels all for one guinea and the workmen spent the day drinking the liquor 'which pleasing task was accomplished to their satisfaction'.

At Bull Bridge on the Belper contract, the navigators suspecting that the 'gaffer' was about to abscond with the wages he had drawn from the main contractor,

> manifested strong symptoms of dissatisfaction, so much so, that the policemen were sent for and by their prompt attendance peace and good order was restored.

In April 1838, constable Thomas Mettham of Mansfield was employed to pursue two bricklayers, Thomas Hughes and G. Russell, who had been working on the tunnel. 'One of them it seems was foreman of a gang, and had to pay his men and had drawn £40 with which he decamped, taking the other with him as a companion'. Mettham eventually caught up with them and on going into the tap room of the Radcliffe Arms, at Bunny ... 'he saw the objects of his pursuit quietly seated there'.

Bull Bridge

North Midland Railway Contracts

Contract	Contractors	Tenders
Derby	J. & J. Nowell	£19,000
Duffield	McIntosh	£43,144
Milford	McIntosh	£93,122
Belper (south)	McIntosh	£20,650
Belper (north)	T. Jackson	£60,500
Bull Bridge	T. Jackson	£63,000
Lodge Hill	J. Nowell	£52,893
South Wingfield	Trubshaw	£103,060
Clay Cross Tunnel	Hardy & Cropper	£105,400
North Wingfield	J. Waring	£39,500
Chesterfield	J. Waring	£32,164
Whittington	J. Smith	£38,876
Staveley	J. Diggle	£58,678
Eckington	Nelson & Kitchen	£30,686
Beighton	Rutherford	£37,572
Treeton	J. Buxton	£39,500
Ickels	J. Buxton	£26,264
Greasborough	Stevenson	£43,800
Kilnhurst	J. Mawson	£25,517
Swinton	T. Gill	£28,023
Darfield	J. Stephenson	£64,464
Houghton	H. Clark	£51,706
Royston	J. Thornton	£43,527
Notton	W. Shaw	£70,864
Oakenshaw	J. Thornton	£82,161
Methley	McIntosh	£26,655
Woodlesford	J. Chapman	£55,112
Altofts	McIntosh	£78,000
Rothwell	J. Mawson	£25,517
Leeds	Bray & Duckett	£57,632

* The N.M.R. line was an expensive line and its total cost inclusive of all the station and branch lines was about £3,000,000.

*Landslip near
Ambergate.
Notice the Limekilns*

Railway versus Road

DR.	To 31st December, 1841.			Since.			To 30th June, 1841.		
	£.	s.	d.	£.	s.	d.	£.	s.	d.
To Payments before act was obtained	41349	12	3	....			41349	12	3
Land & compensation	363825	14	7	6279	15	1	370105	9	8
Works—road	1658541	9	8	21877	7	3	1680418	16	5
Works - stations	194898	8	9	63913	18	9	258812	7	6
Permanent way-rails, chairs, sleepers, &c.	330768	4	3	10,545	0	6	341313	4	9
Engineering—salaries to engineers, clerks, office expenses at Chesterfield, &c. ..	48824	14	6	2692	16	9	51517	11	3
Surveying and land valuing	7538	14	0	61	8	6	7600	2	6
Hire of police previous to opening line	2439	14	7	....			2439	14	7
Waggons, trucks, implements for contractors, &c.	8222	5	10	....			8222	5	10
Law charges for general purposes	20001	0	11	1955	0	0	21956	0	11
Direction	7850	0	0	....			7850	0	0
Miscellaneous charges	8390	3	11	1262	18	7	9653	2	6
Advertising, printing, &c.	2898	7	5	383	7	10	3281	15	3
Office charges—London and Leeds previous to opening line	8460	1	0	....			8460	1	0
Parliamentary & law charges	4163	5	1	250	0	0	4413	5	1
Stamps on debenture bonds	4500	0	0	6	17	6	4506	17	6
Interest on debenture bonds	47669	7	6	....			47669	7	6
Locomotive stock— engines, tenders, implements, &c. ..	121471	6	6	23308	2	0	144779	8	6
Coaching stock—1st, 2nd, and 3rd class carriage bodies, and trucks, horse-boxes, &c	38704	12	8	6226	6	9	44930	19	5
Stores, stock on hand, less this amount recharged storekeepers—£6883 15s 2d..	6883	15	2	....			....		
Stock of road and stations, furniture for									

30

	To 31st December, 1840.			Since.			Total to 30th June, 1841.		
stations, notice boards, signals, &c Three per Cent. Consols,—security for government duty..	1596	0	0	3456	11	7	5052	11	7
	1000	0	0	....			1000	0	0
	2929696	18	0	142219	11	1			
Deduct as above ..	6893	15	2	...			....		
	2922813	2	10	142219	11	1			
Cash at the disposal of the company....	....			....			3065032	13	11
							20978	15	11
							2086005	9	10

CR.	To 31st December, 1840.			Since.			Total to 30th June, 1841.		
	£.	s.	d.	£.	s.	d.	£.	s.	d.
By cash received For calls on £100 shares..........	1465330	0	0	5895	0	0	1471225	0	0
Ditto £50 shares	562575	4	8	19520	0	0	582095	4	8
Sundry payments on account—arrears of £100 & £50 shares	....			4320	15	3	4330	15	3
Premium on £50 shares..	5666	10	0	....			5666	10	0
Deposit on 3rd shares and advance on future calls	....			97556	13	4	97556	13	4
Interest (balance of interest) account less - £794 8s 5d..	6286	2	9	....			5491	13	4
Loans on debenture bonds	750030	0	0	28900	0	0	778930	0	0
Money on loan—less paid off—£10,460..	137360	0	0	....			125900	0	0
Materials re-sold	1392	5	9	478	4	0	1870	9	9
Rent of cottages	367	8	9	....			367	8	0
Dearne & Dove Canal Co. for works, executed by the N. M R Company	3471	2	2	...			3471	2	2
Midland Counties R. Co., ditto ditto	....			5000	0	0	5000	0	0
Manchester and Leeds R. Co., ditto ditto..	....			1738	13	4	1738	13	4
York & North Midland R Co., ditto ditto..	....			1366	0	0	1366	0	0
£11,254 9s 5d	2932478	13	4						
Deduct as above ..	11254	9	5						
	2921224	3	11	164776	5	11	2086009	9	10

31

CHAPTER TWO

THE NAVVIES AT WORK

The word 'navvy' is derived from the name given to the navigators who built the canals in the eighteenth century and was later inherited by the railwaymen. A popular image of railway navvies is that they were all Irish, but this is simply not true, and the thousands of excavators who toiled with their picks, shovels, crowbars and barrows on the canals and railways were drawn from almost anywhere, including Ireland.

Navvies did the hardest and most hazardous work on the lines of railway, particularly the blasting, cutting and tunnelling, and left the young lads and locally recruited labour to do the menial jobs. The navvies usually worked on piece work rates at so much a foot, either in a gang or set and were only paid for the work done. The ordinary labourers were usually employed on a shift or daily basis and earned considerably less than the navvies.

Pay disputes

The industrial revolution, so far from abridging human labour created a whole new world of labour intensive jobs and railway navvying is a prime example. The early railway workers were, however, amongst the most exploited of all workers. Organised labour along the line was virtually non-existent and the early legislation that gave some little protection to various other sections of the national workforce evaded the railway workers.

Some navvies did attempt to get their grievances settled through the local courts. At Chesterfield Borough Court in September 1837, William Price and John Coates, contractors, both appeared to answer a complaint by George Else, a labourer employed by them. Apparently these two sub-contractors had paid him short for eleven days' work and as he was employed as a day labourer the court ruled in Else's favour and the sub-contractors were ordered to pay 10/- and 9/- costs.

The severe frosts of January 1838, hindered the progress of the tunnel and caused several contractors to reduce the navvies' wages, and a number of aggrieved navvies took their complaint to the Chesterfield Borough Court. During one such case Mr. Waring, the principal contractor on the North Wingfield and Chesterfield sections, was called upon to state the mode of payment observed by the masters in general on the railway. Waring argued that all the workmen were paid for the actual work done, it being immaterial as to the time they were occupied in performing such work. The excavators' case, he argued, was quite different to that of the day labourer. When the weather was bad it impeded work and consequently the men would not earn the same rate of wages as when the weather was favourable. This, he announced, was the custom on all public works, and anyone applying for employment understood it as such. 'If this mode was not adopted neither himself nor any other person would be able to enter into the required contract'. The court ruled that the employer was acting according to custom and the case was dismissed. According to Waring, during favourable weather conditions an able bodied man could earn up to 3/6 per day but at the present time it was only possible to earn 2/- per day. During the height of activity on the Clay Cross Tunnel in June 1838, the average fortnightly pay for this particular contract was estimated at £2,000, with one of the payments for this month amounting to £2,500. The amount of these payments, obviously indicate that a substantial labour force was employed on the tunnel but because of the complexities of the different contracts, day work and shift systems etc., it would be difficult to hazard a guess as to the number employed.

The craftsmen working on the tunnel were much better organised than the ordinary navvies. In November 1837, the whole of the bricklayers employed on the Clay Cross Tunnel struck work and demanded to be relieved from their stint every eight hours instead of every ten hours. Despite several pumps operating continuously for twenty-four hours a day to prevent the tunnel from flooding conditions must have been quite grim, and many of the workers would be saturated throughout the shift. Though the bricklayers had their shift reduced by two hours the navvies were expected to work at least twelve.

The masons on the Horns Bridge contract at Chesterfield struck work in March 1838, for an advance in wages. Another 'turnout' in September by the masons at Bull Bridge was reported to the N.M.R. Board and Swanwick advised the contractors to resist the men's demands.

It is of interest to find a number of these masons appearing as speakers at local Chartist meetings. At Belper in April 1839, a number of workers employed on the N.M.R. line, together with some nail makers and stocking-frame knitters assembled in the Market Place for the purpose of hearing Mr. Heatherington of London, a delegate from the National Convention, talk on the subject of the People's Charter. Although nearly 500 people attended this meeting the press considered it to be 'an altogether failure'. Clay Cross does not appear to have been honoured with a visit from the Chartists until 1842, when O'Neill, a Chartist emissary called upon the miners at Clay Cross and Tupton to demand a wage of 4/- a day and with no half or quarter days to be worked at all.

Further north on the Chevet tunnel, near Wakefield, the excavators refused to descend the various shafts, armed themselves with hedge stakes and picks and attempted to get the other excavators in the neighbourhood to strike work for an increase in wages, but their attempt failed and the contractors paid many of them up and sacked them. At a N.M.R. Board meeting just after this incident, after listening to a report about 'the prevalance of a disturbance and riot amongst the workmen at Wakefield', the Directors expressed their 'approbation of the efficient measure taken by the authority and the parties on the spot for restoring tranquility'.

At the height of activity along the line in July 1838, Swanwick reported that the contractors were complaining of the workmen getting scarce and difficult to manage. The following October, a meeting of contractors on the line at Chesterfield was called for the purpose of appointing an individual to act in the capacity of secretary to an association which they formed and which they were anxious to extend to similar undertakings.

> It appears that on several occasions the excavators and others employed on the N.M.R. line have put the contractors to inconvenience by leaving one contract and obtaining work on another, when they have considered themselves not sufficiently remunerated for their labours; and the association alluded to is intended to check this rambling propensity on their part.

The Work Proceeds

> Clay Cross accordingly presents an animated scene indicative of the pervading vigilance of a master mind and every prospect of a timely completion of the contract. At the southern extremity the ground has to be levelled for a great distance in order to reach the proposed entrance. The width across the chasm at present affords the

spectators of a somewhat terrific conception of the ultimate depth of the intended railway here. At the northern termination of the tunnel the entrance presents itself and is faced and arched with brick, consolidated with Roman Cement to the distance we understand of 60 yards. To form the opening a vast quantity of earth and stone had to be raised and removed. The sight of the rock cut down to the level — the operations carrying on by the glimmer of lamps within the tunnel — the majestic size and due proportion of which as indicated by the wide, arched and elevated entrance — like the east window of an Abbey, relieve the spectator when struck with the labour yet required to sink the trench in that direction in order to connect there with that of the valley before North Wingfield Church. While observing the steady diligence and attention of the men and boys at the mouths of the shaft, together with the never ceasing play of engines, and the prodigious piles of bricks burnt in those kilns for consumption below, one is stunned by the unexpected heavy reports beneath the feet, as one explosion of rock succeeds another. Two invaluable conveniences are found on the spot — suitable clay for making the bricks and plenty of coal for the engines. It is only necessary at present to add, that the length and gentle slope of the hill through which the tunnel passes is apt to deceive the eye, the labour therefore of reaching the shafts is much greater at the summit than might be supposed.

The working and ventilation shafts were the centre of operations and a hive of activity surrounded them and

> one is reminded of the advancement of the irksome labours carried on below, by the vast quantities of rubbish raised through the shafts and wheeled off in every direction, while the numberless many stones thus brought up excite the wonder how it could possibly be effected in these subterranean passages.

During the first year of excavations four working shafts were sunk with another six the following year which enabled the tunnelling to proceed at twenty-two different places at the same time — inclusive of the two ends. Of the nine shafts still standing, eight are working shafts and are about ten feet in diameter and the remaining shaft was obviously a pumping shaft and is about six feet in diameter. At one time, six fifteen horse-power whimsey engines were erected along the line of the tunnel and six twelve inch pumps were working twenty-four hours a day to stop the working from flooding.

> The works at Clay Cross Tunnel are proceeding with vigour and expedition and it will be satisfactory to the proprietors to learn that although there has been a considerable influx of water, the

difficulties usually contingent upon such circumstances, and which were fully anticipated and provided for by the engineers, have been entirely overcome.

A few days after the tunnel had commenced, a correspondent for the 'Chesterfield Reporter' wrote a detailed description of how the tunnelling department was carried on, but thought it superfluous to mention the dangerous process of shafts sinking as every practical collier and lead miner in the county is well aquainted with it. However

the pumping and working shafts being got down to the required depth, the workmen commence by driving a heading, or driftway at the top of the intended tunnel, about three yards in length; into this drift a piece of stoutest oak timber, about four yards in length, and the thickness of a man's body is introduced half a yard at each end, being intended to rest upon the solid. This piece of timber if firmly packed and wedged up to the roof of the drift way, and may be aptly compared to the ridge tree of a building, more earth is cut away on the sides and other pieces of timber put in the form of side trees of a building, and this is repeated until the whole of the earth is cut away

CLAY CROSS TUNNEL No. 8 CONTRACT

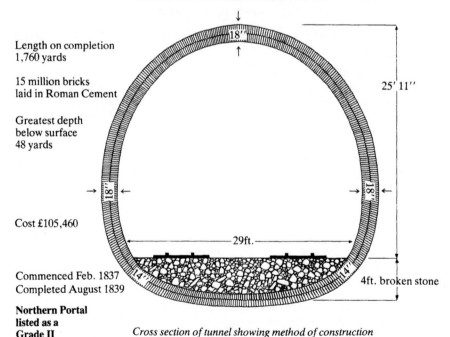

Length on completion 1,760 yards

15 million bricks laid in Roman Cement

Greatest depth below surface 48 yards

Cost £105,460

Commenced Feb. 1837
Completed August 1839

Northern Portal listed as a Grade II

18″

25′ 11″

18′

18′

29ft.

14″   14″

4ft. broken stone

Cross section of tunnel showing method of construction

down to the springs of the arch. Smaller pieces of wood or rough boards are put between the side-trees in the form of spars. The roof being thus supported, and it may be expected that the lower part will stand without timbering, but should the strata prove tender and soft, more polling wood and timber is placed according to the judgement and experience of the workmen. All the earth in a length being cleared away, the bricklayer commences at the bottom of the tunnel. This is to be fourteen inches in thickness, the sides and the tops to be eighteen inches in thickness, laid in Roman Cement. The bricks are not to be laid headers and stretchers, in the ordinary manner of performing brick work but in half brick rings, and it is obvious that the back joints or circular brick work can only be filled up with cement. The top arch is to be a portion of a larger circle than that of the bottom, or invert; the sides are to be segments of a still larger circle, the whole thing being similar in shape to the longitudinal shape of an egg, with the small end downwards. Any void space on the outside of the brick work, must be filled with brick-bats, stone or other hard materials well rammed in. A length being finished another length is begun and carried on as before; the packings under the ends of the large timbers can be loosened, and the timber shifted forward for the next length, one end supported by brick work the other by the foreground; but the polling wood cannot be got out and must remain for ever where it has been put.

It was estimated that two different set of workmen, about ten or a dozen to a set, each working a twelve hour shift, could excavate a four yard length of tunnel in about nine days under ordinary circumstances. At the N.M.R. Board meeting in April 1839, it was reported that ... 'During the last ten weeks one million cubic yards of earth work had been excavated from the Clay Cross Tunnel' — at this date all the twenty-two faces would have been working. On the seventy-two mile stretch from Derby to Leeds it was estimated that 9,500,000 cubic yards of earthenworks were removed by picks, shovels and gunpowder when the excavations were completed. In the 1850's twenty tons a day was considered to be a normal stint for a navvy.

On the deep cuttings north and south of the tunnel a prodigious amount of soil and rock had to be cut through and removed in order to reach the tunnel entrances and there is a vivid description of how this sort of work was done in F. S. Williams' 'Our Iron Roads'.

Runs as they are called, are made by laying planks up the side of the cutting, on which the barrows may be wheeled. The running is performed by stout young men, round the waist of each is a strong belt, fastened to which is a rope running up the side of the cutting, and turning on a wheel at the top, whilst to the other extremity a horse is attached to the barrow being laden ... the signal is given to the driver, who leads the horse quickly out a given distance into the field, and thus the man is drawn up the acclivity; the contents of the barrow are emptied, and the horse being led back the rope is slackened and the man runs down the plank again, drawing the empty barrow after him.

Contemporary sketch showing barrow runs to remove earth from cutting

Much of the soil and rocks drawn up from the southern entrance down Clay Lane, can still be seen and the walk along this part of the line is known as the 'Spoil Banks'. Some of this earthen work was also carted off to help make up the embankments immediately south of the tunnel.

Though there is no evidence of any women actually working on the excavations no doubt many were employed in making the prodigious pile of bricks used on the tunnel and ventilation shafts. Brick-making was a seasonal occupation and the brick make during the summers of 1837, 1838 and 1839, were 4½ million, 7 million and 4 million respectively. It was estimated that the tunnel would absorb at least 15 million bricks and all these bricks, it must be remembered, were individually made by hand.

Accidents and injuries

Tunnelling was perhaps the most hazardous job of all on the earthenworks of the railways, and the navvies frequently toiled twelve hours a day in atrocious conditions, often soaked to the skin throughout the shift by a constant influx of water; in constant peril from falls of earth and explosions, and constantly breathing in foul air. During the driving of the tunnel at Clay Cross at least eleven workmen are known to have been killed and many others were savagely injured. As no records were kept by the N.M.R. company or by the various contractors, the total number of people killed or seriously injured is difficult, if not impossible, to obtain. However, the accounts of at least eleven fatal accidents on the Clay Cross stretch, together with many others north and south of the tunnel, appear in contemporary newspaper reports. Whether or not all fatal accidents were actually reported to the local press is not known, and it is very difficult to trace those people who were seriously injured and later died from their injuries, as they were usually removed to their respective parish of origin as a consequence of the laws of settlement regarding poor relief.

One such person who was removed to his place of settlement at Hucknall was Francis Burton. This man apparently died from injuries he had received seven months previous.

> It appears at Clay Cross between eight and nine o'clock, the flywheel shaft broke, and while Timothy Green, engineer, was taking the shaft out, the deceased tapped the boiler and let the boiling water run into the fire-hole; he then said he would fetch the shovel out of the fire-hole, and he got down a four staved ladder to get it; the water having floated the ladder bottom when he set foot upon it, it shot from under him and caused him to tumble in the boiling water. The men assisted to get him out, and he was taken home . . . and he contined suffering until Friday week when he died.

One of the first reported fatalities occurred on Saturday, November 26th 1837, at the Chesterfield end of the tunnel. A workman named George Linsey, had just sat down to dinner with several of his companions, when he was struck at the back of the head by a chunk of stone from rock being blasted, and was killed instantly. They were seated only a few yards away from where the shot was being fired and no warning was given. The expenses for his funeral were paid for by the newly established 'Society of Excavators'.

Without gunpowder some sections of the different railways, including the N.M.R. would have been impossible to cut through. Alternative routes would have been far too expensive and its use certainly saved the navvies much 'graft'. On some contracts the navvies had to purchase their own gunpowder and its safe storage always caused a problem. On one occasion a woman who kept one of the shanties had a narrow escape in consequence of a workman incautiously placing a quantity of gunpowder over the fire place

> which by some accident exploded and the roof of the place was blown off and the poor woman was seriously injured about the neck and arms.

A 'serious frolick' was reported in February 1839, when Charles Bishop, a bricklayer threw a shovel of burning coals into a waggon containing gunpowder which exploded and blew the 'thoughtless man' a distance of 26 yards. His clothes were torn to pieces and his body severely burnt. In August, the previous year, Thomas Cook working near Clay Cross,

> was in the act of lighting a shot which had been set for the purpose of blasting a mass of soil, and by some means a small proportion was sprinkled on the ground, which ignited and communicated with the blast before the poor fellow had time to get away — he was killed on the spot.

Many of the contractors and engineers refused to use the patent safety fuse and W. A. Purdon, engineer on the Woodhead tunnel in giving evidence to the 'Select Committee on Railway Labourers' 1846, gave the astonishing reply that

> Perhaps the patent fuse is safer, but it is attended with such loss of time, and the difference is so very small, I would not recommend the loss of time for the sake of all extra lives it would save.

Unfortunately, no evidence related to the N.M.R. line was submitted to this particular select committee.

In February 1840, in an attempt to complete the line on the deep cutting at the south end of the tunnel, nearly 200 excavators were busily engaged in blasting and cutting through the rock when a half barrel of gunpowder was ignited by a piece of hot ballast that had rolled down the side of the cutting. This particular barrel of gunpowder was situated in the midst of a group of workmen when it exploded and severely burnt nine of them. One man was reported to have had a miraculous escape. Although he was only a few yards from the barrel when it exploded, he was in a crouching position and so escaped much of the blast. Three others were not so fortunate, and it was feared that they would lose their sight as a consequence of the accident. Several days later there were two other shotfiring accidents on this same cutting. William Johnson of Stretton, beer-house keeper, after preparing a shot and retiring about thirty yards from it, was struck on the head by a large stone and seriously injured when the shot went off prematurely. Two hours later another shot was fired and another overlooker was also seriously injured when

> a large piece of rock descended with such force on the waggon as to break through the plank bottom and crosspieces and cut the overlooker's head most seriously.

Besides the accidents with gunpowder and its careless use and storage, a few explosions of firedamp occured in the tunnel headings and on one occasion a navvy was severely burnt by this 'wildfire'. The Clay Cross Tunnel was driven through about seven different seams of coal, and firedamp (an inflammable gas whose chief constituent is methane) is emitted from coal seams during their working. In November 1882, an explosion of firedamp at the Clay Cross Company's No. 7 pit (Parkhouse) killed 45 men and boys.

Together with the men's own recklessness, ignorance and bravado, and the contractors' determination to complete the work on time and as

View in tunnel at bottom of working shaft (Kilsby Tunnel)

View up ventilation shaft in Clay Cross tunnel

41

cheaply as possible, little or no attention was given to matters concerning health and safety. Indeed, one particular overlooker, who was responsible for the No. 5 shaft on the tunnel, was so concerned about the progress of the work that he called to the men to see how work was progressing; no answer being returned he attributed the silence to inattention, and decided to shin down the shaft's gin rope and 'as the rope was wet he reached the bottom in a state of insensibility'.

Sinking and working about the unguarded shafts along the line of the tunnel was a dangerous and difficult job and at least ten people were reported to have lost their lives during the time it took to complete the tunnel. In February 1838, a miner named Bunting, employed sinking a new shaft near to the entrance at the Clay Lane end, was killed when a truck fell down the shaft and hit him on the head. A few weeks later Bunting's former partner had a narrow escape from a similar accident but just managed to jump clear. In between these two accidents, Daniel Glinister, was passing by one of the shafts at about six o'clock in the evening and as there was a fire on the ground close to the shaft, he did not observe it and fell down the shaft and was killed on the spot. Richard Crompton, William Brooks, John Alvey, James Ferguson, James Walker, Gale, Spencer and Parker were all killed as a consequence of falling down one of the shafts on the Clay Cross Tunnel. Also a stranger

> to the business of tunnelling looked up the shaft as a loaded waggon was ascending when a stone fell off and hit him on the head. The company have ordered him an attendant night and day — but the poor man continues in a dangerous state.

Joseph Edwards a superintendant of the excavators employed on the Milford Tunnel was also killed when he was thrown out of a bucket whilst descending a ventilation shaft.

In the second year of the tunnel's progress, in June, one of the main shafts together with part of the tunnel collapsed. Fortunately no one was injured but the contractor, who would have suffered considerable financial loss. This particular set-back probably contributed to Swanwick introducing Edward Price to take over half of the tunnel contract. When the tunnel was supposed to have collapsed, a rumour quickly spread that thirty tunnellers had been killed and ten seriously wounded and that as a consequence a serious riot broke out, the military were called upon, and a serious engagement took place — the 'Derbyshire Courier' however, refuted both these rumours.

42

The following September, another length of the tunnel fell in and buried a bricklayer, George Platts, from Coloverton, in Lincolnshire. This particular fall was quite considerable, and it took about three days to recover the body from the tons of debris. The inquest was held at the George and Dragon at Clay Cross and he was later interred in the North Wingfield cemetery. It was common practice during the nineteenth century to hold inquest in local pubs and few escaped this duty.

In October 1839, a fourteen year old youth was run over by some soil waggons and killed.

> Nothing can exceed the reckless daring of youths employed on the railway. By far the greatest number of accidents that have happened have been occasioned by utter want of care and this unfortunate case adds one more to the list.

At the Derby, Easter Quarter Sessions held in 1838, W. J. Lockett Esq., questioned the sum of £223 appearing in the accounts for the inquests held in the County during the last quarter.

> It was, a very large amount and for which he saw not the least necessity. In many cases of inquests there had been verdicts returned of 'natural causes', and he believed it to be quite unnecessary in many of these cases to put the county to expense by inquisition.

W. J. Bagshaw then replied.

> In reference to the increased number of inquests held by Mr. Hutchinson, the coroner for Scarsdale, they were in a great measure owing to the many accidents which had recently occurred on the North Midland Railway line.

Medical treatments and operations

The medical men residing in the town during the tunnelling operations were Mr. Brown, who came to Clay Cross with the Kilsby tunnellers in 1838; and William Mackarsie, who was employed by George Stephenson and Company. Mackarsie arrived about the same time as Mr. Brown, and remained surgeon to the Company's Field Club until 1860, when he was succeeded by Dr. Wilson.

At the deep cutting on the south end of the tunnel, a young lad, George Bradley, came to an untimely death when he was run over by a set of soil carriages. The surgeon, Mr. Brown, amputated both legs but the young lad only survived a few hours after the operation. The following year, John Bateman, met a similar end . . . 'but tetanus coming on, the poor fellow's existence was terminated . . .'.

Broken and crushed limbs were very serious injuries and few people appear to have survived any of the operations that necessitated amputations. With no effective anaesthetic available, the injured had to endure excruciating pain and their only relief would be from a swig of whiskey or drop of laudanum (a tincture of opium). Laudanum was sold by druggists and grocers alike, and was administered without any instructions whatsoever, and frequently resulted in many infant mortalities and adult suicides. An inquest before J. Hutchinson, at the New Inn, Clay Cross, in January 1842, on the body of a child between one and two years old, recorded a verdict of death occasioned by an overdose of laudanum. Indeed, Joseph Hays, grocer, of Clay Cross took some laudanum by mistake.

> Mr. Hays retails a few drugs, and finding himself unwell he took a dose of epsom salts, with which he mixed three quarters of an ounce of laudanum for that quantity of tincture of rhubarb by mistake — the bottles standing on a shelf close to each other. Immediately after taking the dose he discovered his mistake, and took a quantity of mustard and water, which caused the dose to be ejected from his stomach.

The report then went on to say

> We advise Mr. Hays, if he cannot guard against the repetition of such mistakes, to dispense with dispensing drugs.

Though there are few details of these gruesome operations being performed on the navvies, the 1840 local newspapers inform us in some detail of some of those undertaken by Mr. Mackarsie. In December 1841, a collier fell down a shaft belonging to Stephenson and Company, and sustained three severe fractures, Mackarsie, with the assistance of two other surgeons from Crich and Alfreton, decided to amputate both legs.

> Stimulants were administered to him and he appeared to rally under their effect, but after the amputation of one leg he began to sink and it was deemed advisable by the medical gentlemen not to proceed with the other operation.

Sometime in August 1843, another collier fell down a pit shaft and miraculously escaped without sustaining any serious injury and was at work again in a couple of days. With regards to this accident, however, the company surgeon wrote to the 'Derbyshire Courier' and requested that the editor should correct an error which had appeared in the previous week's edition.

Will you be pleased to correct an error in your publication of last week, as it may tend to infer absence of duty on my part as surgeon of the Clay Cross Company. Job Bradley, fell a distance of 20 or 30 yards down a shaft and miraculously escaped without serious injury, the second morning I bled him, and repeated it in the evening; the next day he was out at six in the morning and did not return for twelve hours. He was perfectly recovered.

Ventilation shaft, Clay Lane

Ventilation shaft, Market Street

Operating on a boy whose arm had been severely crushed by a railway waggon, Mackarsie put the patient under the influence of ether inhalation

which acted most effectively and the patient appeared unconscious until it was nearly completed. Some portion of the ether remaining in the inhaler, Mr. Mackarsie was in the act of putting it back in the bottle, when the candle came into contact with the vapour and an explosion took place. The persons were much alarmed in seeing Mr. Mackarsie enveloped in a sheet of flame and the room apparently blazing. By prompt exertion the flames were after a little while extinguished no serious injuries having been sustained. Up to the present period the boy is doing well.

In 1847, James Simpson, Professor of Midwifery at Edinburgh University, demonstrated anaesthesia by means of chloroform and in October 1848, we read of its first use in the Clay Cross district when Mackarsie operated on Margaret Elliot of Higham.

> at first she became much excited, but by continued application of the agent, she soon went into a sound sleep, and the operation immediately began. She remained in total insensibility to the very last and only regained consciousness when the stump was being severed. Two hours afterwards, she expressed herself as not having felt the slightest pain and was doubtful that the leg had been removed.

At about this date, the Chesterfield Board of Guardians were advertising for a medical practitioner for their Ashover district, which included Clay Cross, and the successful applicant had to supply his own leeches and equipment for the grand sum of £20 per annum. Indeed, leeches were still being used in Clay Cross as recently as 1916, and Leslie Ball, during a recorded interview in 1979, explains how he used some leeches on his father to help relieve him of a violent headache.

> I couldn't just say whether it was Dr. Chawner or Dr. Wilson, but he was fetched to my father this particular day. He was suffering from violent headaches and the only thing the doctor could suggest was bleeding. The way he suggested bleeding was to put some leeches on his forehead. I had to go to the surgery, as medicines were dispensed there by Mrs. Alison. I was given a box of these, and I'm certain there were four in the box. They were taken down home and two put on his forehead for a considerable time, in fact they rolled off themselves. A towel was placed at each side so that when they dropped off they dropped on the towel. We had to get them on a saucer . . . place them on a copper . . . and they were put in salt, and we waited until tea-time until the next lot was used. Then I think he was done the next day and the day after, and that was the end of the leeches.

The Workhouse and Sick Clubs

Many of the workers that were injured or took seriously ill, and who had no way of supporting themselves and their families usually finished up in the workhouse. In the Admittance and Discharge book of the Chesterfield Union Workhouse, there are several entries of navigators being admitted. Two such navvies, Richard Gardner and George Richardson, both chargeable to the Clay Lane Township, entered the Chesterfield Workhouse in June 1839. The cause of their seeking relief was that they had been severely burnt, which rendered them partially disabled and unfit for any work.

An interesting entry in the Chesterfield Admittance Book, of which there are several similar entries, is of a man abandoning his wife and children. The entry records that he did not belong to the Parish of Clay Lane, but happened to fall there as a tramp. Perhaps he was a navvy and came to Clay Cross with his family in search of work on the Tunnel. The navvies had a tradition of tramping from job to job, sometimes taking their families with them, and at other times leaving them on the Parish. If a navvy could not get any work on a particular line, it was traditional for the other navvies to give him a shilling the 'tramping bob' to help him on his way.

The navvies did, however, attempt to introduce a little self help, and in November 1837, it was reported that the excavators employed on the Clay Cross Tunnel had formed themselves into a society for the relief of each other in sickness and in case of accident, during the progress of the Tunnel. In December, the funds of this particular society (£3 to £4) were stolen from the offices of Mr. Trezivant, assistant engineer to Mr. Waring, and there appears to be no further mention of this Sick Club after this date. The rules for this society appear in the 'Derbyshire Courier' and were very similar to those adopted by the various Field Clubs that were springing up in the coalmining villages in the county.

> If any workman be disabled through drunkeness or fighting, he cannot claim the assistance of the club, and if any be found drinking or entering a public house for the purpose of drinking while receiving relief, such relief will be withdrawn.

According to the 'Courier',

> these rules appear well calculated to add to the comfort of sick workmen and to promote good conduct, affording sufficient proof that railwaymen are not the reckless characters they are generally considered.

During the time it took to complete the N.M.R. line, there appears to be no other evidence to suggest that any of the excavators had organised themselves into a sick club. It was perhaps the prospect of at least two years employment on the Clay Cross section that encouraged the navvies at Clay Cross to raise a fund for their mutual relief in case of accident or sickness. The craftsmen on the other hand had better prospects of employment and together with regular earnings and better pay they usually belonged to a recognised Friendly Society which also offered them some security against sickness or injury.

In 1841, George Stephenson's colliers at Clay Cross, held a meeting for the purpose of forming a sick club to raise funds for their mutual relief. Contributions were compulsory and written into the company rules :- Rule VII, stated that

> Every married collier or pit man is required to give 6d a fortnight; every single man 3d; to a fund raised every pay-day for the purpose of procuring medical assistance whenever required for the men and their families.

This company Field Club was for many years under the rigid control of the management and continued to be criticised throughout its existence.

It is interesting to note that the N.M.R. in February 1841, insisted

> That all porters and other subordinate servants of the company who may in future be appointed, be required to enter into the N.M.R. Friendly Society.

AMBERGATE TUNNEL.

CHAPTER THREE

THE NAVVIES AT HOME

Homes

In February 1839, at the N.M.R. general meeting it was reported that about 8,600 people were employed on the line between Derby and Leeds and as the Clay Cross Tunnel was one of the most difficult sections and took two years and seven months to complete, it would obviously require a substantial labour force. Though no exact figures are available as to the number employed on the Clay Cross section, in July 1839, it was reported that 1,700 are employed ... 'within the compass of two miles contiguous to his (Milnes J.P.) residence'. William Milnes resided at Stubbing Edge Hall, approximately two miles from Clay Cross. At about this date the Bull Bridge contract employed 200 horses and 1,400 men on its three and a half mile stretch. At the height of the work, when all the contracts were set, nearly 10,000 men were estimated to be employed on the line.

If hundreds of navigators, excavators, bankers or miners, as the railway workers were sometimes called, were employed on the Clay Cross line; together with bricklayers, brickmakers, kiln attendants, masons, sawyers, carpenters, blacksmiths, engineers, engine drivers, barrowmen, horsekeepers and drivers etc., working round the clock — where did they live?

In Clay Cross and the surrounding districts there was certainly insufficient accomodation to cater for this great influx of workers together with some of their families. According to the 1831 census, prior to the commencement of the tunnelling operations, the population of Clay Cross or the Clay Lane Township was 564; 111 families inhabited 109 houses, and one dwelling house was reported as being uninhabited. As there was an average of five persons to each dwelling, taking in any lodgers would have meant severe overcrowding. It was, however, not unusual for navvies to sleep more than ten to a small room and a number of residents found it quite lucrative to take in lodgers. The 'Derbyshire Courier' in 1837, reveals that

> A great many hands are employed on the deep cuttings of each end of the tunnel, and so large a congregation of course renders cottages and lodgings very scarce and dear at Clay Cross and in the neighbourhood. Our information states that in one cottage consisting of a ground floor fourteen feet square with a chamber in front of it and a pantry backwards; with a small chamber or loft over that there are eighteen of a family; and they may be more thickly huddled together in other places for ought we know to the contrary. A cottage of this description was let out for about three shillings per week. This scarcity of cottages and lodgings has caused about 30 houses, or rather cabins to be built with sods in the neighbourhood; and notwithstanding the great mart for human labour, troops of men are daily applying who cannot obtain any.

The main contractors on the tunnel expressed their concern about the lack of accomodation and complained to the directors of the N.M.R. and ... 'which causes several of their best hands to leave and to go to other places'. Soon after, this matter was discussed at the N.M.R. board meeting, and in August 1837, it was recorded that

> order be given to the engineer (Swanwick) to furnish an estimate for the erection of buildings on the Clay Cross Tunnel contract, for the accomodation of about 100 of the superior workmen, for which rent is to be paid.

The plans and the estimates for these cottages were soon approved and Mr. Swanwick was

> requested to carry into execution accordingly keeping in view the possibility of a part of the building being hereafter applicable to the permanent use of the company's officers or servants.

These particular houses were completed early in 1838, and were appropriately called the East and West Tunnel Rows — sixteen houses in the East Row and fourteen in the West Row. Both these rows were situated either side of the Turnpike road on the High Street, with East Tunnel Row almost on the top of the tunnel and just a few yards away from the ventilation shaft that still proudly stands in front of the new Social Centre. West Tunnel Row was demolished in 1875, to make way for the Victoria Buildings erected by Mr. Linacre. The East Tunnel Row was demolished in 1970, and the area has since been landscaped by the District Council. The total rent collected by the N.M.R. for the Tunnel Rows in a 20 month period was about £367-8-9.

East Tunnel Row c. 1908

Though the Tunnel Rows were considered for the permanent use of the N.M.R. 'servants' the majority of their workers resided at Tupton which was nearer to Clay Cross Station.

After the tunnel was completed both these rows were purchased by George Stephenson and Company in 1841, to accomodate the miners for his expanding labour force who were to work at his No. 1 and Tupton pits. In a letter to the N.M.R. directors, George Stephenson wrote

> I find on examining the cottages which the company offered to us at Clay Cross, that many of them are in a most ruinous state owing to them having been shamefully used by the workmen engaged in the tunnel. I trust therefore you will take into consideration the priority of making us some allowance to enable us to put them in a habitable condition.

In June 1841, George Stephenson and Company's minute books reveals

> To purchase of 30 cottages and one house (Hill House) situated at Clay Cross, £2,684 3s 9d.

An indication of the state and condition of the place is perhaps highlighted by a newspaper report of July 1840.

> FEVER AT CLAY LANE — We are sorry to hear of the extent to which the malignant fever prevails in the parish and hope that prompt efforts will be made to stop its further progress. It is painful to think that the inhabitants have by their culpable carelessness and uncleanliness brought disease upon themselves; and this fact should operate as a caution to other districts not to neglect what may appear trivial, but are in reality exceedingly dangerous and disgusting nuisances. The public seem not sufficiently awakened to a sense of this danger, but we can inform them that in the exact language of our authority which is best, in two or three cases last week, the clergymen of North Wingfield would not admit the corpse into church from motives of prudence. The warmest thanks are due to Mr. Oldham, surgeon of Alfreton who first called attention to the existence of the nuisances and not less are the public indebted to the Chesterfield Board of Guardians, who in this, as in every other matter which has come under our observation, have displayed an anxious desire to promote the interest of the community. We would advise that, at once, subscriptions be raised by the inhabitants for the purpose of whitewashing and effectually purifying the houses of the poor.

In George Stephenson's account books for 1841 and 1842, there are a number of entries for the supplying of lime for the cottage gardens and . . . '9cwts for whitewashing cottages at 7/6d per ton'.

Local folklore and school history continues to teach us that both the Top and Bottom Long Rows were built for the tunnellers but in fact they were built by Stephenson and completed early in 1841. 'To glazing 88 cottages at £1 8s 6d each'.

Because of the scarcity of houses the navvies who could not secure rented accomodation erected their own homes, and the huts and shanties they built were usually made of wood, turf, mud, stone, bricks or anything else they could lay their hands on. Tarpaulins were frequently used to cover their shanty roofs. Sometime in July 1837, a reward of two guineas was offered for the recovery of a new tarpaulin that was stolen from a stack yard at Stretton

> and if two or more are concerned in the robbery, if any one of them will impeach his accomplice or accomplices, he shall receive the reward, and all the means to obtain his pardon.

At Crich, 96 square yards of calico used as a stack cover was also stolen.

In May 1838, a fire broke out in one of the 'huts' erected on the tunnel section,

> which communicated to two adjoining ones and being chiefly composed of combustible materials, the whole speedily ignited, and so rapid was the progress of the flames that the whole of the furniture, together with the beds and bedding were entirely destroyed. As a result several families were rendered homeless by the calamity and the workmen employed on the line of railway in the neighbourhood of Clay Cross had a collection for them.

Womenfolk

In the early years of the railways it was the navvy custom not to marry and most of the men and women on the lines of railway simply lived together. Indeed, on some lines it was the custom for a navvy and his woman to step over a brush and the marriage ceremony was complete — hence the saying 'living over the brush'. Selling wives was common and when it was time to move on, many women and children were left on the parish, as was Sarah Young and her four children. Mr. Rooth, the Clay Lane Guardian of the Poor, complained bitterly to the Chesterfield Poor Law Union about this particular case.

> The woman not being able to give any account as to her place of settlement, he was afraid it would impose a burden on the parish.

The Chesterfield Union, however, were legally bound to support Sarah and her children until they had established her legal settlement.

Despite the propensity not to get married, the North Wingfield Marriage Registers between 1837 and 1839, record several navigators and excavators getting married according to the rites and ceremonies of the established church. In July 1839, Thomas Lightfoot, navigator, was married to Mary Aram who was registered as a widow. Their place of reisdence at the time of marriage was Smithymoor, which is situated at the south end of the tunnel, and no doubt they probably lived in one of the huts or shanties erected at that place. It is quite possible that Mary's previous husband was also a navigator, her father, Samuel Brown was registered as a navigator and Thomas' father was registered as a brickmaker.

Often a woman who was widowed or left behind hitched herself to another man and usually her children took his name. Other women left on the parish would do almost anything to escape the workhouse, which deprived them of their liberty and took their children from them. In

June 1839, Mary Royston, a native of Wakefield had travelled to Chesterfield with the expectation of marrying an excavator who was working on the N.M.R. line there. She had been on the tramp for three days and after being turned down by the excavator she procured two ounces of arsenic at a druggist shop in the town and then went to the Crispin Inn, on Knifesmithgate, where the person who had disappointed her was sitting with some other navvies. She then purchased some ale and put the arsenic into it and drank it off in his presence saying ... 'now I am done for myself'. A surgeon was sent for and a stomach pump was applied without much effect — a verdict of temporary insanity was later returned.

Women who followed the navvies on the railways as their mistresses were known as 'tally women'. Whatever we think of their morals, we must sympathise with their attempts to make a home in a typical navvy hut.

Unfortunately, no description of the living conditions in these huts at Clay Cross has yet come to light, but it is not difficult to imagine what it was like eating and sleeping in an overcrowded, verminous, earth-floor, sod hut, with no sanitation and huddled together with 'untrained' running dogs and bulldogs!

Pastimes

The running dogs, usually lurchers, were used for poaching and the bulldogs for fighting, which was one of the navvies' favourite pastimes. George Stephenson's colliery rules at Clay Cross, did not allow any of its employees to keep fighting dogs, or fighting cocks in any of the company's cottages, or to introduce them on the works. (Rule VI)

Another of the navvies' favourite pastimes was prize-fighting. They would gather from all quarters to witness such a spectacle as they did in May 1838, when numerous railwaymen flocked to a fight at Selston. On their return to Riddings and Alfreton a number of the navvies rioted, and a detachment of the 10th Hussars was alerted but having no orders to remain they returned to their quarters.

> The unseemly conduct of persons employed in the neighbourhood in the construction of the North Midland Railway, continues to excite fear of the peaceful inhabitants. The men thus employed are of the lowest ranks of society, untaught and uncultured.

The degrading sport of prize-fighting continued to be part of the scene at Clay Cross for a considerable time and in March 1847, we read of such a fight in a field between Clay Cross and Stretton.

> The combatants were Jacob Kenning of Clay Cross and a person whose name we could not learn, who is commonly known by the cognomen of 'Cuckoo of Ashover'. The wager was £1 a-side. They had 70 rounds (a knock-down constituting a round), and were fighting about three hours, both men were dreadfully bruised. Kenning was finally declared the victor. What necessity there exists for vigorous efforts on the part of those whose labours are directed to the moral elevation of the people; when men so degraded can be found as will voluntary subject themselves to such physical injuries, merely that they applaud the victor in the injuries he receives. We hope the time will come when such scenes will no more disgrace our country — when every man will strive to render his fellow man happy.

Booze

The excavators were notorious for their fierce drinking habits. Their customary drink was beer and on the lines where the water was contaminated there were few alternatives. Indeed, one youth employed on the Clay Cross section was taken seriously ill after drinking water that had run off the ironstone, and as there was little hope for his recovery he was taken to Nottingham 'where his friends lived'. Pure clean water was scarce and expensive and in October 1837, Mary Sanforth of Brampton was fined 10/- and 13/- costs for stealing water from the Chesterfield Water Company. In June 1840, two shares for the above mentioned company were advertised for sale and were bought for 100 guineas each, and the original price per share was only £25.

During the two and half years it took to drive the tunnel, the beerhouses and beer-huts together with the established pubs such as the George and Dragon, Angel Inn, Shoulder of Mutton, New Inn and the Old Buck were the dominant institutions to which the navvies escaped after their labours.

> This hamlet continues to present an aspect of activity altogether unprecedented until the railway tunnel was undertaken. So great a number of workmen are in constant employment and occasions a consumption of malt liquor never witnessed in the place before, and we wish the days immediately succeeding those of payment were not marked by the intemperate drinking, but it is worthy of remark that no less than seven agents of so many different breweries made

their call at one house in the brief space of half-an-hour; and that five out of the seven were connected with firms from Staffordshire, Yorkshire, Leicestershire, Nottinghamshire and Derbyshire. This fact appear evincive of punctuallity on the part of the Clay Cross victuallers, or so much solitude to serve them would not be manifested in so many quarters.

Though a number of pubs and farms brewed their own beer prior to the navvy invasion they no doubt abandoned this practice in preference for a quicker product from the breweries and an increase in trade. At this date Clay Cross had a malt house which was situated down Clay Lane, and the 1841 census records George Ellis as the maltster.

The Beerhouse Act of 1830, permitted almost anyone to sell beer provided they paid a small excise fee, and ordinary houses and shanty-huts could readily be turned into beerhouses. Indeed, many of the beer-huts in Clay Cross were illegal as their excavator landlords did not bother to pay the excise fee. Yellow Sam, a sub-contractor hit upon an evasive contrivance to avoid taking out a licence, to all those who wanted liquor he sold them a pea and gave the drink. In December 1837, another Clay Cross landlord appeared before the Alfreton magistrates and was fined £5 for selling beer without a licence. 'Nixon was in the habit of evading the law by selling peas and giving beer'. The following year in December, William Marshall, John Fliver, Richard Smith and George Lancaster all excavators in the neighbourhood of Clay Cross were summoned to Chesterfield Borough Court, for having sold beer without a licence. Only Smith was found guilty and fined £5 with 15/- costs.

> The friends of the parties who escaped the penalties, amounting to about fifty, decked themselves in ribbon and hired carriages to convey them in triumph to Clay Cross.

The following month William Marshall was back in court for the same offence but did not escape a £5 fine the second time.

As a consequence of the proliferation of unlicensed beershops, the magistrates of the county signed a petition.

> relative to the state of the beerhouses in the county and praying the legislator to take such measures for their better regulation as thought expedient.

In July 1840, the 'Courier' reports that

> The number of public houses has increased at Clay Cross in the last few years from 4 to 17, and three more good houses are erecting which are intended as being opened as public houses.

With this deluge of beerhouses in the town, there would obviously be some competition for custom, not only between retailers but also between breweries. To attract custom beer would be sold as cheap as possible and to enable the retailer to do this, the prevalent practice at the time was to dilute the beer with water and then make up for the lack of strength by adding cocculus indicus, a dangerous poison containing picrotoxin. Other stuffs used as cheap substitutes for malt and hops and to give false appearance and strength and taste, were multum, capsicum, copperas, quassia, harts-horn shavings, orange powder, caraway seeds, ginger and a variety of mixed drugs. Storage was a problem and expensive for the large breweries and to make the beer mature faster for a quick sale they added sulphuric acid.

Adulteration was a deliberate fraud for the sake of gain, and its most pernicious effect was on the health of the consumer. Unfortunately, it was regarded as a normal and almost legitimate method of carrying on trade, and druggists who supplied much of the ingredients for adulteration practised their trade quite openly.

There appears to be no prosecution locally for this systematic adulteration, but the excise man was quite active and he summoned quite a number of landlords and grocers for giving short weight. At the June Quarter Sessions in 1837, six landlords in the Clay Cross district were prosecuted for possessing measures 'not according to the standard of the exchequer'. A local grocer and chemist were also fined at the same court for similar offences. At Eckington in February 1839, nineteen different individuals from the district were all convicted for either giving short weight or short measure.

The ability to consume enormous quantities of beer was one of the qualifications that an ordinary labourer had to possess before he could graduate to the status of navvy. An example of their fierce drinking habits was demonstrated by a John Mason who was employed on the line at Ambergate near Belper. Mason laid a wager that he could drink a pint of gin in five minutes, and, surprisingly, he completed this feat in one and half minutes; but not being satisfied, he laid half-a-sovereign that he could drink a quart more gin in five minutes. As soon as the gin was produced he collapsed on the floor and expired in a very short time.

One excavator at Clay Cross hit on a novel way of raising a glass of grog when he called at a public house in the town and pretended to be an overseer employed on the tunnel. Whilst talking to the landlord he informed him that he had the good fortune to have an honest set of men under him, and that he was about to treat them with a gallon of gin as a

A group of Navvies in their working clothes (Leicester Museum)

reward for their industry and good conduct. He then produced a gallon bottle, which he had previously half filled with water, and requested the unsuspicious landlord to add two more quarts of gin which was accordingly done. On request of payment being made he intimated to the landlord his intention of paying a future date, but mine host, having no faith in excavators refused to trust him, and two quarts of the liquor were consequently poured from the bottle after which the wily rascal, 'chuckling at his success' returned with his two quarts of water ingeniously converted into capital half-and-half grog.

A felicide extraordinary happened in the town when two excavators lodging in Clay Cross discovered that sad inroads had been made into their provisions.

> which their sympathetic hostess always attributed to the dishonesty of the cat, whose indiscriminations sharpened the wits of the men of clay in proportion to their diminished meals. Having in vain tried to preserve the fragments; they took a rabbit, ready skinned, and requested their landlady to make a pie for supper, which on being set before them, they pretended to eat it with sundry praises but pocketed their supper, and next day asking for the remainder found

puss had again been exercising her old propensity to the entire demolition of herself. Imagination may picture the looks of mine host when informed she had been eating — instead of the rabbit, her own favourite tabby.

It is of interest to note that No. 7 Parkhouse Pit of the Clay Cross Company, was more commonly known at Catty Pit as a consequence of one of the sinkers being served up with a similar supper of cat-pie.

As the excavators were usually paid in a pub or beershop they frequently drank their pay away and then went 'on the randy'. At times they drank and slept at work and many workmen were killed under the influence, and the Tunnel section, despite its apparent dangers, was no exception. At the Clay Lane end of the Tunnel, an excavator known amongst the men as Rodney, was dreadfully burnt whilst in a state of intoxication. Apparently, he had been drinking at one of the unlicensed beer-huts that 'abound in the neighbourhood', and after taking his fill, he fell asleep by one of the ballast fires and was dreadfully burnt. Though it was reported that he had been admitted to the workhouse, the Chesterfield Union registers record no such person being admitted, so he was probably returned to his place of settlement.

In March 1838, an inquest was held on the body of an unknown man who was found dead, with his face down, in a muddy ditch near Wingerworth Hall. The man 'proved to be a labourer' on the N.M.R. and the coroner presumed that he was intoxicated having fallen down in the ditch, and 'suffocated from the inability to rise again'. Another excavator was also found dead in the Cromford Canal and 'It was supposed he had fallen in the water accidently, being in the state of intoxication'.

Fighting

Navvies worked hard and played hard and frequently indulged in fist-fights, particularly after they had been drinking. As a consequence several cases of manslaughter were reported during the progress of the tunnel. John Craddock and William Haines, two tunnellers, had such a contest after a boozing session, and Haines later died from his injuries and a warrant was issued for Craddock's arrest. Another incident occurred on the line at South Wingfield when Thomas Hardy accused William Keen of saying something disrespectful about his sweetheart. Hardy struck Keen a blow and when the landlord turned them out, in true navvy style, they retired to an adjoining field to settle the dispute. Keen, after receiving two blows to the head fell to the ground and immediately expired. A warrant was issued for Hardy's arrest but he had absconded and probably took up an alias on some other line of railway. Hardy came from Carlton, Nottinghamshire, and Keen from Staffordshire.

On Whit-Monday 1838, three navvies on their way back to South Wingfield, recognised a man in Alfreton Park, who had previously taken up one of the navvies for poaching. Thomas Lewin, one of the excavators left his companions and went to have a chat with the person concerned. A fight ensued and Lewin received a stab in the abdomen from which he died. A man named Shipley was later arrested and committed to Derby Gaol to take his trial at the ensuing Assizes. Shipley pleaded guilty to manslaughter but because of the provocation by Lewin and Shipley's previous good conduct, he was imprisoned for nine months — usually anyone convicted of manslaughter at this period in time was transported for life.

> The Reverend I. Halton has known prisoner for six to seven years, who was once in his service as a gamekeeper. He was always a peaceable, inoffensive man, and his character remarkably good.

Profaning the Sabbath

Work on the Tunnel proceeded day and night with the exception of Sundays and even on this so-called day of rest, the navvies' behaviour provoked offence and led many people to sign a petition to the Mayor of Chesterfield urging him to prevent

> the most disgraceful scenes, which are continually exhibited on the Lord's Day, by a set of profligate and unprincipled characters.

At Staveley, as a result of representations made by the Rector, the Rev. B. Moore, the publicans took drastic action and closed their doors in order to withhold drink from the navvies,

> a circumstance highly honourable to them and an example of universal imitation.

Soon after this petition ninety-nine residents of Staveley signed the following letter which they had published in the Derbyshire Courier.

> Reverend Sir, We have observed, with much satisfaction the determination of the Publicans and Beer-house keepers of this large parish to keep holy the Sabbath day and although your own feelings of gratification on such an occasion is your greatest recompense, yet as you have been mainly instrumental in forwarding so desirable an object, we deem it proper to tender you our best acknowledgements, sincerely wishing that your exertions may be

crowned with complete success. And we hope and trust that the parties who have made such praiseworthy resolves, will continue to preserve them — inasmuch as they will not only tend to produce present peace and comfort, but must also tend to promote eternal welfare of themselves and many others.

The previous year Mr. Burkett, a Staveley landlord was fined 10/- for selling ale during divine service, and William Palethorpe of Eckington was ordered to pay ... 'into the hands of Rev. A. C. Broomhead one pound to be given to the poor'. At Barnsley, John Bragg and William Bradley were both fined 3/4 each and 6/6 costs for playing marbles during divine service.

At the justice room at Alfreton in June 1837, George Gregory of Woodthorpe in the North Wingfield Parish, was fined for 'suffering tippling therein during divine service'. Mrs. Lister of Sheffield was also charged with allowing a stage waggon to travel through Chesterfield during divine service and was fined £1 and costs.

In January 1837, a meeting of coach proprietors was convened in London and resolved that 'All the coaches between Leeds and London (except mail) have in consequence been discontinued starting either end of the journey on Sunday'. Both the economic and religious sides of the question were discussed but it appears that it was the economic one that prevailed as some of the proprietors were running at a loss with Sunday travel.

None of the advocates of teetotalism appear to have set foot in Clay Cross until the excavations were complete and a more permanent and settled community began to emerge. In November 1841, a noted champion of teetotalism from Nottingham visited Clay Cross for the purpose of lecturing on total abstinence,

> who did not scruple to take the greatest liberties with the character of the famous old gentleman John Barleycorn, as well as with all publicans and public houses.

The N.M.R. board also received a complaint about the employment of workmen on the Sabbath but Swanwick and the contractors emphasised the

> absolute necessity of not permitting the works on the tunnel to be stopped on Sunday. Only one or two men are employed, without the whole of the works would be completely filled with water, which would require the whole of Monday to pump out.

Despite the little Methodist Chapel (built 1824) being situated directly on the top of the Tunnel, just a few yards from the deep ventilation shaft, services appear to have continued as normal, and in May 1839, two impressive sermons were preached there by Mr. Henshaw of Mansfield and £3 16 3d was collected in aid of the Sunday School. This was quite a good collection for such a small chapel, can we suppose that some of the workers on the line might have attended?

The following memorial was extensively signed in the several Parishes and districts of Derby, and in many of the neighbouring places and sent to the shareholders of the Midland Counties, North Midland and Derby and Birmingham Railways.

> We the undersigned fully believing in the Divine authority of the Christian Sabbath, and that the blessing of Almighty God rests upon those nations, and companies and individuals who keep it holy, and his wrath upon those who profane it, earnestly request you to come to the resolution not to run our trains on the holy day; that thus the numerous servants employed on your lines of railway, may have the opportunity of observing the whole of the Sabbath in a religious manner; and that no temptation may be held out by you to the thoughtless and ignorant persons, to spend that day in amusement and dissipation which a merciful God has set apart not only as a day of rest from bodily labour, but also a day of instruction, edification and comfort for their immortal souls.

CHAPTER FOUR

LAW AND ORDER

Problems of Peace-keeping

During the time it took to drive the N.M.R. line through the county, the shire was almost divested of any permanent or regular police force and many places simply had to rely on the old and unpaid office of Parish Constable to help keep the peace. Though Derby and Chesterfield did establish their respective 'Watch Committees' the employed members of these Watches frequently neglected their duties and were totally inadequate for policing an expanding industrial population. The records of the Chesterfield Borough Watch Committee, emphasise the difficulties of recruiting and retaining suitable policemen. Within a period of about four months, six out of the seven constables appointed in January 1836, had either resigned or been dismissed by the end of April that year. The inspector's reports to the Chesterfield Watch Committee underline the major problem of supervising and securing a sober police force.

> Saturday 26th March 1836. Saw each man twice. All sober and on duty except No. 4 who was intoxicated and asleep a hour and ten minutes and unable to discharge his duty.
> Sunday 17th April 1836. Saw each man twice. All sober and on duty except No. 1 who did not cry half-past two until twenty minutes past three, nor four o'clock until ten past four.
> Tuesday 6th September 1836. All sober and on duty except No. 4 whose beat was at the bottom of the Market Place, and at twenty minutes past two had not commenced the hour, but was coming from Mr. Worsley's at the top of the Market Place with a brown jug containing a gallon of ale.

With the arrival of the excavators the Chesterfield Magistrates in November 1837, decided to swear in a London policeman to help keep order in the district. Indeed, there was so much public outcry about the social disruption and disorder along the various lines of railway in the

Outside the newly-built Derby station

different parts of the country that an 'Act for the payment of constables for keeping the peace near public works (1 and 2 Vict c 80)' was put on the Statute Book in 1838. This act empowered magistrates to swear-in any number of special constables they may think necessary and affix the amount of their pay which was to be provided by the railway company whose line they were to be employed on. The railway companies, however, could in the first instance appoint a number of constables, provided that the magistrate considered them to be sufficient in number for the preservation of the peace. Early in 1838, it was reported that

> the native rural and quiet inhabitants of Clay Cross are in alarm for
> the fear that the morality of the place should be corrupted by so
> great an influx of workmen from all parts.

The N.M.R. quickly responded and applied to the Home Office for a small police force to be stationed at or near Clay Cross

> where the tunnel now in progress has occasioned an immense
> accumulation of lawless and violent men.

In September the previous year it was reported that Clay Cross was becoming a dangerous place to live in, and that the inhabitants should keep an eye on their property. In the same column of the Scarsdale

Hundred report for that week, there were two reported robberies and a nasty fight in the Clay Cross area. Also Mr. Marriot of Clay Lane was robbed of a carcass of sheep and three 'heads and plucks' and a Mr. Oats of Newmarket Lane was knocked down by three men and robbed of twenty pounds and severely injured.

At about the same time, two people returning to Chesterfield after a quiet day's fishing at 'Blue Bank' were met by a party of navigators

> who after a short parley began to assault them, and no doubt would have accomplished their task had not the parties effected their escape by a sudden flight.

During this particular affray one of the navigators was overheard to say,

> that when they rob people on the highway, they should always smash them down and not let them get away to tell people.

It appears that things were beginning to get out of hand in the Chesterfield area. In May 1838, a troop of Hussars from Nottingham arrived in the town to deal with any possible outbreaks by the excavators. Their stay was very brief and the local magistrates denied the need for their presence, but a few days later more Hussars arrived and after further consultation with the magistrate it was decided that

> the soldiers will be stationed here for a considerable time in order to keep the excavators (who are very numerous) in order.

Two months after the London Police had been installed in the Clay Cross area, two of them were called to assist the Parish Constable. Apparently, some excavators connected with the works at Clay Cross ... 'manifested a disposition to be riotous by breaking windows in a public house'. On the Parish Constable apprehending an offender, he was suddenly attacked by a great number of excavators and no sooner had the London policemen arrived when they were also vigorously resisted and in attempting to exercise their staffs of office they were knocked down and trampled on. During the affray a pistol belonging to one of the policemen accidently went off and grazed the face of one of the rioters. Two or three of the inhabitants were charged by the police to assist them and 'behaved extremely well in aiding the civil force'. Warrants were issued for the rioters' arrest but they had immediately absconded.

Further down the line at South Wingfield, a navvy 'by some means' took possession of five sovereigns from an Irish labourer and refused to hand it back. The aggrieved Irishman immediately complained to the Parish

View inside Derby station

Constable who then proceeded to apprehend a navvy named Ward, who at the time of his arrest was enjoying a pint with his comrades in a local pub. Once again the excavators displayed their solidarity and vigorously resisted the Parish Constable, who then called to his assistance John Sharman, one of the London policemen. A severe struggle took place and several of the navvies attacked the constables with pokers, tongs, chairs and anything they could lay their hands on.

> By the courage and dexterity in the management of their staffs they succeeded in securing Ward and two of his companions, whose heads bore evident marks of the blows which Sharman had bestowed on them.

They were all committed to trial at the County Quarter Sessions, and Ward and Robinson were given six months hard labour and the other excavator was given three months.

All along the 72 mile stretch of the N.M.R. line there was much resistance to authority and at Bull Bridge, near Belper, when some policemen attempted to take several navvies into custody, a gang of them opposed the officers and succeeded in holding them off which enabled the delinquents to make their escape. Some offenders even

66

sought refuge in the darkness of the tunnels. At Milford in February 1839, a navvy escaped custody and secreted himself in the tunnel there and could not afterwards be discovered. It was later reported that he had concealed himself in a cart covered with soil and rubbish and in that manner was drawn out of the tunnel and made his escape.

Anglo-Irish Rivalry and the Rotherham Riots

During October 1838, on the Darfield section of the line, there were several clashes between the English and Irish navvies. The cause of their differences was variously stated. By some it was asserted that the Irish labourers worked for one shilling per day less than the English would consent to, which had induced the English to drive them from the line. This assertion, however, was contradicted and

> the rancorous feeling is said to have been engendered by the conduct of the Irish, who have habitually insulted the English workmen . . . and have been known to attack a solitary Englishman in parties of three and four, and beat and abuse them in a most extraordinary and vindictive manner.

One of the riots commenced when the English navvies assembled at Darfield and broke into the sod huts of the Irish, threw their provisions out and

> committed sad destruction on the small properties of the Irish. Another party of Irish navvies armed themselves with their spades and picks and made a resolute stand, and a desperate fight would have ensued if Mr. Stephenson (Robert) had not intervened and promised to protect the Irishmen. Stephenson took them to the Rotherham and Sheffield Railway Station, supplied them with a quantity of ale and exhorted them to be peacable. About 300 of them sought refuge in the railway station and they bitterly complained of the injury which had been inflicted on them by their enemies and stated that two or three of their party had already been killed and that they were obliged to act in self defence.

A number of the N.M.R. directors addressed the English navvies and by the promise of a quart of ale each they induced them to return to their work. As a further precaution forty artillery men, with a field piece, were dispatched from Sheffield, and the Rotherham Troop of Yeomanry was also called in.

Two of the West Riding magistrates addressed both parties and begged them to be quiet, telling them, that in the case of riot, they would assuredly find the law too strong. During the evening all seemed quiet

Clay Cross station : Print c. 1842

and the military were dismissed but one hundred special constables were sworn in; fifty patrolling Rotherham during the night and the remainder going to Swinton to maintain order. The Irishmen remained at the station during the night and the next morning repaired to the line to rescue their wages. The Englishmen, however,

> supposing they were come again to work, left their employment and armed themselves with planks, bricks, iron rails, bludgeons etc; and furiously attacked the Irish

and drove the unfortunate 'Paddys' back to Rotherham. A good number of the Irish lived in West Gate Street, and the houses in that street were broken into and searched; and if any unfortunate Irishman was discovered he was dreadfully beaten and ill used. A large body of the rioters also assembled outside the house of the contractor and threatened to pull it down because he had offered protection to the Irish the previous day.

The Yeomanry were immediately recalled and together with the civil force, led by the magistrates, they proceeded to West Gate, where the Riot Act was read by Henry Walker, Esq. of Clifton. As the mob did not disperse, the cavalry received orders to clear the streets, which they quickly effected, and took prisoners of the most active of the rioters, who were placed in gaol. The cavalry then proceeded to Rawmarsh to disperse another body of rioters that had assembled there.

> Nothing could exceed the consternation of the inhabitants of Rotherham at those hostile proceedings; on the first flush of which they securely fastened their windows and doors, and took every other precaution for the protection of their property. The town continues in a state of the most utmost excitement and alarm. It is difficult to say what has become of the poor hunted Irishmen, but they have one and all dispersed; and people prognosticate that they are assembled at some rendezvous (probably in Lancashire) for the purpose of renewing the fight.

When returning to Wentworth, Earl Fitzwilliam, was met by two English navvies from Swinton, who had been deputed, to ascertain the fate of the five men still in custody and they were told; if the men return to work peaceably, the prisoners would soon be liberated, otherwise their treatment would be more severe. It was apprehended that an attempt would be made to resuce the five prisoners, so they were immediately removed to Sheffield. After things had quietened down, Fitzwilliam applied to the Home Office for a detachment of London Police, who were to be employed to walk up and down the line, armed with a loaded pistol and without uniform (original S.P.G.). After several attacks on these London Policemen, the Earl made a further request to the Home Office for permission to further arm the policemen with cutlasses.

With the completion of most of the work on the N.M.R. line many people were thrown out of work and there was much resentment against the Irishmen who happened to secure work at lower rates of pay. On the line between Eckington and Killamarsh in February 1840, seven excavators were charged with having riotously assembled and with spades, hammers and hedge stakes attacked a group of Irish labourers and forced them to leave their work. Peter Delaney, one of the aggrieved Irish labourers stated that he was employed on the railway by Mr. Nelson for 3/- per day and that forty or so Englishmen and a man called 'Irish Jack', ordered them to leave their work immediately. Delaney, it was reported did not know why they were driven off the line ... 'except they were Irishmen'. William John Bagshaw, emphasised that

Irishmen and Scotchmen have a perfect right in this free country to offer their labours in the market just like any Englishmen. If the Irishmen think proper to work for less wages and live more humbly, has anyone the right to control him? The prisoners may depend upon it that men like the complainants should always be protected by the magistrates.

The defendants were ordered to pay the Irishmen for their loss of time and together with other expenses they had to pay sureties of £20 each to keep the peace for the next six months, and during that time they had not to molest the Irishmen again.

A few weeks later a number of the N.M.R. navvies attacked another team of Irish excavators employed by Robert Stephenson on the York and North Midland line and

> for this purpose broke into their cottages, assaulted their wives and stole their provisions, and proceeded to such an extent in their lawless and daring outrage, that it was found necessary to send express to Leeds for the police force.

During this disturbance Robert Stephenson was knocked down by a stone and injured.

Even the rural and peaceful Ashover Wakes in July 1837, did not escape a visit from the navvies

> there has been much rude company at Ashover Wakes, among whom were many workmen from the railway. Drinking and fighting were the principal amusements; and in consequence of which the constables were frequently applied for to enforce order.

Navvy or Navy?

The navvies usually wore moleskin trousers (a superior kind of fustian, double twilled and cropped before dyeing), double canvas shirts, velveteen square tailed coats, gaudy handkerchiefs and white felt hats with the brims turned up. This traditional navvies' dress was very distinctive and to a 'landlubber', it would look very much like a sailor's dress.

An indication of their distinctive dress appears in a number of contemporary newspaper accounts. Mr. Langston, surgeon, on returning to Chesterfield, was confronted by three men 'dressed as railway contractors' and

> he immediately drew a pistol from his pocket and the footpads instantly decamped across the field.

Mr. Langston's son suffered a similar fate when returning home from Clay Cross, when he also was stopped by two men 'dressed as navigators' and was robbed of his money.

In January 1839, Mr. Thomas Ford, of Coal Pit Lane, Sheffield, left home with the intention of going to Chesterfield, when three men dressed like sailors fell in with him. They journeyed on together until they reached a spot called Smith Wood, where he was suddenly seized by two of the men, whilst the third placed his hands on Mr. Ford's mouth; they then dragged him down a cartway, tied him to a tree and rifled his pockets of £2 10/-. The 'sailors' threatened to bash his brains in if he made any attempt to give the alarm, and he remained in this position for about two hours, until he was released by a boy who was passing on the highway.

This daring highway robbery, was an extremely serious offence and the severity of the punishments for similar offences were severe and are well documented. At the Midsummer Sessions in 1838, John Jackson, excavator, pleaded guilty to 'burglariously' breaking into and entering the dwelling house of Miss Sarah Hardwick, of Deerleap in the Township of Clay Lane; and because he carried an offensive weapon

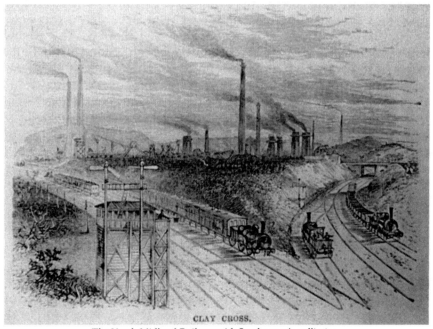

CLAY CROSS.

The North Midland Railway with Stephenson's collieries

71

(crowbar) and 'used great violence against her', he was sentenced to be transported for the rest of his natural life. He was eventually placed on the convict ship 'Ganymede' which was docked at Woolwich.

In February 1839, four men also dressed like sailors were charged at Chesterfield with having used abusive language, and with annoying several respectable inhabitants when begging in the neighbourhood. These particular navvies had previously visited Hardwick Hall, soliciting for alms, and although they were relieved with some money, they refused to leave until some clothes were given to them. They were all convicted on the above charge and committed to serve six weeks hard labour in Derby Gaol.

The Locals fight back

Obviously, the resident population resented the invading army of navvies. At the Shoulder of Mutton at Clay Cross, about half-a-dozen excavators quarrelled with a company of agricultural labourers and came second best. The following day a large number of tunnel men collected at the Shoulder of Mutton to seek their revenge, and being disappointed at not meeting those who had annoyed their comrades, wreaked their vengeance on the furniture of the house — the whole of which they demolished. They finally took their leave after taking down the sign board and smashing the windows and shutters. This riotous behaviour and damage to property may have been just too much for the owner of the Angel Inn immediately opposite, and in May 1838, that pub was put up for sale.

At Eckington in July 1838, Joseph Parr, a butcher from Mosboro and six other inhabitants, together with a number of others, were charged by John Pearce and six other navigators, with having committed an assault upon them. The navvies, it appears, had gone across some land which was not designated as a regular road and as a consequence a conflict between the local inhabitants and the navvies ensued. Parr knocked three of the navigators to the ground,

> but the railwaymen eventually got the advantage ... when the
> alarm was given, and the whole of the neighbourhood was up,
> armed with hedge stakes and other weapons and they eventually
> drove the other party (navvies) off the ground.

The local magistrates were extremely lenient and only fined Parr £1 and 21/- costs and all the others were discharged — the penalties imposed on the navvies for similar offences were much more severe and clearly indicates the bias of the local Bench.

Soon after this confrontation, Richard Henderson, a navvy, employed at Eckington was brutally murdered. He was in fact struck with a scythe blade and

> the blow divided his scalp from the corner of the eye, across the top of his head, almost to the neck behind and completely severed a large portion of the skull and the projecting parts of the brain.

At the inquest held at the Bear Inn, Eckington, the jury returned a verdict of wilful murder against John Guest, who was sent for trial at the ensuing Assize Court in March 1839, and was fortunate to be found guilty of manslaughter only.

> Bearing all the circumstances in mind and considering that there might not be time after the provocation for allowing your blood to cool (and this is a very nice distinction between the crime of manslaughter and that of murder), the jury have properly brought you in guilty of manslaughter, the sentence of the court therefore, is that you be transported beyond the seas at such time and to such place as Her Majesty by the advice of her Privy Council shall think fit for the term of your natural life.

Supplementing their diet

Sheep stealing was a very serious offence and proliferated along the entire 72 mile stretch of the N.M.R. line. A few weeks after the excavations had commenced in the Clay Cross area we learn that

> The frequency of the crime of sheep stealing is at the present unprecedented and we have for weeks past had occasion to mention robberies of this nature; and although several considerable sums of money have been offered for the detection of the offenders, no persons as yet, we believe, have been apprehended. This circumstance strongly indicates that the robberies are affected by a determined band of marauders, the existence of which we had occasionally to allude to.

The following May 1837, after the theft of a fat ewe sheep at Staveley, a reward of 105 guineas was offered for the apprehension of the offenders. As a further inducement, a Royal Pardon was also offered with the reward to any person concerned in the crime and furnishing such information as might lead to their conviction.

In December 1837, John Smith of Fens in Lincolnshire, who had been on the tramp for three weeks in search of work, surrended himself to the Chief Constable of Chesterfield for having killed a sheep at Hasland. He explained to the police that he was unable to obtain work on the

Sheffield and Rotherham railway, and being unable to get anything to eat he killed a sheep to get sent to prison, where he knew he would be maintained.

At North Wingfield after the discovery of a carcass of sheep, a posse of neighbours led by the parish constable was immediately collected. After watching the area until two o'clock the next morning they succeeded in capturing two men in the act of taking it away. Both these men were employed on the railway and were committed to trial at the next Quarter Sessions.

Again in January 1838, it was reported that

> sheep stealing continues to be carried on to an alarming extent in the vicinity of Clay Cross and Mr. Rooth has offered a reward of £10 in addition to the sum allowed by the Tupton and North Wingfield Association for the Prosecution of Felons.

Early in February, a servant of William Milnes J.P. of Stubbing Edge Hall, discovered that a sheep had been slaughtered and its head, fore-feet and intestines left in the park.

> Mr. Milnes lost no time in procuring the aid of John Jackson, a London Police officer, stationed near the line of the North Midland Railway, and there being some snow on the ground, marks of blood were distinctly traced, until they arrived at a house which had lately been occupied by a man of the name Wickin, an excavator. Milnes entered Wickin's house with Jackson the policeman, and they found him in a room upstairs in the act of cutting up a sheep which had been recently slaughtered and also found the skin and two hind feet. Two rabbits and some mutton were also found in the house.

Wicken was taken into custody and brought before William Palmer Morewood Esq. of Alfreton Hall, and committed to take his trial at the next Assizes. Wicken was a native of Kent and had long been suspected of sheep stealing and

> it is generally believed that he has been implicated in all the sheep stealing which has been carried on in this neighbourhood, to an alarming extent; not less that twenty sheep having been killed and their carcasses stolen since the month of May last.

Despite Wickin's arrest on the Saturday, another sheep was stolen from a field at Woodthorpe, near Clay Cross on the following Tuesday. William Wickin alias Mark Hatfield was transported for fifteen years.

Further south on the line near Belper, it was reported that

> The depredators are expert hands, the skin was taken off the carcass as neat is if it had been done by daylight and by an experienced butcher.

Though there is no evidence to show that hungry navvies supplemented their diets with horse meat ... 'a curious robbery' was reported at Handley Lodge, near Clay Cross. Apparently, Mr. Taylor, who was resident at Handley Lodge, had the misfortune to lose a valuable mare and on the following night the carcass was stolen

> but the most valuable, as well as the most portable part of the animal — the skin — was carefully taken off the carcass and with the legs left behind.

Joseph Gratton, the surveyor who had prepared the plans of the strata on the tunnel for the N.M.R. lived at Timberfield House, a few yards from the deep cutting at Stretton and was visited by depredators ten times within eighteen months.

> six store geese stolen therefrom. On the following night, between six and seven o'clock, the cry of several geese were heard from a railway hut in the neighbourhood. It is hoped that this may lead to the detection of the thieves.

Railway Policemen

After the tunnel and the line were eventually completed the N.M.R. decided to appoint five of the London policemen to act as their superintendents and be responsible for their fifteen 'Perambulating Police'. These policemen were stationed along the entire stretch of the N.M.R. line and each policeman was responsible for a stretch of between four and five miles. Each policeman was expected to perambulate his own stretch several times a day and particularly before the passing of the earliest train. On one occasion the policeman on the Clay Cross stretch attempted to warn an oncoming train from Derby about a landslip at the south end of Clay Cross Tunnel ... 'however being drunk he neglected to perform his duty and he failed to stop the train'. Railway discipline was exacting and demanding, and there was simply no excuse for failing to perform your duty, and Peter Taylor the policeman in charge of the Clay Cross stretch, was no doubt, instantly dismissed. Indeed, a few weeks later Samuel Ward, was reported as being responsible for the Clay Cross stretch. Thomas Master, one of the London Policemen employed as a superintendent for the N.M.R. was based at Clay Cross and lived in Chapel Street.

CHAPTER FIVE

THE WORK COMPLETED

Celebrations

On August 22nd 1839, it was reported that

> The whole of the excavations are now complete in the Clay Cross
> Tunnel and the last brick of the arch will be laid in a few days' time,
> when it is intended to give a treat to the men employed in this great
> work.

The last brick, however, was not laid until 18th December, and on this
occasion a silver trowel, bearing a suitable inscription was presented to
the engineer by Mr. Price the principal contractor on the tunnel.

> A number of gentlemen afterwards partook of an excellent and
> elegant entertainment and passed a very pleasant evening together.

During December great efforts were being made to complete a single
line of rails to allow coke from Stephenson's coke ovens at Clay Cross, to
be conveyed to Whittington and Derby. Clay Cross coke was supplied to
the N.M.R. for its engines until the line from York to Darlington was
opened and the superiority of the Durham coke drove the Clay Cross
coke out of the market. The 1841 census returns reveal that 13 coke
burners were resident in Clay Cross and ten of them were recruited from
outside the county.

At the end of February 1840, a number of directors, engineers and other
gentlemen connected with the N.M.R. traversed the line to an extent of
fifty miles and the scenes at Chesterfield presented a very lively
appearance.

> the day was fine and it being the fair a great number of people were
> in town. The station, which is close to the town, was decorated with
> flags, and a band of music which had previously marched through
> the streets with banners flying, was placed on the platform. When
> the carriages arrived, the band struck up 'See the conquering hero
> comes'.

By March, double track had been laid between Chesterfield and North Wingfield and after some tidying up, the line was officially opened on 30th July 1840. By August, third-class carriages were ready for use, and on the first day they were filled to capacity.

> This will be a great accommodation to the humble classes of the community at a cost of 1d per mile.

Though there appears to be no report of the celebrations at Clay Cross on the completion of the tunnel and the opening of the N.M.R. line, the contractors on the Duffield contract gave a dinner to the workmen that had been employed on the line there, and nearly two thousand were regaled with good old English fare.

> The dinner took place at one o'clock, after which there was a variety of sports according to announcement — horse racing, foot-racing, wrestling etc., in a field adjoining the line.

The seventy two and three-quarter mile stretch from Derby to Leeds included 200 bridges, 7 tunnels and 26 stations. The six other tunnels along the line were — the Milford Tunnel (836 yds); two very short tunnels near Ambergate; the Lodge Hill Tunnel (250 yds); Catt Hill Tunnel (140 yds); Chevet Tunnel (684 yds); and the Hagwood Tunnel. The stations along the line were designed by Francis Thompson who was paid £400 per annum for his services.

Effect on roads

Running directly through Clay Cross and virtually over the centre of the Tunnel was the Duffield to Sheffield Turnpike Road. This particular road was established by an Act of Parliament in 1756 (Act 29 Geo II c65) and played an important role in the expansion of Clay Cross, particularly around the cross roads. (See Tithe Map.) By 1837, this road had nine tollgates in its 32 mile stretch and seven side-gates, and incorporated the Birdholme and Clay Cross Gates and Chains. The Toll House at Clay Cross was situated where the post office now stands at the junction with Holmgate Road, and the Chain-bar was situated almost opposite the Shoulder of Mutton. In a report to the Royal Commission on the State of the Roads, in 1840, Mr. B. M. Lucas, clerk to the trustees of the Duffield and Sheffield Turnpike, reported that in 1838, £144 11s 6d had been spent on the road's management and £2,112 4s 5d on its upkeep and that the road was in a tolerable state of repair. Lucas also anticipated that the position of the road would be seriously weakened with the completion of the N.M.R. line.

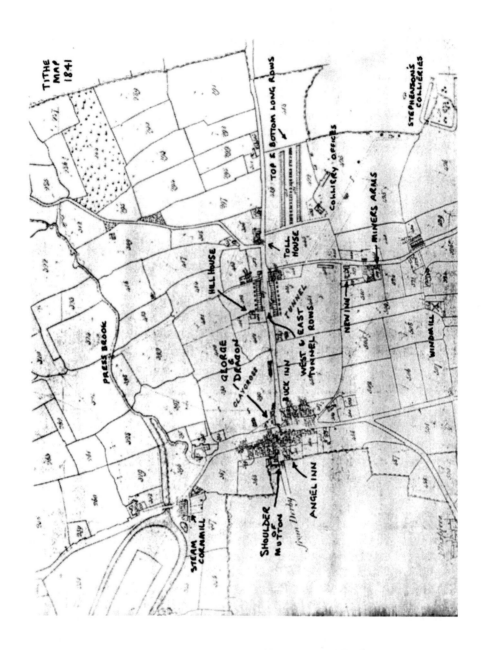

Tithe Map of 1841 showing line of tunnel under Clay Cross

78

Soon after the excavations on the tunnel commenced in 1837, there was an obvious sharp increase in the traffic on this road, which can be clearly seen by comparing the value of the 1836 and 1837 leases for this stretch of turnpike.

	1836	1837
Heely Gate and Side Gate	£838	£1,055
Holmley Common Gate	£658	£930
Stonegravels and Sheepbridge Chain	£716	£955
Birdholme and Clay Cross Gates and Chains	£466	£630
Stretton Hillside and Hallfield Gates	£190	£300
Makeney Gate and Side Gate	£56	£115

In 1836, the trustees of this road obviously anticipated an increase in traffic and they

> intended to consult about ordering and if deemed eligible, order two chains to be put across the road, one on the south side of Clay Cross and the other at or near the north end of Whittington Common.

Lucas's forecast about the reduction of traffic on the road, when the N.M.R. line was completed was absolutely correct and the 1841 leases for the road show a drastic reduction.

Birdholme and Clay Cross Gates and Chains

1831	£452	1837	£630
1832	£454	1838	£650
1834	£456	1839	£697
1836	£466	1840	£625
		1841	£288

When the tolls were auctioned off in 1841, they were leased for a period of three years instead of one year as was usual when the road was busy. The Heeley Gate was let separately and the Makeney Gates were not included in the lease and were probably given up by the trust. In his evidence to the House of Commons Railway Committee in June 1845, with regard to the Sheffield, Chesterfield and Midland Junction Railway, Thomas Fall, the surveyor of the roads for Chesterfield, stated

> the amount collected during the last year at the tolls on the road from Duffield to Sheffield, a distance of 32 miles was £2,250; inclusive of £1,800 collected on the road between Chesterfield and Sheffield, a distance of 12 miles. The traffic of coal on these roads

was considerable, and the reason for that sum collected in the 20 miles from Duffield to Chesterfield was less than the amount taken between Chesterfield and Sheffield was, that the traffic on the road from Duffield to Chesterfield had been much diminished by the extension of the N.M.R. and considered that the 12 mile route from Sheffield to Chesterfield would be similarly injured by the new line.

In 1844, the Heeley Gate and Side Gate was leased for £700, and all the other gates from Duffield, up to Hallfield Gate, were leased in block for £1,290. The last stretch of this road was now covered by the Heage and Oakerthorpe Gate and leased for £102. In 1847, the Heeley Gates show an increase in the lease of £100, but all the other gates, now combined, were leased for a total of £1,450, showing an increase of only £50.

Though both the Keepers for the Toll-bar and for the Chain-bar at Clay Cross, are recorded as such in the 1871 census, the Clay Lane Local Board of Health minutes for April 1876, read

> Clerk was to instructed to write to Messrs. Shipton and Hollwell pointing out the danger arising from the tollgate posts and requesting that they should be removed as soon as possible.

This particular request appears to have been ignored and in May, the clerk gave notice for them to be removed within fourteen days. The trustees eventually gave the road up on 1st November 1875, and offered the new Local Board of Health both tollhouses and land for the 'improvement of the road'. One of the tollhouses (Holmgate junction) was termed 'a great nuisance which will be required to be pulled down at once'. The toll posts, perhaps those used for the gate and chain opposite the Shoulder of Mutton are still intact and can be seen proudly standing at the bottom of the drive of Windmere Point, situated on the old turnpike road at Stretton Road.

With the opening of the N.M.R. line, there was a marked change in the pattern of long distance road passenger traffic. The four daily coaches from Chesterfield to London (Royal Mail, Express, Courier and Royal Hope) and the three to Derby and Birmingham (Royal Mail, Quicksilver and Telegraph) had all disappeared by 1846. The number of coaches to Sheffield had fallen from seven to three and the coach to Manchester no longer ran.

In December 1841, the directors of the N.M.R. decided to reduce the fare from Sheffield to the various stations north and south of the town.

the peculiar situation of the town (Sheffield), lying six miles from the railway — rendering such a necessary step. The altered fare from Chesterfield to Sheffield will be about the same as those charged by the coach proprietors although the distance is eight miles more and the fares to the other places will be reduced in proportion.

The carrying trade was also affected. The Chesterfield carriers no longer advertised their services to the various parts of the Kingdom, but a number of them, including Pickfords, undertook to convey goods by rail to Sheffield, London and other parts of the country. On the other hand there was an appreciable increase in the local carrying trade from Chesterfield and the number of carriers had increased from seventeen to thirty-two by 1846.

Metamorphosis

Without doubt, the completion of the N.M.R. line and the establishment of George Stephenson's Company in 1837, had a profound effect upon Clay Cross. The transformation from an agarian based economy to an industrial based one is well illustrated by a comparison of Stephen Glover's occupational returns for Clay Cross in 1829, with the occupational structure deduced from the 1841 census returns. Glover in 1829 discerns 103 houses and 465 inhabitants; with 49 chiefly employed in agriculture, 24 employed in trades and handicrafts, and 32 employed variously. By 1841, the population had risen dramatically. There were 305 houses with 1478 inhabitants; these included 273 miners, 41 general labourers, together with 41 farmers and 40 agricultural labourers.

The Derbyshire Courier sums up the metamorphosis very suitably.

The formation of the Midland Railways and the establishment of Messrs. Stephenson's and Company's collieries have opened up and developed the riches of the district, professional gentlemen, mechanics, colliers and labourers have flocked to it from all quarters, and from being a scattered and obscure hamlet, it has assumed the appearance of a manufacturing town.

Miles from Derby	
1	On the left, Derwent Bank, the residence of the Misses Strutt; Little Chester; Darley Abbey, Samuel Evans, Esq.; Darley Hall, the Misses Evans—the Church—the cotton and paper-mills of Messrs. Evans.
2½	On the right, Breadsall Church, handsome spire—and village. Principal proprietor, Sir George Crewe, Bart., M.P.
4	On the right, Little Eaton, and Breadsall Priory.—Left, Allestree Hall, William Evans, Esq., M.P. for North Derbyshire. Beyond (not in view), Kedleston, the splendid Hall and beautiful domain of Lord Scarsdale.
5¼	DUFFIELD STATION.—The beautiful village on the left; the Church, the Derwent and bridge, right.
6	Milford Tunnel, 850 yards long, with a rich Saxon arch at the northern entrance.
7¼	BELPER STATION.—A market town; population about 5,000. The railway passes through the town in an excavation.
7¾	The works enormously expensive—not less than 12 bridges in the space of one mile. At the farther end, the large cotton-mills of the Messrs. Strutt; and the mansion of G. B. Strutt, Esq., upon Bridge Hill, the eminence on the left.
8½	The Line crosses Belper Pool, a beautiful expansion of the Derwent, by two long bridges, containing 200,000 cubic feet of timber: the first, 9 spans, the second, 8 spans, of 50 feet each.
10	Proceed through delightful scenery on the banks of the Derwent—lofty slopes, adorned with wood, rising on each side of the valley. Cross the Derwent—Short tunnel.
10¼	The united streams of the Derwent and the Amber, and the turnpike road from Derby to Matlock, crossed by a splendid viaduct of oblique arches.—Hag Wood Tunnel.
10½	AMBER GATE STATION.—Omnibus and posting conveyances to *Matlock*, 6 miles distance westward; a place of fashionable resort, celebrated for its baths, and for the unrivalled beauty and grandeur of its romantic scenery. At Cromford, one mile from Matlock Bath, are the extensive cotton-mills of the Messrs. Arkwright; where their ingenious and enterprising grandfather, Sir Richard Arkwright, commenced his cotton-spinning on the improved principle, in 1771. Proceed in the Amber valley—the turnpike-road and the river crossed by an elegant stone bridge. Stephenson's lime-kilns on the left.—The Amber again crossed. The Cromford canal carried over the Railway by a new wrought-iron aqueduct; a work admirably executed. The Railway crosses the Amber. Bull Bridge village, left.—
11½	Lodge Hill Tunnel, 260 yards. South Wingfield on the left—the noble ruin of Wingfield Manor, an ancient castellated pile, on the summit of a lofty eminence, surrounded by beautiful silvan scenery—it belongs to Wingfield Halton, Esq. Mary, Queen of Scots, passed

a portion of her captivity here, under the custody of the Earl of Shrewsbury. The Manor was greatly damaged in the civil wars, and in 1646 was dismantled by order of the Parliament.

WINGFIELD STATION—for Alfreton (east 1½ mile), Mansfield, &c.—A long embankment, about 2 miles; fine view of the lovely scenery of the valley.   14

Crich cliff seen to the left—on the summit, the column called Crich Stand.—Ogston Hall, Mrs. Turbot.—The village of Higham on the right.—A long excavation succeeds, deep at the north end.   16½

SHELTON STATION.   17¾

The Derbyshire summit, and highest point of the whole Line.—Immediately after, enter the Clay Cross Tunnel; length 1 mile, 20 yards—ornamental stone fronts at the entrances; the northern resembling a magnificent Moorish gateway; cost of the tunnel about £140,000.—Enter the Rother valley.   18½

CLAY CROSS STATION.   20

Stephenson's colliery railway joins on the right.—North Wingfield, to the right.—Left, Tupton Hall.   20½

Wingerworth Hall, Sir Henry Hunloke, Bart., on the hill to the left.   22

CHESTERFIELD STATION.—A beautiful building, in the Elizabethan Gothic style. The town is in a remarkably pleasant and favourable situation, yet it has comparatively few manufactures; it has a spacious and handsome Market-place, with a market on Saturday; population 5,775 in 1831. Its ancient Church, a fine edifice, has a remarkable and curious wooden spire, built in a crooked or twisted form, inclining towards the south-west. On the hill to the right, Tapton House, the residence of George Stephenson, Esq., the renowned engineer; who, by the power of his genius, and by dint of perseverance, without the advantages of early education, has raised himself from an humble station to the highest grade of his profession. From his construction of the first railway for passengers, and his skilful adaptation of the locomotive engine, he has been justly designated "the Father of Railways."   24

The Chesterfield canal (to the Trent) on the right. Whittington Hall, Mr. Dixon, and village, on the left. Dunston Hall beyond.   26

STAVELEY STATION.—Staveley upon the hill to the left; Mr. Barrow's iron-works in the valley.   27¾

Extensive and picturesque views from the Railway.

The Line then enters Renishaw Park—Sir George Sitwell, Bart.—and passes through it more than a mile. The magnificent Hall on the hill to the left.   29¾

ECKINGTON STATION, for Worksop, &c., in Renishaw Park. An ornamental building, with circular tower; slen-   30¼ der storied tower in the Park.

31   Eckington village on the left; noble woods of Renishaw Park, &c., beyond.

32¼   KILLAMARSH STATION.—The village, and rolling-mills, on the right.

Road carried across the Railway by a fine viaduct of 7 arches. Arrive at

34   BEIGHTON STATION.—The village on the left.

34¼   Pass the boundary into Yorkshire.

35¼   WOODHOUSE MILL STATION.—Handsworth on the hill to the left; and Woodhouse Mill, 5 miles from Sheffield, on the road to Chesterfield.

36¾   TREETON STATION.—Treeton on the right.

38½   Tinsley on the hill to the left. Canklow wood, right.

The Line is leaving the beautiful valley of the Rother, skirted by undulating hills clothed with wood. On the hill to the right, a shooting-box built by a former Earl of Effingham, and called by him Boston Castle, in honour of the American patriots who distinguished themselves at Boston in 1775, in their struggle for independence.

The Line crosses the valley of the Don, the river, canal, and turnpike-road, and then the Sheffield and Rotherham Railway, by two splendid viaducts (the former called Ickles Viaduct), consisting together of 30 arches, each from

39¾   25 to 50 feet span, and a bridge of two arches, each 70 feet span over the river.

40   MASBRO' STATION—for ROTHERHAM and SHEFFIELD.

Masbro' is separated from Rotherham only by the river Don. Population of Rotherham 4,083; market on Monday. At Masbro' are the great iron-works belonging to the Messrs. Walker, where the magnificent bridges of Southwark and Sunderland were cast: they are seen on the left, when approaching the Station. Here is a college of the Independents, for the education of students for the ministry. A short branch connects the Sheffield and Rotherham Railway with the North Midland, and the carriages with Sheffield passengers are attached to the North Midland trains or detached from them. The property in the neighbourhood belongs chiefly to Earl Fitzwilliam and the Earl of Effingham: the latter lives at Grange, 3 miles N.W. of Rotherham.

SHEFFIELD is 5 m. on the left, situate at the conflux of the Don and the Sheaf, on a gently rising eminence. The second town in Yorkshire; market on Saturday, and for corn on Tuesday; population 110,891 in 1841; sends two Members to Parliament. This town is famous for its manufactures of cutlery and various hardware, Britannia metal and plated wares, and silver plate; for foundries of iron and brass, type, &c, and many other works. The Railway to Rotherham, opened in 1839, is a prosperous undertaking.

Barbot Hall, Lord Howard, on the left. Rotherham, with its beautiful spire, seen to advantage on the right. $40\frac{3}{4}$

Junction of the Greasborough Railway, from Earl Fitzwilliam's collieries. $41\frac{1}{4}$

KILNHURST STATION.—The Don Pottery on the right. Beyond the river, Thribery Hall, John Fullerton, Esq.; richly wooded Park. Left, Rawmarsh—Greasborough—the fine spreading woods of Wentworth House, the seat of Earl Fitzwilliam, with the grand mausoleum erected in honour of the Marquis of Rockingham. $43\frac{3}{4}$

SWINTON STATION—for DONCASTER, 7 m. on the right; conveyances by omnibus, and by boat on the canal and the river, flowing through a beautiful valley, under the stately ruins of Conisborough Castle. Doncaster, a great agricultural market, on Saturday; population 10,801; famous for its races. Mexborough, on the right; Swinton, left. A Railway is projected to Doncaster. 45

Cross the Dearne and Dove canal by a fine bridge of four arches. Arrive at

WATH STATION.—Wath on the left. The spacious valley through which the canal passes affords fine extensive prospects on each side. On the right, Bolton-upon-Dearne; the distant woods of Hooton Pagnell, Hon. William Duncombe; Hickleton, Sir F. L. Wood, Bart.; Melton, Fountayne Wilson, Esq.; Sprotborough, Sir Joseph Copley, Bart. On the left, Wombwell wood; more remote, the woods of Wentworth Castle, F. W. V. Wentworth, Esq.; Wortley Hall, Lord Wharncliffe, and Wharncliffe Hall. The woods and monument of Wentworth House are also still in view. 47

Cat Hill Tunnel, 154 yards long, over which the Barnsley and Doncaster road passes. $48\frac{3}{4}$

DARFIELD STATION.—Darfield on the hill to the left; Houghton on the right. Traverse the winding valley of the Dearne, interspersed with fine woodland and picturesque scenery. $49\frac{1}{4}$

Leave the valley—New Park Springs on the right. 52

BARNSLEY STATION, at Cudworth bridge.—Omnibus to Barnsley, $2\frac{1}{2}$ miles on the left. A flourishing town, with a market on Wednesday; population 12,307. Seat of the linen manufacture, and wire, hardware, &c. 53

Monk Bretton on the hill to the left.—Royston and Notton Park. The Line crosses the Barnsley canal, at a very acute angle, by a bridge of iron and wood. 54
55
56

ROYSTON AND NOTTON STATION.—The Yorkshire summit. Chevet viaduct, 110 yards long. On the left, Notton—Woolley Park, Godfrey Wentworth, Esq. $57\frac{1}{2}$

Chevet Tunnel, 684 yards long, through Sir William Pilkington's land; Chevet Hall (not in view) on the left. $58\frac{1}{4}$

Walton village.—Crofton village on the right, and the woods of Walton Hall, Charles Waterton, Esq. Left, the 59 village of Sandal, with its ruined Castle on the wooded hill behind; the spire of Horbury remote in the back ground. A succession of splendid prospects, including the town of Wakefield.

59¾   The Barnsley canal crossed by a splendid viaduct of five arches of 60 feet span, and 65 feet high; the loftiest on the line; succeeded by the highest embankment, to Oakenshaw.

60   OAKENSHAW STATION—for WAKEFIELD, 1½ m.—regular conveyance by omnibus. The building is beautiful. Wakefield has a market on Friday, the largest for corn in the north of England; held at the Corn Exchange, a handsome modern building—population 12,232.   Great trade in wool and dying—has an ancient Church, with a handsome lofty spire.   Elects one Borough Member—place of election for West Riding.

A long cutting at Warmfield, the deepest on the Line.— Newland Park, Sir Edward Dodsworth, Bart., on the left;
62¼   the house not visible.   Junction of Manchester and Leeds Railway.

63¼   NORMANTON STATION.—The place of junction with the Manchester and Leeds, and the York and North Midland Railways.   New Station, offices, &c., are erected here, for the use of the three Companies.   Normanton on the hill to the right.

63¾   The south branch of the York and North Midland Railway joins on the right; Altofts on the left.

64¼   The Calder and the canal crossed by a magnificent viaduct, comprising one arch of 90 feet span, 5 of 60 each, and 2 smaller arches; cost £18,700.

65   Second junction of the York and North Midland Railway.—Cross the Leeds and Pontefract road.   Methley Castle, Earl of Mexborough, seen on the left for some miles.

66¼   METHLEY STATION.—The village on the right.—Enter the Aire valley.   Swillington Hall, Sir John Lowther, Bart., on the right: beyond, Kippax, Ledstone, and Ledsham.

68   WOODLESFORD STATION.—Woodlesford and Oulton on the left; Swillington bridge—house and brewery of Henry Bentley, Esq., right.

68¾   Leventhorpe Hall, Kirkby Fenton, Esq., and the Church of Church Garforth beyond, on the right.

69   The noble woods of Temple Newsome, Lady William Gordon, an ancient demesne of the Knights Templars, on
70   the north side of the valley.   River Aire and Leeds and Goole ship canal on the right.   Cross the Leeds and Pontefract road, Haigh Park to the right.   Cross the Leeds
71   and Wakefield road, Stourton Lodge, right.
72   LEEDS STATION.

SOURCES

North Derbyshire Chronicle 1836-1841
Derbyshire Courier 1835-1846
Derby Mercury 1835-1840
Quarter Sessions Order Book 1835-1840
Chesterfield Borough Watch Committee Minutes 1836-1840
N.M.R. Acts of Parliament 1836-1840
Leeds and London N.M.R. Committee Minutes 1835-1842
N.M.R. Railway Guide 1842
Report of the Royal Commission on Children's Employment; Mines 1842
Census Returns 1801-1971
Life of George Stephenson   Samuel Smiles 1857
The Midland Railway   F. Williams 1876
Frederick Swanwick; a sketch   F. Smith 1888
The Derbyshire Miner   J. G. Williams 1962
The Railway Navvies   T. Coleman 1965
Chesterfield History Vol. III   J. M. Bestall 1978
Clay Cross: A Product of the Industrial Revolution   C. Williams Unpublished

Time Line

August	1835	Selection of N.M.R. route
January	1836	Test boring on tunnel section
July	1836	Carr Glynn appointed chairman of N.M.R.
July	1836	North Midland Railway Bill received Royal Assent
July	1836	George and Robert Stephenson appointed engineers
September	1836	Frederick Swanwick appointed assistant engineer
November	1836	Plans and specifications for tunnel complete
December	1836	Tenders for tunnel invited
January	1837	N.M.R. offices established in Vicar Lane, Chesterfield
January	1837	Hardy and Cropper secure tunnel contract
February	1837	Excavations on tunnel commence
April	1837	Waring secures contract for northern section to Hasland
April	1837	Trubshaw commences contract from southern section up to South Wingfield
August	1838	Mr. Price takes over half of the tunnel contract
August	1839	Tunnel completed
December	1839	Northern entrance completed
May	1840	N.M.R. line opened from Derby to Masboro
June	1840	N.M.R. line opened from Leeds to Derby
July	1840	N.M.R. line officially opened
March	1841	Cooke and Wheatstones electric telegraph in use at Clay Cross Tunnel

Lightning Source UK Ltd.
Milton Keynes UK
UKOW030933230911

179157UK00003B/1/P

The Size of a Stamp

Art Collection

Water Colour & Black Ink Drawings

"My True North" Series

Marie Anne O'Mordha

First Published in Ireland, in 2019, in co-operation with
Choice Publishing, Drogheda, County Louth, Republic of Ireland.
www.choicepublishing.ie

Paperback ISBN: 978-1-913275-12-9
eBook ISBN: 978-1-913275-13-6

A CIP catalogue record for this book is available from the National Library.

Available now in paperback from www.choicepublishing.ie

MY GRATITUDE

My Gratitude goes to my parents for having been great people, to have had the courage to migrate in their early 30's for my mother and early 40's for my father from a well-established very comfortable lifestyle in Mauritius, built over four generations by their erudite French forebears of the former *Ile de France*, to the unknown: a new life in Australia to start all over again for the future of their children in the Land of Myriad Opportunities. They were great parents and guides to me in my childhood and adult life, they taught me well and instilled in me a reverence for life and a passion for learning, to develop the innate skills I was born with. We arrived in Australia in the City of Sydney in my teen-age years, I was in secondary school with three and a half years for my Highest School Certificate, and mammoth work to do for entrance into University, a duty I applied myself to everyday for obtaining the University Entrance marks in my Highest School Certificate Examinations. *My gratitude goes to my teachers* during those decisive years, as my ambition was to graduate from an Australian University with a degree in my hand, making me the first generation of women in my family with university education.

My gratitude goes to the Australian Labour Government of the Day under Prime Minister Gouth Whitlam, for the abolition of university fees in 1974, which continued for a decade or so, thus opening the University doors to students from all walks of life with Scholarships for fee-free University Education on the basis of merit rather than wealth, an unprecedented Event in the history of Australia. This was the best news of all for me, as we were new as a family in Australia and my University Scholarship freed my parents from the financial burden. University Education usually availed by the wealthiest in Australian society as in other parts of the world and usually by the men folk was now open to Australian women for University degrees, previously a rare phenomenon. Women formed half the Australian population and free University Education for those who gained entrance into University meant that the potential now being developed by university-educated females was ready to be ploughed back into the economy of the country, their latent potential could now be harvested from the variety of skilled work that they were now capable of doing and some in the highest echelons of the workforce. I, myself, came from a family where the women were the home-makers with large families and they had the care of their children and families till the end of their days. These women mostly had the basic education, and when it came to my turn: I asked the question: *"What if?"* for another way of life… and like other educated women in the workforce, I worked in various positions where higher education was a requirement, and with heads held high and no regrets, I with other educated women and men contributed at a higher level to the country's economy through our paid-taxes and specifically in supporting the families, today's new generation raised by women and men who did not/could not avail of the same chances. Everyone has a wish-list in life, however at times all may not fully be accomplished. Fortunately, a society is the sum total of its individuals, the collective.

My gratitude goes to my husband Tom Moore for inspiring me to develop my life-skills, to acquire new ones and to keep on learning & up skilling as he always was, to move and change with the time if this was for the better. I am grateful to have met my husband as a young adult in my 21st year. Tom Moore, at the height of his career with world-wide international managerial positions at the highest levels, he was a total Inspiration for me. And now a teacher/lecturer of Management Studies in the Melbourne Colleges of Technical and Further Education, he was taking his students to the next higher levels in their own careers and I listened to all the history Tom Moore told me about his life, work and world travel; I learned a lot from my dearest friend and beloved husband. And I am grateful for our lifetime together: *Tomas O'Mordha, My True North*, my east & my west, my north and my south, my sunrise and sunset, my midnight and daylight, my everything in the world…

DEDICATION

This book is a Stress-Buster and therefore dedicated to everyone, as everyone at some time can fall prey to stress and in need to grapple with stressful situations.

It is a known fact that stress is a killer, whether short-term or long-term, stress affects everyone who is faced with it.

One's response to stress in fact bears on the way that one's health is affected. A negative response to stress lets in bad health and resulting consequences, which can sap the joy *"joie de vivre"* out of one's life.

A positive response in *stress-blasting* in fact acknowledges the cause of the stress, while taking into account all the positives of the past in stored memories, it's a caring response which allows the gentleness and kindness of healing to take place in order to keep one's health in body and mind and keep on going on one's path in life.

There are huge stressors in life, the top one being bereavement for a loved one, and there are other stressors in life, all very real to each. However there is always a silver lining in beating stress, on top of the situation, *"standing and unbowed"* to keep afloat and keep well.

This book is written for the healing process to take place, as it gives one a little time to escape, to recover and recharge one's batteries, in a moment of silence and reflection, shielded in the powerful quiet and serene space as in a cocoon.

So sit down quietly in your favourite space, and enjoy the journey…

ACKNOWLEDGEMENTS

Ever since my childhood, I loved words and languages, the musicality and cacophony of sounds in familiar and foreign languages, their sounds projected in the past and present stored in memory. I loved poetry and the emotions conveyed in words which forged a lasting interest for writing: essays, stories and poetry started in my teen-age years and I thank Brenda Woods from the "Write Space" for her guidance in the completion of my latest work:

The Size of a Stamp Art Collection by Marie Anne O'Mordha
following my first Book in August 2019:
"My True North" by Marie Anne O'Mordha
Published by www.choicepublishing.ie

As a youngster, I loved drawing and painting, my parents recognised it and gave me the jobs to enhance my natural talents. I remember the passing of my most beloved paternal grand-father, my father said to me: *"There are some notes in your grand-father's wallet, so we will use them to buy something in his memory."* I said: *"Yes."* So we went to the Carmelite nuns' gift-shop in Beau-Bassin, and as it was Christmas time, we agreed on nativity subjects to go into the crib made by my great-uncle René; the subjects were beautifully made in France, all in clay and lovingly painted by hand. I was given the job of decorating the crib and made the back-drop to it, in midnight-blue thousand and one star-lit sky with one shooting Star, the skyline in the distance and I made the Christmas Star for the top, then placed the subjects into the crib; it all looked absolutely amazing, everyone marvelling at it…

In this book, I decided to illustrate my stories with my own drawings: some are in water-colour, others in black ink: *The Size of a Stamp Art Collection*

My thanks go to Aoife, a talented up-coming artist, for her expert tuition in the finer points of water-colour painting for my illustrations.

Breda from "Breda Wools of Drogheda": For some time now, I wanted to be able to knit and crochet wonderful garments made by my own hands, the love of a skill instilled by my great-aunts who were aces in this art, producing most enviable garments and items for house & family in their home-making, and I thank Breda for her thorough knowledge of knitting and crochet to teach me the skill and for her patience.

CONTENTS

My Gratitude	03
Dedication	05
Acknowledgments	06
The Emerald Isle	08
Body & Mind Beautiful	09
Nature or Nurture?	12
Mind Challenge	16
The Size of a Stamp	17
Social Interaction and Belonging	18
Learn a new language	22
Stories from far & near	25
The Beach house	26
Geography Quiz	27
The Elephant and his Keeper	30
The Butterfly & Bee Garden	31
Re-live the Poetry	32
The Alphabet in National School 1930's	33
Round the table	37
Spot the difference	42
The Sydney Opera House	43
Take up Calligraphy	45
The Coat and the Mantle	46
Learning something new & keep learning	48
The Handshake	51
The Poinsettia	52
The China Man & the Giant Puzzle	53
The King and the exotic Bird	57
The Governor's wife's Ball	61
Meditation in Practice: instant mind-therapy	64

The Emerald Isle

The Emerald Isle. The Green of Emerald Isle, fabric of one's life.

"The patchwork of green that soothes my mind as I rise in the morning, and toil in the fields through the day, as I lay down my tools for the angelus at mid-day and the packed lunch in my bag. My faithful tools I take up again to work in the fields of green and gold , then hurry back home, jumping over the hedges and into the stream that cool my feet." One can see a cavern at the mountain side: gushing out in a cascade, is the pure clear sparkling water to satisfy any thirst. Pure clear sparkling crystal clear water heading its way skimming the fresh breeze, meandering and winding its way against a patchwork of greens and gold, forest green, lime & yellow, over to the faintest palest white merging into the ocean foam. Dense dark blue sea carrying intrepid ships small & large far far away till at the Captain's call, they sail back home again..

Body & Mind Beautiful

"Body & Mind Beautiful" Appreciation List: Everyone is unique… amazing engineering, athletic, energetic, soft curves, toned & bronzed, full of beans, magical, **easy on the eye**, sexy, dark and handsome, the golden boy, amazing, **charismatic**, chip off the old block, full of vigour & strength, strong legs strong core, supple & flexible, admiringly slender, **strong and resilient**, intelligent, smart, foxy, clever, **intuitive**, gorgeous, select your attributes, impeccable, **resourceful**, knowing, can-do, Queen-bee, svelte, pleasantly plump, perfect, love you to the moon & back, as it should be, light-hearted and easy-going, placid, **self-confident**, smooth, delicate, **flawless**, fine, angel's hair, beautiful luscious hair, **in top condition**, tall and powerful, irrepressible, fabulous, everyone is unique, sturdy, **from small acorn large oak trees grow**, deep deep beautiful eyes, **wonderful light blue eyes**, exhilarating, weightless & ageless, misty & mysterious, golden with sunlight, **youthful & radiant**, glowing, attractive smile, pearly, **lovely**, neat & tidy, **good manners**, like a god, Adonis, **charming**, seize the days, imaginative, friendly, in perfect health, self-sufficient, capable hands, original mind, brainy, excellent nature, unique, happy, positive, upbeat, **forward-thinking**, astute, flexible, inquisitive, searching, **reliable**, **faithful**, truthful, loyal, experienced, practice makes perfect, **creative**, constant, voluminous wavy & curly hair, fine, straight and waist-long hair, **extraordinary**, magnificent, **talented,** articulate, **prodigy**, La crème de la crème, tops, Number One, unique, **winning attitude**, **loving**, protective, spirited, **fast & racy**, competitive, **perfect match**, **orderly**, organized, **systematic**, good, **cooperative & synergizing**, ready, the explorer, nurturing, disciplined, appreciative, understanding, inclusive, supportive, select your attributes, flying, selective, **reaching for the heights**, shining one's light, a guide, **protective**, embellished & adorned, determined, **following one's path**, keeping one's counsel, silent & reflective, literate, **multi-skilled**, colourful, fluent, silver tongue, genuine, enthusiastic, passionate, lively, considerate, add your own, exquisite, **sterling character**, dependable, **leader**, quality work, **great hands**, marvellous **inventor**, prolific, **amazing**, incredible, superlative, **knowledgeable**, worldly, **diplomatic**, as sweet as honey, courageous, **enterprising**, proud, **adaptable**, artistic, accurate, **clear vision**, clarity of purpose, good, sure & steady, rich, **know-how"**

Body & Mind Beautiful: endless positive attributes to the moon and back still waiting to be written.

The negatives are the other side of the coin.

Is the glass half-full or half-empty? Reaction to stress impacts one's life: Dark, dreary & depressed or flying through a paper dragon with resilience and buoyancy? Letting go, learning to let go and minding oneself.

Making lemonade from the lemons of life potentially turns obstacles into Opportunities for personal growth and development that brings positivity to be grateful for: grateful especially for the wonderful people in one's life: past-present-future.

Faith healing and spontaneous recovery…

Hearsay of healings: *there were many, it was about a man by the name of* **Jesus of Nazareth**, *preaching and healing the sick, the blind, the lame, the paralytics and the dying; there were crowds of people by him anytime he was around, this man had followers called his disciples, 12 of them plus a few women who followed and supported him, so the report said. There were other reports: a wedding at Cana, turning water into the finest wine, then feeding the masses gathered to hear him on the mountain, baskets full of fish to feed the hungry; other reports of calming the storm at sea and of walking on water and of having raised Lazarus from the dead. Extraordinary powers not seen or heard of before anywhere in the land.*

☆ Marie Anne O'Mordha©

*These were the reports on **Caesar**'s desk for some time now about the named Jesus of Nazareth, under surveillance by the **Centurions of Caesar** shadowing the man's movements in the territory occupied by the Romans. So the story goes that the Head-Centurion's servant became very ill at death's door to the grief of his master; it was a valuable servant and dear old man known to his master for a long time. Does the Centurion go to the Roman doctors who will surely give him some potion? No. The Centurion has the reports of healings by Jesus, reports given and sent to him daily at his desk by his soldiers. And now, **Jesus of Nazareth** is here:*

*When Jesus had entered Capernaum, a centurion came to him, asking for help. "Lord," he said, "my servant lies at home paralyzed, suffering terribly." Jesus said to him, "Shall I come and heal him?" The centurion replied, "Lord, I do not deserve to have you come under my roof. But just say the word. For I myself am a man under authority, with soldiers under me. I tell this one, 'Go,' and he goes; and that one, 'Come,' and he comes. I say to my servant, 'Do this,' and he does it." When Jesus heard this, he was amazed and said to those following him, "Truly I tell you, I have not found anyone in Israel with such great faith. I say to you that many will come from the east and the west, and will take their places at the feast with Abraham, Isaac and Jacob in the kingdom of heaven." Then Jesus said to the centurion, "Go! Let it be done just as you believed it would." And his servant was healed at that very hour.

*Source: The Bible, New Testament, Gospel by Matthew.

Nature or Nurture?

Nature or Nurture? Who wins? It's for each to decide.

Everyone is dealt with a set of variants at birth: *Country, parentage, socio-economic background, health status and an innate range of strengths and talents.* To be able to thrive, firstly one's nation needs law and order in its house with individual safety a given characteristic together with peaceful relations and cooperation with other nations. One's country needs to oversee the welfare of its citizens in setting up right economic conditions for creating employment, good living standards and health-care.

The nuclear family and wider community are the providers of physical, mental and emotional well-being. Suitable and secure housing, supply of good balanced nutrition & positive inter-active relationships with one another provide stability to one's life. Imperative also is the access to education and ensuing opportunities to develop one's strengths and capabilities & to overcome any weakness.

When it comes to nature versus nurture: ***Nurture has the upper hand*** *given the right environment, right from the very beginning, for optimum health.*

One Condition: to take control and responsibility for one's own health daily in all aspects engendering strength & optimum health.

   a) *Suitable foods in the right portions* following the food pyramid.

   b) *To enjoy a good moderate varied lifestyle* with work-life balance for mental and emotional fitness.

   c) *Plus daily must-do exercise* to remain capable & ageless.

Endurance and Stamina Exercises: *cardio-vascular for optimal heart and lung function.* The exercise should be briefly intensive followed by a pause and repeat. The body invigorated by movement, to sweat & keep one's organs in good working order.

Strength Exercises: *strong and well-toned body.*

Balance Exercises: *keep upright and out of harm's way.*

Mental and Emotional health workout: *good social interaction within one's family & community.*

To keep the brain active and fit:

Learn new skills and keep updating them.

These are the Keys for peak fitness throughout life.

Healthy body, healthy mind engenders a healthy community.

What type of sport is each innately drawn to?

Would it be high-intensity exercise to fire up the metabolism & to dissipate stress or exercise to calm & soothe?

Stress: the known cause of dis-ease over time.

Anti-dote responses to stress as it occurs through the right exercises & pathways are vital for healthy body & healthy mind.

Everyone is looking for a quick-fix:

So here's one, and a very effective one too!

Antidote to Stress: SOS   A call for help!

Sleep: good sleep is essential for repairing body & mind and to recharge one's batteries. Good sleep is a daily must-have. While asleep, one's body and mind are letting go of the stresses of the day and the body intelligence repairing the immune system and repairing damage done. Good sleep gives one energy and good health. Sleep is not a luxury or something one can do without, not at all. Good sleep is an essential vital component to one's health and good skin which is one's largest organ, and as it's said: *"Your Health is your Wealth!!"* Going to bed at the same time every night and switching off the television about one hour before retiring as the blue light affects one's restful sleep. It's good to do some quiet reading before sleeping if it helps to wind down, or one can set a particular ritual that will assist with good restful sleep: this could be hot chocolate or warm milk with some cereals, a favourite *"mid-night snack"*.

Outside: Going outside to enjoy the sun and fresh air, and if it's cold, one can go to a shopping centre where it's warm and do some window shopping or some browsing to keep oneself up-to-date with current fashions. Going out to meet with friends and relatives, having a coffee together, going out for a walk, joining a club or a sport, trying out the gymnasium, getting a personal fitness coach, keeping oneself busy with various general activities such as shopping, cooking, gardening, a change in patterns or jobs, the activity could be in the general care of house and child-minding or looking after one's loved ones may help; the decision rests with oneself and foremost remembering to give oneself space and flexibility to adapt and move with change.

Any activity in time of stress should be light enough to be able to cope easily. To lessen one's burden, and as it's said: *"You don't need to be holier than the Pope!"*

Sharing: To share one's problems with someone of trust and who will listen to one's feelings without judgement, that helps to deal with the situation being experienced. *"A trouble shared is a trouble halved."* There are a number of organisations one can call if there's no-one close by to listen: e.g. Samaritans, local Churches and organisations which advertise their services.

Solidarity: Seeking out old friends, ringing up acquaintances and relatives. Writing a letter to an old friend, it will be a delight to have an answer back and through the post with a stamp on it! Nowadays, most communications are by email or social media. Seeking the support of people one knows, to ease one's stress and pain. Out of the people's solidarity is the sun behind dark curtains of stress that stifles one's natural inner joy. Joy and the enjoyment of life are essential in one's life, the joy of living to keep healthy and to keep dis-ease out of one's life. *Joy is an innate emotion that one is born with*; healthy children are naturally happy and joyful.

Music Therapy: Music is an international universal language, going beyond borders and frontiers and binding people together, many times and without words to lift the soul.

It is widely recognised that people respond to music that they grew up with, people remember the times when they were carefree and enjoying life, it could be the music of their student days, or when they met the other half, when they were raising their families, all going their way. The happy memories are still there in the background lodged in their cellular memories and the positive feelings come flooding back in the moment. Exercising with such familiar music gives the individual the extra boost needed to flood the immune system with feel-good factor, and this in itself has powerful healing benefits.

Great Music of the 70's & 80's: *Abba's Dancing Queen, BeeGees Staying Alive & Jive Dancing, Music from Box Office movies is pop-corn for the mind: Flashdance music with Irene Cara, Grease with Olivia Newton-John & John Travolta, other favourite songs: Simply the Best by Tina Turner, Eurythmics Travel the World & the seven Seas, Men at Work Down Under...*

Everyone has favourite tunes associated with good-times drawing out positive feelings to live with in the moment, younger, ageless and in the flow of life. Listening to the music one knew as a young person brings positivity in one's life & the joy to live in the moment. To allow powerful healing to take place. Each generation will have its own musical favourites specific to the time in youth in one's 20's and 30's: generally the happy & decisive years.

IMAGINE:

Group-exercise programmes to include all youngsters, girls and boys, from an early age right up to their early adult years, to encourage & develop an instinctive love for team-sports, a liking for being active and engaged with their friends, progressively developing social & life-skills, to create balance in this technological age for well- rounded young people, physically & mentally fit and brimming with health to meet the world in their chosen fields and to enjoy their lives and give joy to their families.

Name the following city/country/symbols represented by icons below:

| 1 | 2 | 3 | 4 | 5 | 6 |

| 7 | 8 | 9 | 10 | 11 | 12 | 13 |

| 14 | 15 | 16 | 17 | 18 | 19 | 20 |

01 ……………………………… 02 ……………………………… 03……………………………………

04………………………………… 05 ……………………………… 06…………………………………

07………………………………… 08 ……………………………… 09…………………………………

10………………………………… 11 ……………………………… 12……………………………………

13………………………………… 14 ……………………………… 15……………………………………

16………………………………… 17 ……………………………… 18……………………………………

19………………………………… 20 ……………………………...

The Size of a Stamp quiz:
Answers to city/country/symbols

(1) *Sydney Opera House* (2) *Aurora Australis from Space* (3) *London* (4) *Scotland* (5) *Wales*

(6) *Ireland* (7) *Aurora Borealis* (8) *Hallgrímskirkja in Reykjavik, Iceland* (9) *Coat of Arms, Spain*

(10) *Eiffel Tower, Paris* (11) *MIR Space Station* (12) *Amsterdam, NL*

(13) *Scandinavian Flags: Sweden, Norway, Denmark* (14) *Coat of Arms, Bavaria DE*

(15) *Tower of Pisa, Italy* (16) *Emblem of Greece* (17) *Taj Mahal* (18) *Moscow*

(19) *Great Wall of China* (20) *New York with Statue of Liberty*

The Size of a Stamp…

The "Size of a Stamp": A picture paints a thousand words…

There's a letter in the mail for you. It may be from a *friend* or *relative* abroad, it may be from *the love of one's life* sending messages of endearment. These *little stamps of mystery*, wonder and excitement & apprehension all at once bring news to the world. Only one knows in opening the envelope and taking the contents in one's hands. Good news or otherwise? Remembering the *friends of yesteryear & love of yesterday*: one puts pen to paper with the words to re-connect memories. The little stamps from far-away places or localities *are the wings* that bring the words of *life's narratives* to one, passion & sympathy alike.

Social Interaction & Belonging

Remember: A program for both Body & Mind, on a 3-legged stand.
It's necessary to keep both spheres: body & mind active.

A)   The Exercise plan.   *B) **Meet people, social interaction.***
C)   Learn something new & keep learning.

Meeting people: social interaction on regular basis is a must-do, and could be a lifeline. Engaging in conversation: one-to-one or in a group, purely for leisure, *just for the craíc* without strain or timelines to watch. Keeping the brain relaxed and active, empowered to deal with stress, to overcome it and reduce anxiety.

Social interaction activates the thinking power of left and right sides of the brain for logic and language, moving over to abstract thought, memory and intuition. *"Practice makes perfect".*
Joining a conversation with others: to give the brain a workout, maintaining its flexibility and strength and keeping it youthful & in good working order. This also brings a sense of belonging and security, being part of a group of familiar faces, week in week out.

Listening to the chit-chat just enjoying the company without passing any remark has its value too. The sense of belonging to a particular group is important and enriches one's life.

Maslow's Hierarchy of needs explains what humans need for fulfilment in life; there is a sequence to every step, the lower requirements need to be fulfilled before the higher can be reached.

The first need is physiological: *food*

The second need is for safety: *shelter*

The third need is for love / belonging: *social interaction*

The fourth need for self-esteem: *purposeful work and prestige*

The fifth need is for self-actualisation: *reaching one's full potential*

The fifth need being the highest to be reached. The ultimate…

Joining an exercise class in your Gymnasium and going for a coffee afterwards for a chat & get to know one another. If there's a canteen in the place, some kind lady in the group would invariably be bringing cup-cakes, or a package of biscuits may appear out of thin air. There could be a lot of people for the exercise class, men and women; people of all ages & the older generation, Minders of the State in their day, people from all walks of life: with family-members locally & abroad in the States, Europe, Australia, in far-flung-places of the world, they could be mothers and fathers, grand-parents, single and married people, people of the older generation and proud of it, their work already completed, apart from minding the grand-children, which keeps them on their toes and youthful.

"Does anyone know about this that or the other?" just ask the group, and the expert will soon make an appearance and extoll the ins-and-outs of the matter and delighted to do so. *Be ready to straighten the world, talking about day-to-day events of the week, and the soapies on TV and no harm done.* There's always one who knows and takes the lead in any given situation. **Mother Machree**, the whole of Ireland's here, former workers: of Iarnród Éireann, Drivers of CIE buses & taxi-men, Mechanics of Aer Lingus, Bakers of Kylemore and of Brennan's Bread, Doctors here to keep everything in working order and Accountants before they lose the run of themselves, Teachers of the Teaching Council to safeguard their most precious possession i.e. their Brain. Chiefs and Indians present: the Captains of Industry and Council workers who

left their High Viz-jackets and muddy boots by the hall-stand back home, MKM Assortment Confectionery and Chocolate Makers.

There's a man saying he's *"a relative of a celebrity, no a distant relative"*, and talking *"about a passion for automobiles & fast engines and the horse that won the race a couple of times"* its name escapes my mind. *"Did you hear about the promotion of Doughnuts on the main street in Dublin, for that price you may as well get the whole box"* and *"Did we not go to Roches Basement Dinner Hall for the Irish Breakfast every Saturday morning, the place was packed full of Dublin people, great breakfast at a great price 4, 6, 8 items whatever you want and a hot pot of tea or mug of coffee with it."* *"That was the company - which looked after its workers with a bonus at the end of the year, a bonus even for its student staff from the college."* *"Oh, yes, you do have to look after your staff."* Snippets of *craíc* here and there: *"she's a diva, there's one in every family, oh, yeah, she's a long-haired chi Wawa"* sitting attentively on a high stool in the photo being shown, *"it's the right size of chi Wawa"* Everyone talking and joining in as its customary in Ireland, as you don't have to know anyone to have a chat with the people. A few would just be sitting down, enjoying the chit-chat and they could be catching their breath, there's an overall a sense of carefreeness and good humour in the room. The whole cast of a new Production is here, under the Directorship of Coaches & Co. and there's Fiona the well-liked Energizer Bunny in her long blond tresses for the workout, in the production of an Exercise Program in the gym. *In fact, it could be the football warm-up itself that you've enrolled yourself in.*

There's always the restaurant that stands out, everyone seems to be a patron, always packed, the atmosphere jolly and buoyant, the menu is what people like to eat, home-made everyday food *"All-day breakfast, Bacon, cabbage and spuds, CBS, Roast beef or chicken and vegetables,"* favourite deserts to indulge in *"apple pie and cream"*. The owner & staff recognise the regulars and know the people by name: *"Hello dear, how are you? What would you like today?"* The patron taking a little time to see, the owner would ask: *"What did you have for breakfast today?"* and the reply *"The Missus made me a good breakfast today, the full Monty."* One feels at home, the destination for a few minutes' rest or before the work-out. People would be sitting together, in small work-groups or in pairs having a coffee or at large tables to celebrate a child's birthday with the family get-together. There's often the one who loves talking and telling interesting stories with gestures to illustrate, everyone glued to every word. There's a table of four enjoying a meal, talking things over, bouncing a few ideas and sharing a joke. I know a couple of these places; I find them great, akin to heart of family, the *craíc* from the tables quite entertaining. Every now and again a party-pooper would rear its head, nearly always the same people: *"All I done for them, and not one word of thanks!"* Mostly, one always tries to find common ground: *"Do you know such and such Avenue in front of the stadium? My grand-ma used to live there."* *"Oh, really"* is the reply *"Is that so? My cousins used to live there too and they went to the local national school round the corner."* *"That's unbelievable! I used to go to the same school as well."* Someone's repartee: *"The further you go, you'll find out you're all related!"* At another table: *"I love going to New York, the food is great, I find the portions enormous though... I leave all my things with my family in the foyer and go shopping for 1 hour, take my coat, my wallet and my card, just for one hour shopping, that's all I need, cause I hate shopping, but I go anyway to see what's there."* And off for the bargains, all designed to appeal and tempt. *"Yes, be tempted, life's too short"* so one says. *"Be happy, have your cake and eat it."* Remember home-made food for optimum health, full of vitamins, minerals & proteins: fruits, veg & dairy, salads, soups and stews plus water for hydration, opt for the Mediterranean diet for longevity. *"Did you hear the latest?"* *"One can reach anyone in any part of the world in 3 contacts. The formula actually works, amazing!"*

*"Did you hear about **the Healing Code** written by 2 American doctors, the Real McCoy MAGNUM FORCE STRESS-BLASTER."*

Learn a new language: it's great for keeping the brain active:

Do you have any school French?

Here are 2 texts in French & English. See how much French you understand in the story. The following page is your translation.

- *Les animaux domestiques*
- J'ai deux animaux chez moi: *un chat et un chien.*
- *J'ai nommé mon chat "Mimi".* Il est d'une belle couleur jaune et ses yeux sont verts.
- Mon chat a trois ans, et il est malin et indépendant. Quand il est dans le jardin, il est comme un petit tigre.
- On le voit tout bas dans l'herbe à épier les oiseaux. Il s'approche d'eux tout doucement, et après, d'un bond, il saute sur sa proie. Mais les oiseaux sont très agiles, et ils s'envolent tous rapidement. C'est un jeu quotidien entre mon chat et les oiseaux. Le soir, mon chat passe son temps devant la cheminée à somnoler les yeux mi-fermés.
- Comme tous les chats, Mimi boit du lait et il mange du poisson. Quand il est content, il ronronne.
- *Mon chien est mignon. Il s'appelle Médor.*
- Il est fidèle et très attentif. Il est tout noir avec de beaux yeux marron. Il aime se promener avec moi au parc, et il joue avec les autres chiens qu'on rencontre.
- A la maison, il passe son temps dans la cuisine devant la porte, ou dans le jardin.
- Il aboie quand quelqu'un s'approche de la maison.
- Généralement il aime la compagnie des gens car il est sociable.
- Mon chat et mon chien sont tous les deux amis, l'un de l'autre, car ils se connaissent depuis longtemps quand ils étaient encore petits. Ils sont tous les deux très aimables.

Learn a new language; it's great for keeping the brain active:

Do you have any school French?

Here is the English translation of the story written in French.

- *Pets*
- I have two animals at home: *a cat and a dog.*
- *I named my cat "Mimi".* He is a beautiful colour of yellow and has green eyes. My cat is three years old, and he is clever and independent. When he is in the garden, he is like a little tiger. He is seen low in the grass, spying on the birds. He approaches them slowly, and in one leap, he jumps on his prey. But the birds are very agile, and they all fly away at once. It's a daily game between my cat and the birds.
- At night, my cat spends his time in front of the chimney, dozing with half-closed eyes. Like all cats, Mimi drinks milk, and he eats fish. When he is happy, he purrs.
- *My dog is cute. His name is Médor.*
- He is faithful and very attentive. He is all black with beautiful brown eyes. He likes going on walks with me in the park, and he plays with the other dogs we meet.
- At home, he spends his time in the kitchen in front of the door, or in the garden.
- He barks when someone approaches the house.
- Generally he likes people's company as he is sociable.
- My cat and my dog are both friends, as they know each other for a long time when they were still small.
  They are both very likeable.

Write a postcard in a newly acquired language on your holiday:

La Tour Eiffel
Emile Dutreuil

Chers Marie et Antoine,

Nous sommes arrivés à Paris ce matin. C'est un rêve. Nous avons tout un programme devant nous.

Visites à la Tour Eiffel et au musée du Louvre. Déjeuners sur place et rencontres avec des amis du collège. Nous avons aussi des billets pour l'Opéra de Paris.

A très bientôt
Affectueusement

La famille Montrose

Translation: French/ English: *Dear Marie & Antoine, We've arrived in Paris this morning. What a dream come true. We have a whole program in front of us: visit to the Eiffel Tower and Louvre museum. Lunch on site & meetings with college friends. And we also have tickets for the Paris Opera.*
See you very soon. Kind Regards. Montrose Family.

Other Useful phrases to write on a postcard:
Grand Bonjour de Paris/ Lourdes/ Nice.
Je pense à vous et vous envoie mes meilleurs vœux.
Je suis en vacances avec ma famille en ce moment.
Nous serons de retour la semaine prochaine.
Au revoir. Bernadette.

Translation: Wishing you a huge Good-day from .../ ... / ....
I'm thinking of you & send you my best wishes.
I'm on holiday with my family at the moment.
We'll be back next week. Good-bye. Bernadette.

Stories from far & near…

The Size of a Stamp Art Collection: stories from far & near
Watercolour & black ink drawings by Marie Anne O'Mordha

A little time to live in the moment

Totally absorbed in the moment: that's Mindfulness.

Where time is non-existent, flowing in the Continuum of Space, Past-Present-Future all merging into one. It's the flow of Life, there's a time to go with the flow. Powerful Healing Tool for Balance and Well-Being.

As a child I was surrounded by music & song: old songs: I was lulled by the soft timbre of my great-aunt's voice singing about the ebb & flow of the great oceans' waves as the vessel made its way at the whim of nature's idle calm or fierce wrath tearing through land and sea: the little sailor's abode, his whole universe round the world and back home again.

*Va, petit mousse, va petit mousse,

Où le vent te pousse…Entre le ciel et l'onde,

Marchant vers l'horizon, Ton navire est ton monde,

Ton pays, ta maison Va, va, petit mousse

Vole où le vent te pousse

*Source : Michel Cadiou. Les Cloches de Corneville, Act 1. (Grenicheux) Orchestre National de Paris. "Go, little sailor, go little sailor, where the wind brings you… Between the sky and the sea, pushing towards the horizon, your vessel is your world, your country, your abode. Go little sailor. Fly where the wind takes you…"

*"Tropical" The Beach house...*The Gathering was at the beach house, round July & August during school holidays, with parents enjoying the time with their children and elders. *"What a lovely beach house, so cosy and in the perfect spot within reach of the sea lapping gently on the beach!"* one said. *"We'll certainly enjoy every minute of this holiday"* said the other. All agreed. It was a lovely beach house with a thatched roof by the seaside, one could see the wooden rafters inside; there was a large table in the centre of the main room, everyday all would be sharing meals in the family circle, chatting and enjoying one another's company. Daybreak would start with the cooing sound of pigeons nearby in the tall wiry filaos trees, and the all-encompassing roaring tide beyond the reefs swashing powerful white crested waves in the distance; the beach for now an expanse of fine white sand as far as the eye could see in the faint rosy light of dawn before a golden sunrise, the scenery coming alive with the rising sun.

Learning something new...

The following section relates to memory. Countries are listed in groups according to geography or singly or as in travel packs.

(A) Write all the answers you know, mark.../50
(B) See the answers in the 2nd part, learn & commit to memory
(C) Re-do the exercise faster, mark.../50. See the improvement.
(D) Repeat occasionally. Note any difference.

Time quiz: write down the capitals of the European Countries in pencil
The first letter is the clue   *Answers: next page to quiz*

	Country	Capital City		Country	Capital City
1	Ireland	D	29	Belarus	M
2	United Kingdom	L	30	Montenegro	P
3	Iceland	R	31	Romania	B
4	Finland	H	32	Czech Rep.	P
5	Sweden	S	33	Andorra	A La Vella
6	Norway	O	34	Bulgaria	S
7	Denmark	C	35	Slovenia	L
8	France	P	36	Slovakia	B
9	Monaco	M	37	Malta	V
10	Liechtenstein	V	38	Serbia	B
11	Luxembourg	L (City)	39	Cyprus	N
12	Switzerland	B	40	Albania	T
13	Italy	R	41	Armenia	Y
14	San Marino	S M	42	Azerbaijan	B
15	Vatican City (Holy See)	V C	43	Bosnia & Herzegovina	S
16	Spain	M	44	Georgia	T
17	Portugal	L	45	Kazakhstan	N -S
18	Netherlands	A	46	Kosovo	P
19	Greece	A	47	Moldova	C
20	Belgium	B	48	Ukraine	K (K)
21	Austria	V	49	Croatia	Z
22	Germany	B	50	North Macedonia	S
23	Poland	W			
24	Latvia	R			
25	Lithuania	V			
26	Estonia	T			
27	Hungary	B			
28	Russia	M			

	Country	Capital City		Country	Capital City
1	Ireland	**Dublin**	29	Belarus	**Minsk**
2	United Kingdom	**London**	30	Montenegro	**Podgorica**
3	Iceland	**Reykjavik**	31	Romania	**Bucharest**
4	Finland	**Helsinki**	32	Czech Rep.	**Prague**
5	Sweden	**Stockholm**	33	Andorra	**Andorra La Vella**
6	Norway	**Oslo**	34	Bulgaria	**Sofia**
7	Denmark	**Copenhagen**	35	Slovenia	**Ljubljana**
8	France	**Paris**	36	Slovakia	**Bratislava**
9	Monaco	**Monaco**	37	Malta	**Valletta**
10	Liechtenstein	**Vaduz**	38	Serbia	**Belgrade**
11	Luxembourg	**Luxembourg City**	39	Cyprus	**Nicosia**
12	Switzerland	**Bern**	40	Albania	**Tirana**
13	Italy	**Rome**	41	Armenia	**Yerevan**
14	San Marino	**San Marino**	42	Azerbaijan	**Baku**
15	Vatican City (Holy See)	**Vatican City**	43	Bosnia & Herzegovina	**Sarajevo**
16	Spain	**Madrid**	44	Georgia	**Tbilisi**
17	Portugal	**Lisbon**	45	Kazakhstan	**Nur-Sultan**
18	Netherlands	**Amsterdam**	46	Kosovo	**Pristina**
19	Greece	**Athens**	47	Moldova	**Chisinau**
20	Belgium	**Brussels**	48	Ukraine	**Kyiv (Kiev)**
21	Austria	**Vienna**	49	Croatia	**Zagreb**
22	Germany	**Berlin**	50	North Macedonia	**Skopje**
23	Poland	**Warsaw**			
24	Latvia	**Riga**			
25	Lithuania	**Vilnius**			
26	Estonia	**Tallinn**			
27	Hungary	**Budapest**			
28	Russia	**Moscow**			

The Elephant and his Keeper

SABU the Elephant... *Sabu the Elephant lived in the forest with his keeper.* Day & night his keeper Babu looked after Sabu the Elephant and the man's people considered the Elephant as one of the family. All the loving care the keeper gave his elephant made him a wonderful good-looking elephant who loved his work, and one said: *"What a happy elephant he is!"* Both Elephant & Keeper were very fond of each other and every day, Sabu would be ready for doing his work, lifting and carrying the logs that the workers cut down for new houses to be built far & near. The forest owner was a good savvy man with a wide knowledge of the planet, having travelled the world over. He had come from a faraway land, however he decided to settle down in the forest where he valued the indigenous tribes people, fauna and flora. A very wise owner he was indeed, as he heeded the talk of climate change. As soon as the trees were cut down, the forest owner already had a replacement of new trees to be planted. *One day, Sabu the Elephant had a dream:* the elephant dreamt of his keeper, so kind and loving, looking after him Sabu the Elephant with his food, work tasks and bathing ritual at the river every day and Sabu's skin was a lovely grey and texture-soft although he rolled in the mud to keep insects at bay. Sabu dreamed of his keeper, and he dreamed of the next life where he himself Sabu would be looking after his keeper, and in the dream, the elephant asked: *"Can I be your keeper in the next life? To be looking after you as you are looking after me now, so well and loving, that I would like to repay you in the next life, it would be a privilege to look after you in turn."*

The Butterfly & Bee Garden: **Blue, violet and yellow** *favourite colours for bees: sunflowers, lavender, blue geraniums, yellow roses & clover...*

The Scout Bees fly out from the warmth of the hive at the early hours of the day, *"as busy as a bee"*, it's said. These tiny creatures, nature investigators and inspectors have an important task to do. Gardens full of sweet delectable nectar & pollen they have to find hopefully nearby, the closer the better. Their tiny wings flap in the air buzzing around and about, loop in the air, up and down diving and shooting upwards over hedges and walls, till they find their loot. So back they go, into the warmth of their hive, it's tropical in here: a constant 34 degrees Celsius. The little scout bees gather the **Worker Bees** around for their waggle dance, saying: *"Here chaps, that's the path for the best bounty of all today, and you'll be back in a flash"* With the waggle dance, the navigation path is pin pointed. The worker bees use their antennae to see where to fly out today, as it's dark in the hive. What an important task rests on this tiny community to find the trees, plants and flowers to bring the bounty home which will make the sweetest most prized honey the world knows, and simultaneously pollinate all the plants which feed the world.

Poem by William Henry DAVIES

WHAT is this life if, full of care,
We have no time to stand and stare?—
No time to stand beneath the boughs,
And stare as long as sheep and cows:
No time to see, when woods we pass,
Where squirrels hide their nuts in grass:
No time to see, in broad daylight,
Streams full of stars, like skies at night:
No time to turn at Beauty's glance,

And watch her feet, how they can dance:
No time to wait till her mouth can
Enrich that smile her eyes began?
A poor life this if, full of care,
We have no time to stand and stare.

Learning the alphabet in the 1930's in the National School.

I often asked my husband to tell me a story, and this time he told me the story of learning the alphabet when he was in first class in the National School in the 1930's, Point Road Dundalk.

There were some letters which were indelible in his mind: from A to D, then onto S, all said in a musical tone:

A for ***Apple***   **B** for ***Boy***   **C for Cat***   **D for Dog**

S with ***a Long Tail***   **S** with ***a Long Tail***   **S** with ***a Long Tail***

When it came to "S with a long tail", the little boys waved their hands behind their backs to imitate a long tail, which caused many giggles from the girls sitting behind them on the long bench… a tale told with such childhood innocence that I loved the story and grateful to my wonderful husband to have told me this gorgeous story.

I will add other letters to the learning of the alphabet, as some stories still stand out in my mind:

G for goat: Annie's Goat. There was water to fetch from the fountain. There was Annie's goat to watch out for: it would pat its hoof onto the ground, its head bent with the little horns on the ready, and eyeing the children with a wicked look in its eyes. The buckets were filled to the brim with the cold water from the well. The children ran most of the way back home as the geese gave them chase with open wings, buckets now half full on reaching the house, and mother said: *"There're still children to be washed, so you'll have to fetch some more water."* Soon the chase would start all over again…

H for Harmony: Harmony, Love and Song in the Little Thatch Cottages. A cosy home for children to grow up in, becoming most wonderful people to follow their dreams to make the world a better place to live in.

L for Ladder: Irish Naval Reserve, Nr. 1 Company Dundalk. Seamen dressed in their wonderful naval uniforms; the training on the ship would be weekly for all to be learned about seamanship. Sailors boarded the ship with the Ladder; three sailors at one time: one boarding, one in the middle and one at the other end on the quay. The Irish Sea is known to be rough and choppy, so every now & again the unfortunate seaman in the middle of the ladder was thrown into the water with the disappearing ladder underfoot, and the Master said: *"Get the Ladder, get the Ladder!!"*

O for Orchard: There was a wonderful **O**rchard on a large estate full of apple trees; the ripened apples fell to the ground and the children looked at the apples from behind the fence. Soon the children made their way to the apples and soon these would be collected for the most wondrous apple tarts mother made, all eaten!

P for Planet Earth: Our Planet Earth, our cradle and home from the beginning of time. Caring for our **P**lanet: must-do priority and shared responsibility for us all.

S for Saints and Scholars: Tomas told me *"Ireland is known as a Land of Saints & Scholars."* **St. Patrick, St. Gerald of Majella, St. Brigid** to name a few & the mass migration of **Scholars of Ireland** throughout the world in the Irish Diaspora.

U for Unity: Family **U**nity, Unity in the Home, Unity in one's Country, Understanding & Order in society, Order in the World and Peace throughout.

V for Village: It takes a whole **V**illage to rear a Child: learning comes from the warmth of the family home, play & lessons learned from one's neighbourhood and school, from society as a whole. There's a saying: *"Give me a child till he's 7 and I will give you the Man."*

W *for* **Wisdom:** **W**isdom comes with life experience. Nanna always had good advice for Tomas as he was growing up. Nanna was a well-read woman from books borrowed from the Dundalk County Library. She sent Tomas outside to play with his friends on sunny days, and never mind the penmanship homework, *"there are machines now doing all the writing for people"*, she said. Nanna was always the last to go to sleep at night, waiting for everyone to come home by 11.00 p.m. and she would have some nice cereals and warm milk and a hot cup of tea made on arrival. Nanna had her own grief as she was a widow a long time now when her children were still small, however she was strong and held her nerve and kept on going and kept everyone together. Tender Loving Care gently guiding the family and the wheel need not be re-invented.

Round the Table…

Round the Table…Cooking & enjoying a meal
Recipes for Condiments & Grand-ma's cake

Welcome Tomato Chutney:

Serves 4 people

Ingredients:
4 medium size tomatoes
1 small red onion
2 sprigs of parsley
Sea salt & pepper

Method:
Quarter the tomatoes, and cut finely
Slice the onion as fine as possible. Chop the parsley fine
Mix the tomatoes, onions and parsley in a small salad bowl
Add the sea salt & pepper to taste
Serve with your meals. *Looks & tastes great with rice based meals.*

Tropical Coconut Chutney:

Serves 4 people
Ingredients:
8 pieces of fresh coconut in small white chunks.
10 Coriander leaves & same quantity of Mint leaves
1 small Green chilli, 3 garlic cloves, 2tsp Olive Oil.

Method: First, remove the seeds from the chilli, as they are very hot.
Use the electric blender or finely chop all ingredients & crush using pestle & mortar.
Put ingredients into the blending bowl: coconut, garlic, coriander, mint, and chilli without seeds. Pour in the oil.
Blend briskly altogether. Put chutney paste into condiment bowl & serve with hot meals. *Spicy. The coconut, garlic & herb mix tastes delicious.*

Note: It's said that fresh coconut is great for memory, and brain repair!

Delicious Dressings for Salads:

Serves 4 people.
Ingredients:
1 lemon
4 tablespoons of Cold-pressed Virgin Olive Oil
Half teaspoonful of Dijon Mustard
2 large cloves of pressed garlic, 1 tsp finely chopped parsley
Sea salt & pepper to taste

Method:
Squeeze the lemon into a bowl, removing any pips.
Add 4 tablespoons of virgin olive oil, half teaspoonful of Dijon mustard, pressed garlic & finely chopped parsley.
Sprinkle a little sea salt & pepper.
Pour over any salad: Mixed leaf salad or Greek salad: lettuce & rocket mix, cucumber, tomatoes served in quarters, green & black olives, capers & feta cheese cubes. *Dressing is exquisite & tangy, gives salads a boost. Serve with oven-hot garlic bread.*

Honey & Herb Remedy *for banishing colds & sniffles:*

Ingredients: Makes large jar.
30g fresh thyme, 16g (2 tsp) Sage leaves, 12 sachets chamomile, 4 tsp fennel seeds, 2 tsp aniseed, 40 cloves, 4 garlic cloves, a small piece of grated ginger, 1 pinch of cayenne pepper, 1800ml water, 900g organic local honey.

Method:

1. Place herbs and water into a pan and bring to the boil. Cover with a tight-fitted lid. Upon boiling, turn the heat down & simmer gently for 20 minutes.
2. Allow liquid to cool a little and then strain into another pan.
Press the herbs with your hand to extract all the juice. Keep the liquid & discard boiled herbs.
3. Return the liquid to the heat & simmer very gently, uncovered & without stirring until the liquid is reduced to 400ml. The slower the liquid reduction, the better: that's the decoction.
4. Add the honey to the pan. Dissolve slowly and simmer for a few minutes, stirring all the time, until a syrupy consistency is reached. Allow the mixture to bubble for a moment, only for a moment taking care not to over-heat to avoid making a caramel toffee instead.
5. Allow to cool and pour into heat-resistant jar / jars.

That's the *Honey & Herb Remedy: Potent for Chest Colds & Sniffles*.
Tried & tested with family members, and wards off colds especially in cold windy wet weather. Some family members had no need of antibiotics since taking the remedy.

That's wonderful news for the immune system!!
Take a tablespoonful 3 times daily, can be poured over porridge.
It tastes great. Enjoy!

Grand-ma's Sponge Cake: *Grand-ma's cake always delighted us children when we came over to spend some holiday time with the grand-parents. Grand-ma would bake the cake, a large one; when it was ready, the cake would be left to cool and then large slices cut to be eaten. What a delight! There were sultanas and cherries in the cake and it smelled delicious! We'd all sit down round the table, eat the cake with a bolstering cup of sugared tea.*

Method: Mix with an electric blender

4 equal parts of sugar, butter, flour & eggs. All ingredients should have the same weight.

Add raisins & some red candied cherries, plus some almond essence.

Put mixture in tin, lined with grease-proof paper and bake in the oven for 30-35 minutes. Take the cake out the oven, and allow it to cool.

Turn upside down to remove from the baking tin.

Place on a serving dish, and cut in large slices to share. Thank you Gran-ma!

Spot the difference.

Give yourself 10 seconds to spot 5 differences between the 2 images

01 ....

02 ....

03...

04 ....

05 ....

The Sydney Opera House

I was asked by a friend from the University where would I want to go. I replied, "To the Opera House", so the tickets appeared for the Opera House. "What dress will I wear?" I wondered, I had a couple of ideas for a new dress, and with the busyness and thouroughfare of life, the time went on. A few days before the event, my young mum asked: "What dress will you be wearing?" I hadn't got one yet, and she said: "I have a lovely one in my wardrobe, would you like to try it?"It was a two piece outfit with a lovely design & a summery fuchsia shade of pink, so I tried it and it was a tee bit large at the waist, I said: "Thanks." So I went on to secure the waist with some safety pins, and it was fine. On the evening of the excursion, my party came to my parents' house to bring me to the Opera House, with greetings all round. So it was time to go, and we were just about to get into the car, when my mum said in a foreign language which she thought my party would not understand: "Make sure the dress is secure."It was suddenly a very warm Saturday evening. My party said to me quietly: "Are you wearing your mother's dress?" I said: "No."

The journey to Sydney was about 45 minutes away, and the streets of Sydney full of the endless week-end traffic. A space was found up on the heights of the hill beyond, a motorcycle needed to be displaced to make room for the car. We walked briskly to the Opera House chatting and enjoying the mild weather. On arrival, the show had just started and the usher said we needed to wait for the interval, my friend said it was only just a few minutes started, however the usher was adamant we had to wait for the interval about half hour or so. My friend said: "We can't go in right now, the show has already started. The man must have had an argument with his wife." *So we looked out to the Ocean from the large bay windows of the Opera House, sipping on some orange juice, looking out to the ships in the distance with lights shining from their port holes, and to the dark black wavy sea below, lit up by the Southern Cross, it was a magical view in a magical place.*

The Opera cast was a European medieval tale of intrigue and drama, with music from the Sydney Orchestra sung in a foreign language by highly trained operatic voices male & female to fill the hall to vertiginous heights. My friend explained to me the opera was full of intrigue, and he asked me if I liked intrigue, I considered my answer before replying: "No." *The costumes, the singing and the orchestra were absolutely wonderful, in this completely magical place. A treasured memory, a treasured time and place, a treasured friendship. The opera was over, and we walked together chatting and admiring the large paintings of artists and pioneers that had made their mark in this new country of ours. We stopped at one painting, and I said:* "It's so real, that one could say to have met this person sometime." *He asked if I was interested in art, I said:* "Yes." *He said, he knew an artist, he knew one. And I could meet this person sometime. There were many large wide steps walking towards the base of the Opera House, and the weather outside was mild and there was a gentle sea breeze in the air. My friend brought me back home to my parents' house, he was very nice and we liked each other. He accompanied me to the front door and clicked his heels before taking his leave. Old time courtesies, invaluable in today's world.*

TAKE UP CALLIGRAPHY
Beautiful Writing Techniques, to try your hand at
Send your own Greeting Cards to your family & friends…

Calligraphy is quite a skill that requires a **love of writing beautiful letters** *in an artistic way and a little time to write. Define your message and design.*
There's always a blank page waiting for your own distinctive creative style with your message to send to someone dear to you.
And what a surprise it will be! *What a complete joy to receive such a message, to think someone close to one's heart has taken the time to imagine a be-spoke creation made just for me!* I remember making a Mother's Day Card in primary school for my mum, and we were all delighted with our cards made in the class; they looked beautiful, a genuine expression of love for our mums.
To hold the treasured item in one's hand & have it as a keepsake of affection.
There's a soothing healing energy in the keepsake.

Key to card above: Bonjour! / Good-day! Meilleurs Vœux / Best Wishes.
Bonheur & Prospérité / Happiness & Prosperity. French to English translation.

The Coat & the Mantle…

Mother Earth's Little Boys are taught from a young age to be providers of the World. Lessons learnt in the hearth of family life. The little boys, soon to be the men of this world, are handed over this Mantle from Father to Son.

Born in the little thatch cottages overlooking the Irish Sea at the turn of the 20th century, Tomas had big dreams. He was a member of Captain's Mac World Wide Web, and had collected all the badges that came with Captain's Mac Magazines supplied to him by his uncles James & Johnny; he also read the Beano and the Dandy, awesome comic stories full of interesting goings-on and familiar characters to be looking out for. Tomas had dreams of Travel & Adventure and he sought Work to become a Captain of Industry…

My dear husband Tomas loved buying a new coat for me, *"You need a new coat for the winter, let's buy a new coat for you."* This was an expression of love and duty to his wife. And this gave him the satisfaction that I would be warm and protected from the cold and blustery days of wintertime. I remember the very first coat he bought for me, in one of Melbourne's lovely department stores. It was a long navy Cashmere and Wool coat, made in the most beautiful natural fibres, mid-calf in length and in raglan sleeve design, navy buttons in the front to keep the cold at bay, and a belt of the same material. It was the warmest and indeed the most luxurious coat I had ever owned and I told him so. *"Thanks very much Tom, it's the most wonderful coat I've ever worn, it's so warm and amazing and looks great!"*I saw the joy and pride in his eyes. He just looked happy for having bought the coat for me, and able to buy the finest coat for his wife. His work as a teacher was a labour of love, and in his teaching and lecturing over the years, he was in fact passing his own Mantle to his students, through his industrial expertise and vast management know-how of the business-world acquired in five decades of relentless work over 4 continents. Tomas O'Mordha the teacher was now passing his own Mantle to his students to navigate their own careers and with the same passion and dedication that he himself had conducted his own path with. And out of the Passion for his work came Opportunity to meet him and the highest possible heights reached. Tomas used to say: *"The Eagle has landed…"*

Over time, Tomas would buy other coats for me: *"summer and winter coats for rain drops and blustery weather"*, fashion coats to wear on evening soirées, then *"a lovely sporting duffle coat in pink because it looks young & fun to wear and with lamb's wool lining"*, there was another duffle coat in khaki with a hood lined in silk with a dainty blue floral design, and made for the coldest winter days and worn so much that the sleeve edges needed leather binding. The colours over the years were classical and matching the fashion of the day. We both enjoyed buying the coats. *"Try it on!"* Tomas would say and I would know from his eyes if he liked it, and I think somehow the higher joy was on his side, the joy of providing for his family as he had been taught when he was a little boy.

The glimmer of the little boy still at heart, now all grown up in a fine tall distinguished lovely gentleman, the glimmer of the little boy he was so long ago was still there; cherished and adored for it by me. When I wear the coats my husband bought for me, I feel his strong protective presence over my shoulders. I am in fact wearing both the beautiful coats Tomas bought for me and my husband's Mantle.

Learn something new & keep learning

To keep the brain active daily is a must-do at any age, keep the brain flexible and flawless, start early and keep memory and behavioural problems at bay in the older years. To learn something new is to push one's boundaries, forming brand-new neurons, to extend or maintain the brain's capacity at any age.

3 Catalysts: Exercise, Social Interaction & to Learn something new to keep one's independence. What a small price to pay for such enormous benefits! One's innate intelligence Body and Mind keeps the immune system strong combating & preventing dis-ease. One condition remains: that one must treat Body & Mind with respect, providing both with the required daily nourishment and care: physical, mental & emotional.

What is one's passion? Would it be art or the mechanics of vintage cars or train-building or gazing at the stars and galaxies? It could be designing a seasonal garden with distinctive shape and colour.

Would your passion be in raising your family or looking after husbands or wives to love and cherish into their older years? Would it be in climbing the corporate ladder, or being an entrepreneur? You could pick up a childhood hobby and knit the most wonderful garments for the catwalk and start your own business. Whatever it is:

Just pick up a new topic to learn and keep going.

The local knitting and crochet teacher is Breda of "Breda Wools, Drogheda", a Master of her Art. *She's a lady who learned knitting and crochet from her mother when she was a child, as a form of play & to create something useful with her own hands, she so loved the items she made with simple tools and some wool that this became a life-long work of love. One of her ambitions is to pass on her skills to the next generation and those interested in developing the craft, which is enormously grounding and therapeutic especially to anyone feeling stressed.*

The items in the photograph shown further on are all hand-made.
The following were made by Marie Anne in Breda's Wools classes:
Knitted sleeveless vest and belt *to be worn over black*, my creation is lime in colour which reminds me of a beautiful scalloped dress that my great-aunt made for me in my childhood. The intricately eye-catching crocheted dress started

with small shells increasing in size to finish off, over the same colour lining. A treasured memory and work of love that I'll always cherish.

Lace-Crochet Collar in white, worn over a navy floral dress. Set off with a shamrock pin.

Hat & collar in navy furry wool made for warmth on cold winter days.

Other masterpieces crafted by myself and my husband at various times:
The ***all-leather, perforated leather vest*** *in navy was made by Tom Moore for his wife Marie Anne.* A very beautiful sentimental keep-sake, the leather is fine and original, its leather buttons display a floral design & demi-belt of the same material at the back.

The following items were hand-made by Marie Anne:
Crochet Ivory scarf to contrast with the navy leather vest.
The Size of a Stamp Cushion: stamped envelopes with rose-perfumed letters, for the shoes & crocheted white collar.
Felted Eggs *Irish landscape depicting sheep, lighthouse & flora.*
Embroidery *of Australian Callistemon "Captain Cook" and European landscapes,* all 3 graced my office in Australia.
Mat made with latch-hook *with my own vibrant colourful drawing,* I made the mat as an Art project in secondary school. My lovely mum helped to finish it as I had lots of homework to do for the next day.

The last 3 items were beautifully fashioned by my aunt Geneviève, a lady in her 7th decade enjoying life looking after her family and its blessings. She learned knitting long ago while at school and developed the skill further going to local classes and knitting on train journeys to and from work.
Knitted hat & scarf *with flower* in multicolour green & brown.
Teapot Warmer: a beautiful multi-floral tea-cosy to love and appreciate.
Crocheted Shopping Bag which is great to hold a few essentials for a stroll on summer holidays.

The lovely fashionable court shoes in brown printed leather were hand-crafted by Footwear Expert *Tom Moore* on a Commonwealth assignment training demonstration to the Footwear Industry & Government Training Authority of Cyprus before joining the European Union.
Nicosia, Cyprus 1986.

The Handshake

The Handshake. *"There is power in the handshake."* One can decipher a person's character from the individual handshake. I knew Thomas Moore's handshake, I would recognise my husband's handshake, even with my eyes closed. It was firm, warm and welcoming saying: *"Hello, I'm genuinely happy to see you."* I would say that the handshake is characteristic of region and locality. Having travelled the world with my husband Thomas, I know that my husband's handshake is different from most handshakes I've encountered. And I have classified my husband's handshake to be characteristic of the Dundalk older generation male handshake of the 1920's and 30's, because I recognise it to be of the same quality as my husband's. To me it conveys an unconscious message inherent in the people of the older generation of Dundalk: *"We have your back, we've been through the mill and we know..."* Some people convey through a handshake a message of protection and safety, safe hands to carry people through. When I was growing up, I watched the current movies on T.V. and I grew up thinking that people try to get out of prison as in *"Alcatraz"* and the *"Great Escape"*. There is an exception, it's an Irish story. *"Have you heard of people forcing their way into prison? Does the* Black and Tan *mean anything to you? Well, I know a story which my husband told me: During the First World War, Britain was at war with Germany; well the attention was diverted from Ireland, but not fully, and according to popular belief, men from British jails were let loose in Ireland to be the Guardians of Peace and Order in the State. Those people were called* Black and Tan *because their uniforms were of mis-matched tops and bottoms black and tan in colour, whichever fitted.*
Peace and order! Well, all the hell broke loose!
The Irish were pining for their country's independence for a long time and when the Irish revolution started, many were indiscriminately put into jails, and Dundalk was not immune. The Black and Tans *were looking for one of Thomas' uncles, a teen-ager at the time, and went to the little Thatch Cottages to his mother for his whereabouts; she said she did not know where he was as she had not seen him. So the* Black and Tans *set fire to the little Thatch Cottages and secured it locked with Thomas' grand-mother inside; the neighbours saw what was happening, got the grand-mother out and managed to put the fire out, a lot to be repaired."* There is a large round mark cemented over at the edges on the Garda's wall in Dundalk where the break-in occurred on the eventful night that the Black & Tan prison was broken into to seek and get the people out; out from the jailers' claws, out of sight and out of mind.

The Poinsettia: Attractive & Charismatic Garnet Red. Lively & Inviting. **Welcome flower of the festive season**, all cares forgotten for now. Reminiscent of the **Flamboyant tree**, the shade of its extended wing so cool under a noon-day sun & blue skies above where swallows fly carried lightly by the sway of whimsical southern air currents of the Tropics. Memories of Christmas past and those here further up north where the Green Flash plays out an amazing display on the horizon. Mother would say: *"The weather is Baltic out there, come in you, out of the cold!"* Expectations run high, housewives busy with the Christmas fare of roasting goose simmering gently in the hot stove; the pudding hanging by the chimney side, dog and cat lazily lying one eye open in front of blazing hot flames flickering in the fireplace. *"It's great to be home!"* says father. The children are playing quietly eyeing the tantalising feast on the table and the wafting menthol & pine scent of the fir fills the warm air, ready for the toys that Santa will bring before the strike of midnight; all would be quiet then with children asleep till the morning of Christmas Day.

The China Man & the Giant Puzzle...

In times past, little boys played foot-ball because their fathers were interested in the game, fascinated on seeing it being played; a genius of a sport, devised to keep the players' *World in Order* in the far-flung places of Empire, a sport engineered to focus minds on the *Strategies of the Game in the Men's Club,* replete with men living away, often for a life-time; the game strategies would be soldering their togetherness and belonging to the Club, the tactics would show up their strengths, prowess, expertise and know-how in the most advantageous of positions, the total focus on winning, their wit powerfully pitted against other teams.

Rolling back time in the Empire, on the shore of the South China Seas, such a game was a regular occurrence and as canon-ball surprise to the natives. So there was this very enterprising China Man, always thinking what he could invent for the populace as this was his natural incline; as a child he had this incredible drive to create and invent and had already made several feisty-looking kites and festive Dragons for his school-mates and indeed items for his own house such as the silk-net umbrella for food and measures that his mother could use in the kitchen, and delighted so she was, and said: *"Great, that will come in handy, have some more noodle"*, her child was a born-inventor and she knew it, he took after his father, so busy with trade missions round the country. So with the arrival of the Foreigners in the proximity of his house, there was yet another puzzle to solve: He could not understand the ferocious shouting over the wall. The China man had to find out what this weird carry-on was all about, and in the half-light of dawn, he had climbed into the lychee tree high up on a bushy branch seeing into the field, to find out exactly what was going on with his own eyes and this is what he saw: grown-up men running after one ball, all running and fighting and shouting and pulling at each other and rounding and crouching around this one ball, jumping high up raised by the throng to catch it and there were injuries, cuts, bruises and a broken wrist on that day and the Chinese doctor called to mend it; to top it all, right through, there was a man running with the herd with a whistle. The China man recognised the men: they were the *"blue-eyed, yellow-haired foreign savants"* with tall ships in the harbour, houses, and regal uniforms, some of them on horse-back and servants and luxuries at their beck and call... The China Man thought to himself: *"What a mesmerizing whopping puzzle! A total disgrace for all I see!! What a scrappy melee of bodies, heads, elbows, feet, head-to-head and risking life and limb, despicable all-round, bloodied and muddied for all the fighting and if I did not know these people, they could well be the scrum of the earth."* This mystery was an unbearable puzzle in his mind, burning to be demystified and sorted out. Most of all, the China Man liked Order in his house, and to find a solution, he must find one and a good one!! The fracas made people uneasy and the whistling agitated the birds. His neighbours came over to see him, as they knew this China man from their childhood days; he was their friend and would sort it all out as he had done before, in their play-ground fisticuffs. So our man said to his friends: *"Don't you worry, I'll put my thinking cap on and sort it all out!!"*

So after much calculation with the abacus, deliberation and debate in his mind, various models and contraptions made, some scrapped for other uses, the enterprising China man soon came up with the perfect Solution in the loft of his house, his laboratory with a window open to the world. And to set it in motion, the China man invited his closest friends to discuss the plan of action: it was decided to call for the far-and-wide-travelled Monk living in the mountains nearby; that man the monk, it was said, knew foreign cultures and lingo. So the day came for their meeting, there was much discussion in the China Man's courtyard over Mother's scrumptious banquet of food and Chinese green tea, the more food there was to share, the more the people talked and the Monk enlightened his audience with tales of the foreign land and the fighting spirit called *"sport"* which gave the foreigners their *"oomph"*; the monk described the *"sport for skill performance"* as he himself had studied the game and with skilful expression in the slender flowing way of a zen movement he explained it, and he explained the tangle to land the ball on the team's side and he had all present company to have-a-go so they would at least understand the state-of-play and soon all were in a tangle of elbows, feet, legs, their faces squashed to the ground and some facing upwards looking at the sky, all in a fine mess. Mother wisely decided to watch the confused spectacle from the height of the balcony. *"Aaah, sooh!!"* *"Aah, sooh, so that is a sport!!"* they all said, then they all sat round the table again drinking Chinese green tea with ginseng that mother had prepared, they expounded their ideas late into the night till the small hours of morning broken by the dawn chorus.

The plan was hatched: *An INVITATION!!* The Invitation *to the Captain & Company of the Foreign Savants* to be sent by courier on foot, by the trusted Envoy dressed in formal black silk attire and slippers, the pride of his long-tail of glossy straight jet-black platted hair to complete his ceremonious appearance.

Came the Day of the Invitation: the China Man's courtyard was lavishly decorated, numerous red lanterns and globes lit up the space between heaven and earth; the guests wore their handsome impeccable uniforms and the Chinese their rich traditional dress made with the finest silks embroidered in intricate designs to show their affluence. In the centre of the courtyard, was a round table with 19 seats round it, there was a large revolving plate onto the table with a plethora of wonderfully appetising dishes of various types and smell of roasted duck, lean beef, marinated pork, and stir-fried king prawns to tease one's appetite and satiate any hunger, this royal feast was served with green vegetables on large platters, several sauces of sweet & sour, black bean, and soya variations; there was also crispy crackling prawn crackers in accompaniment; then the prized 100 year-old eggs delicacy of the county unhurriedly marinated in the family recipe, after which came the sweet-meal of round rice-cakes and there was the delectable exotic lychee in a light syrup to finish off this wonderful cornucopia and throughout, pots of hot green Chinese tea for all to share. This was all served in small bowls with chopsticks; the talk was courteous and affable, some words already known to both parties; the Monk the interpreter between the China Man & friends and their Guests: the Captain and Dignitaries.

As entertainment, there was a Show of Chinese Acrobats & Dancers, with Dragons, Music and Colour ribbons; the height of the Show was the Ball, lots of balls skilfully twirled, juggled and played by the acrobats, one ball to each acrobat and as they were twirling their ball they displayed their acrobatics all in continuous circular motion and showing the most wonderful tricks imaginable with each Ball, one to each Acrobat. The Show was a delight and there was much talk about the ball, and clapping of hands to show appreciation, so the China Man said to the Captain: *"I would like to present to you the gift of a Ball for everyman in your Brigade."* The Giant Puzzle was finally solved and trade links already taking root:

"A Ball for Everyman on the field!!"

And the Captain graciously accepted the Gifts, and delighted with them, and he said: *"That's great!! Thank you very much!! They will make lovely presents for our children at Christmas Time!!"*

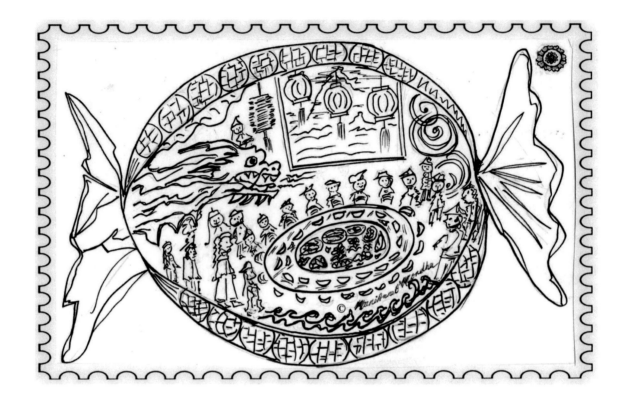

The King & the exotic Bird

Louis XIV, the Sun King was all for the Magnificent, the Elaborate, the Extravagant and Superlative in the Palaces of Versailles, of Paris and beyond gracing the land with his majestic Presence. One gasped in utter amazement at the wealth on display where beauty, indulgence and opulence reigned. The Gardens, most exquisite creations, colours of the rainbow, the King's favourite: the Blue Agapanthus rectangular border around a serene pool of fresh water where the swallows dipped their beaks on a long flight, and the finest people delivered by golden horse-drawn carriages to royal invitations for rejoicing and celebration, the sky all-lit up by a wonderful spectacle of fireworks, sparkling blue, white & pink effervescence.

The successor, Louis XV was pious and reserved. Heir to the throne, at the tender age of five years of age, was raised by the palace clerics and grew up detesting extravagance and high living in the royal household. Gone were the merry days of Louis XIV, the current reign of Louis XV very dull in comparison. The latter had a grand-son named Louis-Auguste: a gentle soul, a sensitive boy, his father passed away at the age of 35 making Louis-Auguste an orphan and the future heir of the kingdom. The little boy's great solace was to play in the Palace Carpenter's work-shop, located beyond the woods on the grounds; he grew up happy in the Carpenter's house, away from the daunting palace, the hated ballet & pageantry, its tutors and tedious royal duties. He learned to use his hands, fashioning all that could be made in wood. He was pious and attended the daily service in the royal chapel, thus developed a reverence for scripture and the faith. One day, Little Louis-Auguste carved some wood making a Chalice as Christ would have used at the Last Supper, the image of which he saw on a large Jacquard tapestry hanging in the palace dining-room, the present of it he made to a small dainty chapel of a nearby village. At the passing of King Louis XV, many breathed a silent sigh of relief and whispered: *"We'll bring back the days of the Sun King, and the champagne will be flowing again!!"*

Little Louis-Auguste was made ***King Louis XVI***, at 20 years of age; all were delighted to welcome their new King…

The talk about a bride for the King was endless: she needed all the attributes of youth and virtue to be married to their King. There was lots of talk of Maria Antonia of Austria, and a meeting of the royal elders about this particular princess... On that night, King Louis XVI had a dream... *"I dreamed of a bird, an exotic bird that I'd love for my forest-aviary and I dreamed that I was making an enormous cage for the rare bird with black ebony wood."* Little Louis had heard an old sailor talking about the rare bird in the magical ebony forest on his sea travels, and this bird was nowhere to be found in the country. His mother said: *"My Louis, we will go to the end of the world to find this bird and the wood you ask for."* The Chief-Librarian, Geography, Archaeology, & Ornithology Masters were called to consult the *"Carnets de notes et images de voyages de mer"* French mariners' log books brought to the Kingdom from their voyages in far destinations abroad, those were dusty with time and spread on the table; there in the *Mascareignes* was the *Dodo Bird found on Ile de France!!* illustrations of dense native flora of Ile de France and of a very strong black wood, *the Ebony*, specially prized by ship-makers for durability & flexible strength to last the course. Another narrative told of other ships there at the time, Dutch ships moored at Grand-Port, their crew members ashore the unoccupied island. There were the keys: the *Dodo Bird and the Ebony Wood.* It was scripted at a later date of the *"extinction of the Dodo and the Ebony wood was no longer on the island"* the bird devoured by the Dutch mariners and the ebony wood made into new ships! Hope seemed lost in the insurmountable obstacle!! The elders were weary, even fearing the marriage of the new King to the Austrian princess... Came news of a Clairvoyant nearby, and men on horseback sent to fetch her; she came with her Crystal Ball wearing a long dark cloak, her long silvery hair tied with grey silk ribbon, an air of aloof authority about the woman, demanding respect and with aplomb she said in her Corsican accent: *"I will find out what you need to know, the crystal ball always tells the truth, however I need my fee in advance, I have little ones to feed at home, the crystal ball does not lie, whatever your answer is, I need my remuneration!"* So the treasurer was called to give the woman her fee in advance. The Clairvoyant and the Crystal Ball went to work, herself and the royal Elders sitting round the table...about the imminent marriage. So the clairvoyant started, talking to her Crystal Ball in her Corsican dialect, repeating the names of the King Louis XVI and of Maria Antonia several times, looking dazed and far away, somewhat frazzled, saying the names into the distance, then she said in her Corsican dialect emphasizing certain words: *"....c'est l'enfer, le désastre .. désastre complet... royaume ...la mort ...*"a mesmerizing mumbo-jumbo of words which meant destruction and death, suddenly she let out a scream*"AAAaaaHH!"* which jolted the seated members, the woman looking haggard, now frightened, even terrified, directing her gaze in particular to one of the elders, the one who held the royal purse, and the crystal ball flew out of her hands and through the window to crash in smithereens on the pavement below by the rosemary bush! The cloaked woman sprung out from the table, starting to run down the stairs, out the gate, the elders unable to stop her so swift she was, they looked through the window, and could see the woman slipping away through the woods with the surprising suppleness of a gazelle, she was gone and could not be seen for dust and never to be seen again!!!

*"So what did that all mean?"*The senior elder had an instinct of an ominous marriage between the two, disastrous, a premonition deep in the pit of his stomach, and he spoke out: *"We'll need to get our King another princess..."*All agreed, all in unison. The elders probed everything leaving nothing unturned, and got to know of the King's wish for his birthday present, *"Voilà!! Mes Sires, voici notre réponse, le souhait du Roi!"*The answer would be in the King's birthday wish…A letter was speedily drawn calling for the *Ambassador of the Pays-Bas* for a very serious misdemeanour indeed that he would have to explain to the French Court. A special Envoy on horse-back was sent to deliver the *missive* with his Royal Majesty's red stamp. The letter said: *"Mr. Ambassador, you are summoned at the Elders' Meeting in the Court of Louis XVI. We have come to the knowledge of a very serious matter between our two countries that will need to be resolved at the earliest. So will you please present yourself at the Palace to discuss and to explain, as your invaluable cooperation will be sought by ourselves to sort out this most unfortunate incident, and was signed by his Majesty's Judge of the Court."*On the day, the Ambassador arrives, he is squat and smallish in appearance, wearing a dapper suit of dark grey flannel and a white shirt with small frills at the neck, a small navy cravat; his face is round and hair light brown in colour, he's wearing small rounded glasses with a gold frame and holding a black leather document-holder under his arm. He is accompanied by one of the Palace's guardsmen to the library where the elders are waiting for him. So the meeting starts and the *Ambassadeur of the Pays-Bas* is informed of the wish of the King Louis XVI for a very special kind of rare bird for his aviary and a cage made with ebony wood, for his birthday soon to be by the calendar, the items searched and it appears that the truth of the matter a very unfortunate one indeed, and therefore Mr. Ambassador of the Pays-Bas

now called to explain and seek a solution of Reparation to the King of France Louis XVI. The Dutch Ambassador was rendered speechless, tongue-tied trying to explain to his best advantage, how was it his country men's fault that the bird was eaten and the wood used in ship-building. So the Court-men said: *"The very Bird that King Louis XVI wants is extinct at the hands of his country-men, it was the only bird of its kind on the planet, and the special type of black ebony the rarest, also one of its kind on the planet. His country men's so-called misdemeanour is for sure down-right infamous, for two precious god-made creations to have been made defunct by their hands."*

The Ambassador now has drops of sweat to his brow, as the Elders of the French Court are all looking his way for explanations and reparation, this matter could turn sour, so as the Dutch Ambassador, he tries to resolve the question, speaking with a strong accent, his words punctuated with *"js"*, his eyes wide with disbelief, and he needs to find how to get out of this impasse, the majestic clock already sounding two hours gone, over the talk of reparation to be made and there is a welcome recess to think the matter over... and to breathe in the fresh air coming through the window, to have another cup of lemon tea, maybe something stronger, no there's none. The window is open, the thought of absconding briefly crosses his mind, only briefly, could be a bad idea with d'Artagnan & the King's musketeers trailing him...The Elders of the French Court and Ambassador are back sitting round the table, the senior of the Elders speaks: *"M. Ambassadeur, as you know, we want our two countries to be on friendly terms and there is a lot in this new world of ours that can be shared and enjoyed and to the advantage of both our peoples... so we may be able to overlook the unfortunate incidents of the lost Dodo Bird and of the Black Ebony Wood.."* The Ambassador listens attentively, wiping his brow with a large lace handkerchief with the Dutch royal insignia; he feels a solution coming round the corner. The senior Elder of the royal French Court speaks, *"You know the King is to be married in the near future and we have an eye on one particular girl in your kingdom and it would please the company of the Royal Palace of King Louis XVI for her visit with her parents next month to make her acquaintance."*

The Dutch Ambassador breathes a sigh of relief and he asks: *"What is the maiden's name?"*

"Her name is Marguerite, her father proprietor of a Dutch Trading Fleet; he is an aristocrat and we would like to forward an Invitation to Marguerite, her father and mother to the Royal Court of Louis XVI. A union between the two young people would be advantageous to both our nations and the people."

The Governor's wife's Ball...

The date was set for the most glorious ball at the Governor's House in Beau-Bassin. The Governor's wife was a very highly placed lady by birth and very astute in the art of social engineering having been taught the life-long art by her father who moved in diplomatic circles. Her Ladyship herself wrote *"The Invitation to the Governor's Ball"* to all gentry of the isle. The Governor's wife said to her husband: *"This will be a grand occasion to mark Your Arrival, the arrival of the Governor at the station. Invitations will be sent by postal service to people who navigated their way here during the French Revolution, one named «La Pimpernelle Rouge» carrying Musketeers and the equerry... I heard the King's carpenter was on-board, Aristocracy and Royalists, in their company the finest craftspeople, artisans and professionals of their time in the Arts, Sciences and Commerce; there will be Proprietors of Sugar-cane plantations, people of Port-Louis& Grand-Port, Beau-Bassin, Quatre-Bornes, Vacoas, 15-Cantons, Henrietta, Floréal, Curepipe, Grand-Bassin, Bel-Air, St. Aubain & Moka, Britannia & Souillac, Le Souffleur, Benares& Flacq, Chamarel, Terre-des-7-Couleurs, Plaisance, Rivière Noire & Pieter Both, Flic-en-Flac & Pointe-aux-Sables, Marie Reine de la Paix, Grand-Baie, Triolet, Trou d'eau douce & Pamplemousses. A most luxurious occasion to meet and greet her Majesty's subjects: a great asset to us in this new ownership, Star & Key of the Trade Route, in the Grand Scheme of our Royal Ownership of the World. The fare, a formal dinner-dance with full orchestra playing, our Welcome and courtesies to seal friendship and loyalty, and you the Governor will be the Master of the Occasion with me at your side."*

Preparations for the Governor's Ball were drawn up: it would be the finest Occasion to be seen for ages at the beguiling old French Grand House, the Governor's House would need to be resplendent, the silver shining and the Crystal gleaming for the finest wines and mature cognac. The House steeped in history, would be displaying the most breath-taking floral artistry in the dance-hall and the lavish dining-room, the gardens alive with the incendiary red Flamboyant trees, softest-pinks, reds and green Anthurium under the fruit-laden red lychee trees, a bounty of the Jack Tree, Fruit-à-Pain and lilac wisteria clad to the orangery while sky-blue long-stemmed Agapanthus and clusters of fluffy powder-pink Hydrangea borders would be lining the Grand House; in the middle of the lawn a gigantic smooth-white curvaceous shell to catch downpours of fresh rain-water, purple-brown passion-fruit with small green leaves and delicate green spiralling stems winding round the balcony's iron filigree work surrounding the terrace, chameleons lazily sunning themselves on the sun-drenched wooden boards and parakeets, almost hanging upside-down from the branches above, gorging themselves on the softly ripened oval-shaped yellow papayas, and in the air the heady scent of Tiaré Mimosa, Azaleas and Jasmine wafting about the most magnificent of locations by the edge of the precipice overgrown by ivy and vines of blue and white trump-shaped flowers, the spritzing sound of a gushing waterfall in the distance and the powerful belling of a majestic stag from the untamed depth of the forest below.

The Governor would be wearing his wonderful impeccable Governor's white Suit, his medals on show, his mighty presence for all to note; her Ladyship would be in a beautiful ball-room gown in the lightest blue chiffon lined with frosted-opalescent silk, the attractive top of the dress adorned with the finest small white and pink pearls of the warm Indian and South China seas, threads of silver through its base to glisten by the light of chandeliers and the adornment of *"nacre"* mother-of-pearl brooch on dainty slippers fashioned in white silk to cushion her slender feet. Her Ladyship would be looking absolutely regal, her complexion ever so slightly glowing and rosy by the mild afternoon sun, wearing the perfume of the heady rose scent from her Majesty's garden back home, and she said: *"The Governor's Ball will be a grand occasion, the talk of the Parlour and find its way over the seas to our great advantage."* The letters were written by her Ladyship's hand, folded and carefully placed in each envelope; pearly white in colour, smooth in texture, and on each envelope was a stamp for the postal service. Her ladyship looked at the stamp in admiration, there was a knock on her door, a messenger to advise of a mistake on the stamps already adhered to the envelopes, marked *"Post Office"* instead of: *"Post-paid"*.

The message caught her breath, and she placed her hand onto her heart which seemed to skip a beat. The Craftsman responsible for Post Office printing was the very knowledgeable miniature painter, jeweller and watch-maker from Europe, come as a stow-away on a ship leaving France, he was looking for adventure and allowed to disembark on arrival by the lenient custom officer.

The craftsman said that the error would soon be rectified and for the time being, letters could be sent with the stamps already printed, to her Ladyship's relief. There were only 240 stamps made; new material ordered already on their way and a new plate to be made by himself. Today's rarest of stamps, most lost to the pages of history and the few ultimate resting in wealthy private collections round the world…

Meditation in practice.

"What a busy world we live in!! Are we made for non-stop activity and endless rolls of tasks? Are we made to take in all the noise?"

It's a modern world full of noise, responsibilities and information overload. One needs to remember that Modern Man, *Homo Sapiens Species that we are*, live in bodies evolved at least 100 thousand years ago and everyday one needs to be still in the treasure-trove of Silence to give our bodies and minds space to breathe & to reflect.

Stillness of mind: finding quiet time to be still & rest.

Breathing in silence, focus on Breath: breathe in, breathe out.

Instant Mind Therapy: in meditation & the enjoyment of a task.

Reflect over the colours of a stained glass window.

Each colour brings forth an emotion: cool and warm colours as in the seasons of the year. Go with the colours that you are attracted to:

Primary Colours are Red, Yellow & Blue.

Red: Colour of Garnet for fostering Appreciation and Sociability.

Yellow: Colour of Topaz or Citrine for joy and communication.

Blue: Colour of Lapis Lazuli *Blue* for Acceptance of one's Good.

Red & Yellow: Carnelian **Orange** for Courage & Goal Achievement.

Blue & Yellow: Emerald colour **Green** for Creativity.

Blue & Red: Amethyst **Purple** for Intuition and Respect.

Colours of the Rainbow: Red, Orange, Yellow, Green, Blue, Indigo, Violet.

"All colours of the rainbow through a Prism produce White"

White: Opalescent **White** for Tenderness and Compassion. The Lotus.

Clear: Clear Quartz Master Healer, for clearing & powerful healing.

White & Red: Quartz in **Pink** for Love.

Brown & Blue: **Black** Onyx for Protection.

Reflect in Silence, absorb the serenity of protected space on the earth's ley-lines, where Churches and Holy Sites stand. Sit quietly at home in your favourite space, doing the breathing exercise, giving your mind and body a well-deserved rest.

The hymn "Ave Maria" is very inspirational going back in time.

In times of Joy at my Parents' Wedding. The church entrance of the young 18 year-old bride with her father was accompanied by the *Ave Maria* sung with reverence by a Cantor with an impressively powerful & mellifluous voice to fill the church. The choir's response angelic, the French horn's cushioning and enveloping sound expressive of floating on air… a whole lifetime of blessings lay out in front of the couple in the promise of tomorrow…

« Ave Maria, gratia plena, Maria, gratia plena, Maria, gratia plena,
Ave, Ave, Dominus, Dominus tecum. Benedicta tu in mulieribus, et benedictus,
Et benedictus fructus ventris (tui), Ventris tui, Jesus. Ave Maria!
Sancta Maria, Mater Dei, Ora pro nobis peccatoribus, Ora, ora pro nobis;
Ora, ora pro nobis peccatoribus, Nunc et in hora mortis, In hora mortis nostrae
In hora, hora mortis nostrae, In hora mortis nostrae. Ave Maria! »

The newly sanctified Pope John Paul II's voice is on CD reciting the Ave Maria in Latin: it's a very comforting voice, the rosary before the night's rest and last moment on earth, eternal rest for the soul. The rosary: *"Our Father, the Hail Mary and the Glory be, Amen."*

ORIGINAL
MORGAN

ORIGINAL
MORGAN
4/4, Plus 4 and Plus 8

John Worrall and Liz Turner

Photography by Paul Debois
Additional photography by Mick Walsh

Edited by Mark Hughes

BAY VIEW
BOOKS

Published 1992 by Bay View Books Ltd
13a Bridgeland Street
Bideford, Devon EX39 2QE

© Copyright 1992 by Bay View Books Ltd

Designed by Peter Laws
Typeset by ICON, Exeter

ISBN 1 870979 29 X
Printed in Hong Kong

CONTENTS

Foreword by Charles Morgan   7
Introduction   8

4-4 Series I, 1936–50   **14**
   Production Data   38

Plus 4, 1950–69   **39**
   Plus 4 Super Sports   56
   Plus 4 Plus   61
   Production Data   64

4/4 Series II–IV, 1955–68   **66**
   Production Data   73

4/4 from 1969   **74**
   Production Data   88

Plus 4 from 1985   **90**
   Production Data   95

Plus 8   **96**
   Production Data   118

Restoration   **120**
   Specialists   127

ACKNOWLEDGEMENTS

Grateful thanks are due to the owners of the cars photographed in detail for this book. They are: Dave Rudge (4/4 Series I two-seater and 'Uncle George's Winter Carriage'), Anne and Ray Salisbury (4/4 Series I dhc), Peter Rogers (4/4 Series I four-seater), Pat Kennett ('flat-rad' and 'interim-cowled' Plus 4s), Haydn Williams (Plus 4 two-seater), John Worrall (Plus 4 Super Sports), Leigh Sebba (Plus 4 Plus), Cecily Jelliman (4/4 Series II), Anthony Lo Pinto (4/4 Series IV), Roger Curtis (4/4 Series V), Bob Williams (4/4 1600 four-seater), Brian Cowell (4/4 Twin-Cam), Allan Cameron (Plus 8), Tim Ot (Plus 8), Jim Robinson (Plus 8) and David Moss (Plus 8).

Mike Duncan, John Worrall's partner at Heart of England Morgans, kindly filled in some photographic gaps with pictures of recent cars and restoration details. Several other owners supplied shots of their own cars: our thanks to Malcolm Lamb, John Lloyd, Andy Biddlecombe, Rob Wells, Bill Fink and Gerry Willburn. The Morgan Sports Car Club's archivist, Brian Downing, provided a photograph of a Plus 4 four-seater coupé.

The assistance of the Morgan Motor Company Ltd, and particularly of Peter and Charles Morgan, in confirming the manuscript's factual accuracy is greatly appreciated. The authors, editor and publisher are honoured that Charles Morgan should agree to write the foreword.

FOREWORD

As products change with more and more frequency the availability of spare parts for those products becomes more and more of a challenge for the manufacturer. Many companies have stopped supplying spare parts for products that are of more than a certain age. Many companies also have a policy of artificially raising the price of spares to account for the expense and inconvenience of maintaining tooling and of keeping stocks for long periods. Many companies do not keep records of their older products or their customers for longer than an established date so it is impossible for people to find a record of the original specification or the customer at the time of manufacture.

Thankfully the policy of the Morgan Motor Company has been different to most companies. The factory has continued to manufacture new spare parts to the original specifications and to make available records of individual cars, how they were built and who they were built for. This has enabled new owners to restore vehicles to their original condition with the help of the factory and even in many cases to contact the original owner for whom the car was built. The situation today is that a high number of the vehicles made by the company are still to be seen on roads and racetracks.

The method of manufacture makes rebuilding a Morgan easier than most cars. The Morgan is coachbuilt, and unlike many vehicles has always been assembled using screwthreaded fixings. This enables a careful restorer to dismantle and reassemble the car including the bodywork. New parts can then be chosen from a kit of parts comprising the seventy or so pieces of ash hardwood and the different panels of sheet metal in aluminium or steel. Replacement of one component does not require replacement of the whole assembly. This makes repair comparatively affordable and enables the enthusiast to tackle the job as well as the specialist.

This book is written by a specialist for the benefit of the enthusiast. Aside from those who continue to coachbuild the car at the factory none is more qualified to write this book than John Worrall. John has rebuilt five of his own Morgans and has had experience of practically all the four wheeled models. But these have been no ordinary rebuilds. They have achieved the standards of the most critical judges in the country and

have been awarded the highest accolades. John has won the Benson & Hedges concours with his Plus Eight WOR 8, as well as fifty other concours trophies. He is now chairman of the Morgan Sports Car Club, one of the fastest growing car clubs in the country, and in that capacity has been a judge of Morgan concours since 1987. As a result he can give precious advice to anybody beginning the restoration of a Morgan sports car, and this book provides a wealth of valuable tips. I would advise any genuine Morgan enthusiast to read it, and I would add that the factory itself welcomes visits by such enthusiasts who may like to watch some of the techniques in action in the process of building a Morgan.

But John is not a dry specialist and the book is filled with humour and anecdotes. Morgans offer a dose of individuality in an increasingly uniform world. The cars are designed and built with care and thought to bring as much fun as possible into the lives of the people who drive and look after them.

Charles Morgan, Malvern 1992

Introduction

It is time the Emperor put on some clothes. The Morgan is not an Aston Martin, neither is it a sacred religious artefact. It was, and is, an inexpensive sports car.

From the moment the first three-wheeler ceased to be a twinkle in H.F.S. Morgan's eye up to the present day, the Morgan motor car has been nailed, screwed and glued together, admittedly with love and skill – but the aim was to create a vehicle in which to have fun. It was never intended to become an icon, nor to last forever. This creates problems, or at least some tough decisions for the Morgan nut who considers restoring the dream on wheels which has just become reality in the drive.

The first tough decision is this: if the car is up and running, dare you touch it at all? If it has not been restored, you can guarantee that the news is going to be bad. The ash frame rots, the steel chassis and body rust, and even though you can get all the panels they will not fit. Being of coachbuilt construction the ash frame acts as a jig for producing the panels. As every Morgan is different, any new panel will have to be adapted to fit.

The second tough decision, to be taken once you have had a very stiff drink and decided to be brave, is to decide to what condition your car should be restored. With most cars, 'the way it came out of the factory' would be a good aim, but no-one would be cruel enough to do that to a Morgan *twice*. Would you really leave the ash frame with only paint for weather protection, as it was up until 1986? Would you leave the steel chassis quite bare and crying out for rust? Would you consider putting the car together and *then* spraying it, leaving all the hidden metal unprotected, without even a smear of primer? And then there is the presentation. Would you seriously choose to finish off your engine bay with a layer of black chassis paint, applied with a hairy old paint brush to ensure just the right amount gets splashed all over the wiring and the name plate on the air filter?

The accepted wisdom is 'no'. Morgan owners generally restore their cars at least to the standards adopted by the factory for its contemporary product, and frequently beyond. A chapter on recommendations for restoration comes later.

So comes tough decision number three. If your Morgan has had a long and active life, to which former 'original' condition should you restore it? As it was in the 1940s? Or how it looked when it won that hillclimb in the 1950s? Or perhaps the way it was when

Dave Rudge's 1937 4/4 Series I two-seater roadster has a slatted radiator stoneguard and a rare 'flying M' mascot. When the dip switch is pushed, the headlamps extinguish and the pass light is illuminated.

This four-seater owned by Pat Kennett is one of only 19 interim cowled models made. It has been called the 'bean can model' by Peter Morgan, as its headlights sit in straight tubes like catering-sized baked bean tins. It has period accessory aeroscreens for protection when the windscreen is folded down.

it was rallied in the 1960s?

The trouble with Morgan people is that they were not generally the kind of children who kept their toys in the boxes. They took them out, raced them, pranged them and upgraded them. If a new, bigger engine came along, the old one came out. Bodies were updated, particularly in the 1950s, to make the cars look more up to date (a concept close to sacrilege now). Some cars had changes thrust upon them. For example, one 1952 Plus 4 still on the road suffered a shunt from the rear in 1957, so it was sent to Malvern to have a new back end grafted on. The result is a 'flat-rad' front, with a slightly higher 1957 rear end and single spare wheel.

Even now, Morgan owners frequently upgrade suspension or instrumentation to improve performance in historic rallies or races. For example, Morgan agent Rob Wells, proprietor of Libra Motive, ordered a very strange car in 1988. He wanted to race a Plus 8, but felt the width of its body was a

disadvantage. So he ordered a Plus 8 with a narrower Plus 4 body and wire wheels from the factory, and at the time of publication he is still racing it with great success. If this car ever ends up under a bale of hay in a barn, it will certainly confuse the people who eventually rescue it.

Having made your decisions, the problems start. 'RAB' Butler once described politics as "the art of the possible", and the same tag could equally be given to the restoration of a Morgan to its original state. It is not that the car is difficult to work on, or the parts so very hard to find. But the information as to what equipment, trim or lights, or even knobs and switches, a certain car would have had is not always forthcoming, although it can sometimes be obtained with help from the factory.

The first stop for any research into your car's history must be the Morgan factory and the famous Car Register. From the first, the details of every Morgan produced were entered in one of a series of huge tomes, and

even today they are still written out in beautiful and loving long hand – you could almost imagine with a quill pen, by candlelight.

The Car Register lists the chassis number, engine number, gearbox number (until recently) and the colour of the paint, generally followed by a paint code number if the colour is not standard; somtimes it will also give trim details. It gives the date of the final road test with any faults noted and rectified, the date of despatch and the address to which it was despatched. This can give you the name and address of the first owner, but more frequently it will be the name of the agent (purveyors of Morgans are agents, not dealers). One very useful point about the Car Register is that notes are always added if the car ever came back to the factory for work or modifications.

However, of other details, such as lights and instruments, the road test book makes no mention. The factory has never used part numbers or listed them for particular models. Plus, unfortunately, there is no hard

and fast way of checking what was fitted when, for a number of very good reasons...

Before the Second World War, chassis numbers were allocated to orders, not cars. As not all orders were taken up, particularly as the war loomed, some numbers simply do not exist and the remaining numbers do not give an accurate account of production figures. Many cars were also supplied in 'rolling chassis' form at this time, to be bodied by individual garages and coach-builders.

After the war, this confusing system was changed and replaced by another, equally confusing, one. Now the car was given its chassis number as it left the factory. If a car had to wait for a part, it could get pushed into a corner to languish for weeks. So, cars often have earlier, or later, parts than the chassis number would indicate (this still happens).

A good example of this is chassis number P2761. According to the general rule, the Plus 4 flat-radiator models ran from chassis

numbers P2100 to P2756 – except for P2761. This was a 'flat-rad' which crept out of the factory after cowled production had begun. The last 'flat-rad' Plus 4 coupé was actually sold as a cowled model two years later. No-one had wanted it, as it looked too old-fashioned, so it hung around at two separate agents' premises until it was finally sent back to the factory and re-bodied. Only the older chassis number remains to tell the tale.

Mike Duncan, who worked at the Morgan factory in the 1960s, also remembers a rolling chassis, complete with number, being sent to Italy to be bodied by a coachbuilder. For reasons unknown, the poor thing ended up sitting on the docks for two years and came back as naked as it had left, but covered in rust. So it was rebuilt, bodied as a drophead coupé and sold, finally leaving the factory far later than its chassis number would indicate.

Or there was the case of Rene Pellandine, the agent in Los Angeles, who, in 1961,

Cecily Jelliman's 4/4 Series II is an exceptionally rare machine – a Series II 4/4 with its 36bhp 1172cc Ford sidevalve engine still in place. Most Series II to V cars have had their lacklustre power units replaced by 1600 or 1600GT engines by owners keen to keep up.

John Worrall's Plus 4 Super Sports is one of 101 made. This model was based on Chris Lawrence's Le Mans car. Its engine was stripped and rebuilt by Lawrence, who had the flywheel, con rods and crankshaft balanced by Jack Brabham Motors.

bought a car in pieces and without an engine as he planned to build a steam-driven Morgan. He gave up years later, and returned the results to the factory to be put back together as a petrol-engined car.

This brings us to the next obstacle to finding out exactly how your car would have looked and been equipped during its first years. In most cars production changes come together. So the 1950 Burblemotor would be replaced by a 1951 Burble MkII with a bigger engine, better brakes and changed body style. Not so the Morgan. Many of the Morgan's production changes happened when a certain component ran out, and a change to one part would rarely tie in with the end of the year, or a facelift to the body.

Definite changes such as the ones from flat-rad to semi-cowled to cowled can be traced, but often even the exact date of a change of engine was muddied by customers paying an extra fiver for the new engine before supplies of the old one had run out.

And so the next variable – the original customer. In theory the customer could have anything he or she wanted, so long as

the cash was forthcoming. And, as customers have always been encouraged to come to the factory and watch their cars taking shape, someone might spot a feature intended for another model, and ask for it to be incorporated into his or her own.

Finally, when it comes to smaller features like lamps and instruments, the spanner frequently flung into the restorer's research is that of supply. For example, the spotlamps on Series I cars were supposed to be Lucas FT37s, but if the factory ran out, a lad might be sent down the road to buy whatever he could find, or the Morgan men would make use of something that happened to be lying around. This, surely, is the only feasible explanation for the 1949 steering box John Worrall recently found happily sitting at the end of a 1952 Plus 4 column. A number of earlier gearboxes have also turned up on later Plus 8s.

If all this depresses rather than amuses you, then perhaps you should trade in your Morgan and buy a Model T Ford – which definitely would have been black.

Owning and restoring a Morgan is not for the faint-hearted, but the task is not impos-

sible. It just needs a different approach and an open mind. If you are lucky, you may trace the original owner, or an early owner or acquaintance, of the car. However, the best most people can hope for is to return the car to an authentic, rather than an exactly original, state.

Therefore, the aim of this book can only be to provide a practical guide to the way a Morgan of a certain age was most likely to have been. We cannot say that a Plus 4 of a certain age definitely had this running gear or that trim; we can only relate that, in John Worrall's extensive experience, it probably did. Even then we cannot say that this running gear or this trim is 'correct', or the only equipment to have. Morgans just are not like that, and people who know and love the marque would not have it any other way.

Having given such a stern warning, this is probably a good place to point out some of the advantages a Morgan restorer may have over his or her fellow car nuts. Think, for example, how many classic car restorers can go back to the original factory which made their car for spare parts or advice? Despite

A 1983 Plus 8 (above) owned by David Moss. It is powered by the Rover V8 in SD1 form, using Stromberg carburettors with an automatic choke. Marchal driving lamps mounted on the front valance can be identified by the cat's head sticker in their centres.

Rob Wells' 'Baby Plus 8' was built for racing and has proved very successful. To make it more manoeuvrable than a normal Plus 8, Wells ordered Plus 8 running gear with a Plus 4 chassis, body and knock-on wheels. Delivered in 1987, it will no doubt cause confusion and consternation to some future restorer.

the problems with rot and rust, the Morgan is still an easier car than many to restore because of its very simple construction. And the fact that the basic elements of the car have remained the same for so long means that many spares were shared and used by the different models for decades.

Another advantage is that the cars have always been loved, so a real pool of knowledge and expertise has built up over the years, in book form and in the combined memories of the Morgan Sports Car Club membership. Many of the old enthusiasts remember cars as if they were old pals, and use registration numbers as though they were first names. You may even find former owners with information, photographs and anecdotes about your car's history to help with the restoration details or with the decisions listed above.

Finally there is the thought, even in your darkest moments, of the reward: to slip behind the wheel and roar off in a genuine Morgan. It might have been a cheap sports car, but it also happens to be one of the most beautiful, charming and enjoyable sports cars ever built.

4-4 Series I, 1936-50

Ray Salisbury's 1949 drophead coupé is powered by a Standard Special engine. It has no louvres in the top of its side-opening bonnet, although these could be specified for a coupé at extra cost.

This rear view of the coupé shows the twin spare arrangement, with the chromed flip-up petrol filler cap at the top centre of the rear panel.

Peter Rogers' 1938 Coventry Climax powered four-seater has 17in Easiclean wheels. The roadster and four-seater have deeply scooped cutaway doors; door handles were extra. The four-seater has a hood frame cover rather than the short tonneau cover used on a two-seater.

This two-seater roadster (below), owned by Dave Rudge, uses 16in wheels with dummy spinners and carries twin spares on the back. The three tread strips can be seen clearly on the running board.

It could only happen at the Morgan Motor Company. The first production four-wheeler was called (phonetically) a 'four-four' because of its four wheels and four-cylinder Coventry Climax engine. Until production was suspended at the outbreak of war, the name was always written as 4-4. But, once the factory had stopped producing Spitfire parts and aircraft refuelling mechanisms, and gone back to building the same car, the name was suddenly written as 4/4 – this is how it has been expressed ever since. No-one knows the reason for the change, but it took the journalists at *The Motor* magazine a year to catch on, as the Brooklands road test reprints show!

The first 4-4, bearing chassis number 1, was the original four-wheeler prototype. It was actually based on an F-type three-wheeler, complete with its 933cc side-valve Ford 8 engine, but with four wheels. The colour was described as 'grey'. It was never registered as it was driven only on trade plates. The new Morgan first appeared in

This two-seater roadster has a fold-down windscreen and torpedo-shaped sidelights mounted on the top of its squared-off front wings. At this stage, the hood fastened to the top of the windscreen with eight studs. As the car grew wider in the mid 1950s it gained a 'nine-point' screen, and finally a 'ten-point' one from the late 1960s for the 1600 4/4 and Plus 8. Replacement eight and nine point screens are now very hard to find.

public when HFS entered it, now powered by a Coventry Climax engine, in the standard production class of the London-Exeter trial on 27 December 1935. The Coventry Climax prototype was later sadly crashed and destroyed.

Chassis numbers 2 and 3 were also prototypes, both now powered by 1122cc Coventry Climax engines and with Meadows gearboxes, and both painted green. Number 3 was tested at Brooklands by HFS Morgan and later driven around that track at 70mph in July 1935 by a journalist for *Light Car and Cyclecar* magazine, although the report did not come out until Christmas 1935, just in time to create some publicity for HFS and Number 1. Like the first car, number 2 was never registered or sold, and no four-wheeler Morgan was ever sold with the Ford 8 engine. Number 3 was later rebuilt and sold as chassis number 11: the factory records state under chassis 3, 'See also Number 11', and vice versa.

So our story begins with chassis numbers 3 (or 11!) and 4 – the first four-wheelers to be delivered. Chassis number 3/11 was delivered to Messrs Bowman & Acock (the agents in Malvern) on 3 March 1936 and the factory records show that the invoice was paid on 11 March. There are no records of where chassis number 4 went, but number 5 was delivered to Maskells (who

had been Morgan three-wheeler agents in London for many years) on 27 March 1936. Interestingly enough, the factory records state by chassis 5, 'See also number 13'. All the early cars were green until chassis number 32, which was blue.

The first 4-4s were two-seater roadsters, but a four-seater was added in 1937 and a drophead coupé in 1938. The difference between a roadster and a coupé may sound confusing as both were two-seater convertibles. The roadster had only a separate, removable hood, and separate sidescreens, trimmed in the same material as the hood, with fixed celluloid windows. The coupé had a folding hood which rolled back, together with a higher door line continuing at the same height as the scuttle, carrying more rigid sidescreens with chromed frames and sliding glass windows.

These cars were the first of a dynasty, but no-one could have guessed that their basic look and mechanical layout were destined to outlive some of their original owners!

BODY

The first production four-wheeler Morgan was a two-seater roadster, built then, as now, with a steel chassis, and a frame of Belgian dried ash, jointed, screwed and glued together, with steel body panels

screwed and pinned on to it.

The wood frame has always been made from scratch in Morgan's own 'woodshop'. Most of the wooden members are of a complex shape, and simple formers are used to produce the correct shape. The wheel-arches are made by a complicated process in which thin ash boards are coated with a special hardening acid, beetle cement is applied and they are laminated. They are clamped into shape between specially-shaped blocks of wood, using strong bolts, and left in a heated cupboard to harden. Early Series I wheelarches were cut from the solid. As it is constructed, every joint in the ash frame is screwed and glued together using countersunk wood screws and waterproof glue. The doors are all fitted individually to make certain that they fit, as the dimensions of the apertures vary from one of these individually-made cars to the next.

Unfortunately, as mentioned in the introduction, no weather protection was applied to the ash frame before 1986, although occasional exceptions received a coat of black undercoat. The frame therefore rots with a vengeance, particularly if the car has been frequently subjected to rain and road spray rather than being hidden in a garage. A 'damp course' of felt material (as used by builders), covered on both sides by mastik, is

This coupé has no 'Flying M' badge on top of the radiator, and the wings are squared off and cover more of the wheel than was the case on earlier cars. Coupés have a chrome strip down the side which could be painted over if the customer required a 'delete option'.

laid between the wood frame and the steel chassis. However, the body panels are secured to the frame using steel screws and panel pins, so water held in the wood causes the screws and pins, and then the panels, to rust.

In these early days a body was coach-painted (painted with a brush) using enamel coach paint, rather than being sprayed. And, though it may seem incredible now, the body was assembled before being painted right up until 1986. So the paint went over the top of the piping between the body and the wings; when the body flexed, the paint would crack along the joins and water would seep in to attack the unprotected metal behind. As a result, many owners deciding to restore their precious cars have stripped the body only to find a ragged saw-edge of rust where there should have been half a wing.

Four separate wings are bolted onto the body frame from underneath. The 4-4 had full wings (as opposed to the cycle wings fitted to three-wheelers), and three rubber tread strips with aluminium surrounds were provided on each side to protect the running boards.

The bulkhead and the valances (Morgan-speak for inner wings) are made of timber. A steel tool box, the width of the car, is mounted on the bulkhead beneath the

bonnet, but the only tools provided with the car were a jack handle and wheel nut spanner! The tool box is a notorious rust-trap as rain water penetrates through the top edge of the bonnet and just sits in the bottom of it. A starter handle was also pro-vided and fitted into a hole, hidden behind the panel holding the registration plate, which is hinged along its top edge.

The centrally hinged bonnet, hand-louvred on the top and sides, comes in two

Peter Rogers' four-seater with a Coventry Climax engine has the early-type cutaway front wings (known technically as 'droopy wings'), which leave most of the front sliding pillar suspension exposed. The four-seater windscreen is 1in higher than that of the two-seater.

This roadster uses 16in wheels like those of the coupé, but with an alloy dummy spinner in the centre of the hub cap. The 'pork pie' light on the rear provides the only illumination at the back. Twin spare wheels are mounted on the back either side of a bar rising up from the trunnion tube between the rear leaf springs. An aluminium bracket fits onto this bar and is secured with a chromed T-bar.

The coupé runs on 16in wheels with plain, domed, chrome hub caps. Its twin spares are mounted with the same T-bar and bracket arrangement as on the roadster. Its only rear illumination would have been originally provided by this Beutler-type lamp in the centre; the D-lamps have been added later.

halves and is fastened on very early cars with external spring-loaded catches, bought from a local source. At some stage before 1937 these catches were replaced by a circular chrome plated knob with concentric circles engraved on the face. The knob works a sliding spring beneath the bonnet, and slides up and down within a chrome backing plate (or escutcheon).

The roadster has a fold-down windscreen, with a chromed metal frame secured by bolts through the bodywork. Its wiper mechanism is a classic example of Morgan's mixture of the advanced and the primitive. The wipers are electric, so Morgan owners never had to suffer the vagaries of vacuum wipers, but the electric mechanism is very crude. The motor sits in the left-hand lower corner of the windscreen (or the right-hand corner on left-hand drive cars) and two rods poke out from it, through two small holes in the glass, to operate the left-hand wiper, which then pulled the right-hand wiper with it on a horizontal bar. This mechanism is very similar to the one used by Land Rovers today.

The roadster's cutaway 'elbow-out' doors are fixed by large external hinges, made of brass and fastened into the pillars with three $3/16$in diameter screws – one machine screw and two wood screws – in each face of the hinge. The first 50 roadsters had rear-hinged 'suicide doors', but from then on two-seater and four-seater doors were hinged on their forward edges.

The back panel or tonneau deck has a double curvature, creating a sloping 'Z' shape. The steel body panel sweeps down and fastens around a wooden back frame rail. The separate number plate plinth is fixed to this frame rail with screws coming up from beneath. The 9-gallon fuel tank sits beneath the tonneau deck, mounted high up to avoid the differential casing; the extra height means gravity can help the fuel supply along.

Two spare wheels are supported by a metal cage which is welded to the trunnion tube. A vertical round bar rises from the tube and is threaded internally at the top to house a chromed brass 'T-bar' to secure the aluminium bracket (looking like a cartoon seagull) which sits over the top of the twin spares. This bracket carries a 'Morgan wings'

This is the unique prototype coupé which became known as 'Uncle George's Winter Carriage' because it was used by the works manager, George Goodall, for trialling in the winter. It began life with a Coventry Climax engine, but became the first car to have a Standard Special engine, because it was used as an experimental works hack. Owned by Dave Rudge, it carries its spare wheel beneath a metal cover on the sloping rear deck. Morgan decided this feature would be too expensive to produce, so production coupés have twin spares carried in the same manner as on the roadsters.

badge on its rear edge.

Morgan introduced the four-seater in August 1937. It is identical to the two-seater in its running gear and its looks from the front back to the rear quarter. In fact, Morgan took the body further back, at the same height as the quarter panels for the two-seater and on the same wheelbase, to give the four-seater quite a large overhang at the back.

The rear passengers sit high up, right on top of the rear axle, so the ride is bumpy and draughty to say the least. A 10-gallon fuel tank is set lower down behind the back axle to make room for the rear seat. As a result, the back panel is higher, and more vertical, and supports only a single spare wheel.

In 1937, HFS wanted to make a coupé, as MG had done, so a Morgan chassis was sent to Avon Motor Bodies to be given a very pretty coupé body. Sadly, the design of this car was too complex for Morgan to make economically, so the design was altered and Morgan produced its own 4-4 coupé, introduced in August 1938.

The Avon-bodied car became a factory development car and as such was later fitted with the very first Standard Special engine – thus it was the first coupé and the first Standard-engined Morgan. It was used mainly by works manager George Goodall,

who used to trial it during the winter, so it became affectionately known at Malvern as 'Uncle George's Winter Carriage'. Early in its life it was also used by Peter Morgan's sister for her wedding. It now belongs to Dave Rudge, Series I Registrar for the Morgan Sports Car Club. Pictured here, it is driveable, and on the road, but needs total restoration.

The production 4-4 coupé has the same chassis and running gear as the two-seater,

and a similar back panel carrying two spare wheels. However, its hood can be rolled back all the way or only half way, in coupé de ville fashion. More on this in the 'Weather Equipment' section.

The windscreen does not fold, so it was given a solid wooden surround instead of the bolt-on metal frame, and the two uprights rising from either side of the scuttle were made part of the ash frame. The windscreen wiper mechanism was totally

This car has the correct Morgan 'wings' badge on the front of the grille. The slatted stoneguard screws into the radiator itself.

The 'Flying M' mascot (below) screws into the top of the radiator cap; these badges are very rare as they were cast in Mazak and easily damaged. The earliest Morgan 'wings' badge was flat, because it was stamped out rather than cast.

different from that of the two- and four-seater models. The electric motor was hidden away on the bulkhead and the rack beneath the scuttle. The arms operate with a 'praying hands' in/out motion.

The coupé's pear-shaped doors are much more robust and complex items than those of either roadster. Instead of having a cutaway scoop at the top, they remain at the height of the scuttle, giving the coupe a higher waistline. They are always 'suicide doors' – hinged at the rear. As these doors are so much heavier than the two- and four-seater doors, they are mounted on more substantial hinges with a solid pin, which was screwed into the ash frame using four $^1/_4$ in screws in each face.

Another distinguishing feature of the coupé is that its bonnet had no top louvres, unless the original owners specified that they wanted them and paid for the privilege. For extra cooling to the interior, a single air vent, which can be opened and closed, was added on either side of the scuttle ahead of the doors.

Only 58 coupés were made before the production of all cars ceased for the duration of the Second World War. However, Morgan went back to making all three models in 1946, and the only discernible change was the replacement of the model designation's dash by a stroke. So, despite this, the post-war 4/4s are still classed, in retrospect, as Series I cars. Since steel was scarce, with quotas for motor manufacturers based on exports, cars produced during the

first years after the war were often made with cycle wings, or were supplied as 'rolling chassis'.

BODY TRIM

The Morgan has never been a car suited to large chunks of chrome decor. Its badges have always been discreet, and these early models did not even have bumpers.

Series I 4-4s had an external flat radiator, hence the colloquial name 'flat-rad'. This

was covered by a simple mesh grille, screwed onto the front like a flyscreen. A 'Morgan wings' badge, made of a piece of engraved and chromed flat steel on early cars but later a deep chromed casting, was fixed into the centre of the grille's domed top.

In 1938, on coupés only initially, the mesh grille was replaced with more solid vertical slats fixed to a broad section of chromed brass which could be screwed, top and bottom, to the radiator. All post-war models carried this configuration.

The windscreen of the two-seater roadster and four-seater is mounted on a metal frame and folds flat. The wiper motor is mounted on the passenger side of the windscreen. The windscreen scuttle brackets are of chromed Mazak.

The coupé windscreen does not fold. Its surround is made of wood, the screen pillars being a continuation of the scuttle 'down boards'. The dash top and doors are wood-capped to match. The wiper motor is fixed to the top of the bulkhead. The mirror and washers are later additions.

Flat radiator cars generally have three tread strips on the running boards.

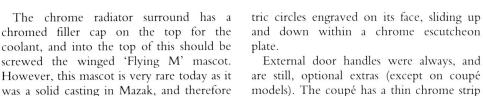

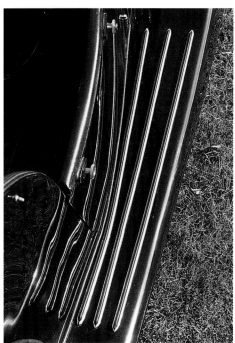

The chrome radiator surround has a chromed filler cap on the top for the coolant, and into the top of this should be screwed the winged 'Flying M' mascot. However, this mascot is very rare today as it was a solid casting in Mazak, and therefore quite easily damaged.

The earliest cars have external spring-loaded bonnet catches, bought from a local source. During 1937, however, these were replaced by a sliding spring arrangement with a circular chromed knob with concen-

tric circles engraved on its face, sliding up and down within a chrome escutcheon plate.

External door handles were always, and are still, optional extras (except on coupé models). The coupé has a thin chrome strip running right down the side and tailing off over the rear wing.

At the rear, the spare wheels are held in place with the alloy bracket described earlier. This carries a 'Morgan wings' badge similar to that at the front, and is held in

place by a chromed 'T-bar'. A flip-top fuel filler cap of chromed Mazak is mounted on top of the tonneau deck in the centre.

The bucket front seats in a four-seater tip forwards for access. The 'hide 'em banding' between the elbow panel and the wooden frame has always been 1in wide on Morgans – wider than any proprietory alternative on the market – and is always made of the same material as the interior of the car. The original floor covering would have been flat fluted rubber.

INTERIOR

Early two-seater roadsters and coupés have bench seats. The occupants sat on two separate 'Float-on-Air' cushions, which had an opening at the front underside and a blow-up cushion inside made of a fabric similar to that of a modern Lilo. The idea was that you could take the cushion out and blow it up or let air out to your desired level of discomfort. Since these cushions are no longer available, most restored cars have foam-filled cushions.

The seat bases were mounted on wooden box-like structures held captive by the chassis cross-members only, so no fore/aft adjustment is possible. The one-piece backrest has a sprung cushion like a small mattress. It is supported across the width of the car by a wooden rail, which is affixed via brackets to the inside of the elbow rail. The hood frame was mounted onto this rail on a two-seater car.

The four-seater has separate bucket seats with fold-down backrests to allow access to the rear – these are known as drop-leaf bucket seats. Each one is mounted on a tubular steel underframe, again bolted straight through the floor via wooden blocks. The base of the rear seat fits over a metal panel screwed into the wooden frame covering the back axle, and the cushion sits loose on top of this.

The seats were originally covered in either Rexine or hide, and the standard trim was black. But the customer was free to choose any colour if he or she was willing to pay for it.

The floor in early cars is made from sturdy tongued and grooved pine floorboards like those inside a house. Two holes would have been provided originally for the Stephenson 'Quick Lift' jack (see below). However,

The front seats of the two-seater roadster and coupé had separate bases mounted on loose wooden frames. Comfort was provided by 'Float-On-Air' cushions. The backrest is a single bench which rests against a fixed wooden bar.

The pear-shaped coupé door (below) is much more solid than that of the roadster and is hinged at the rear – a 'suicide door'. The unique metal-framed sidescreen has sliding glass and a timber base. It pegs into the top of the door and is fastened with two $^3/_8$ BSF nuts and a spring washer under the top of the door recess.

most people prefer not to have holes in the wood these days, so the Stephenson is replaced with an ordinary scissor jack. Another hole is provided in the tunnel cover, behind the gearbox, to allow access to the propshaft UJ grease nipple.

Originally the floor boards would have been covered by black flat fluted rubber, loose on the floor areas but stuck down with glue and upholstery nails to the bulkhead and firewall. However, owners restoring their cars often prefer a carpet to match their seats, and this is considered acceptable in concours competitions.

The rear luggage compartment in a two-seater would have been plain, uncovered wood, but most people now trim this area in leather or vinyl. The flat floor is just a wooden panel and can be pulled out to get at the batteries.

The internal door handles are simple catches screwed into the door casing with wood screws; the door then fits into the body with a D-rubber and dove tail. The door panels are made of plywood, and both these and the quarter panels would have been trimmed to match the seats. The door tops have the fabric stretched over foam.

As the coupé doors are higher, and the occupants cannot put their arms out over

the top, a neatly-lined arm rest is provided inside. The coupé also has a polished wood top to the dash to match its wood wind-screen frame and the theme is continued with polished wood door cappings.

INSTRUMENTS & CONTROLS

Down in the footwell, the brake and clutch pedals are mounted on a shaft bolted to the front cross-member. The accelerator pedal is a revolving alloy roller bolted to a forged steel angled shaft screwed into the bulkhead of the car with three wood screws.

The coupé has a timber surround to the top of the dash and the trafficator switch sits above the control panel. This car has the optional Brooklands steering wheel with, as always, a plain chromed nut in the centre. Dating from 1949, this car has black on cream instruments and a metal ashtray set into the top of the dash.

Some features of 'Uncle George's Winter Carriage' were carried on into the production coupé. For example, the shape of the doors with the recessed arm rest inside and the wooden surround to the dashboard. However, as it is a prototype car it still has tandem wipers, with the wiper motor now tacked onto the dashboard. It has the rare light-rimmed Brooklands steering wheel which was available for all other models; although this one is rather tatty, it retains the incredibly rare 'Bluemels' blue badge on one of the spoke clamps.

Series I dashboards have two open gloveboxes and in pre-war cars the instruments are white on black. Two dash lights jut out either side of the large central speedometer. The wiper motor is mounted on the passenger side of the windscreen with rods poking through the screen itself to operate the tandem wipers. The wiring originally would have been taken along the edge of the screen rather than coiled as seen here. The gear lever is for a Meadows 'box and has a hooked rod on the side for the pull-up reverse.

The handbrake lever sits to the left of the driver on right-hand drive cars (vice versa on left-hand drive cars) and is bolted, together with the ratchet quadrant, to the torque tube. It is the 'fly-off type' – one touch and it's off.

Series I 4-4 (and 4/4) dashboards are made of polished ash, produced in the Morgan saw mill, and have an open glove-box on either side. The boxes themselves, made of steel, are screwed into the back of the dashboard with wood screws and lined with either flat fluted rubber or the same material as the seats.

In the centre of the dashboard is an inset steel panel, sprayed crackle black, with the dials and switches mounted in it. The central speedometer, by Smiths, includes an inset wind-up clock. It is flanked by two gauges, the left showing oil pressure and amps, the right showing water temperature and fuel. All three dials have black faces with white digits and chrome bezels. On some cars they are lit from behind by a white bulb showing through celluloid cut-outs, and on others by twin external panel lamps much like an Austin Seven instrument panel.

There is a plain but solid horn push on the dash. Some are black, some are white, according to what had been bought the month the car was made. Also, the horn tended to migrate around the dashboard according to where whoever it was decided to drill a hole. A pair of jack plug holes are set into the top of the dash panel, so an inspection lamp can be plugged in to help with mechanical work (useful if you break down at night).

The ignition switch is set into the dash in the lower corner of the far side from the steering wheel and is surrounded by a ringswitch, which turns once to switch on the sidelights, and again to bring up the headlamps. The foot-operated dip switch is mounted on the bulkhead beside the clutch. Once the key is turned in the ignition, the car starts with a pull-out starter knob. Another similar knob marked 'pull/rich' operates the choke, but these knobs, like the horn, can be black or white.

No indicators were provided as standard equipment on the two- and four-seater models, the driver being expected to stick an arm out over the door, using the opening flap in the sidescreen if the weather gear is on. However, as this is not possible in a coupé, this model has semaphore-arm trafficators set into the body sides to the rear of the doors. The switch, sitting in the centre at the top of the dashboard, has an arrow and is turned to the left or right (similar to the switch on the A35 or Metropolitan).

The coupé hood can be fixed in three positions. When completely up, the wooden bar at the front fixes onto the two pegs at the top of the screen. Visibility is very restricted as there are no rear quarter windows. In coupé de ville position, the hood is held back by two straps fixed with press studs. With the hood folded right down, the metal side screens can either be left in place, as here, or removed and stowed in the back. Note the standard exterior door handles, which are of a different design to those offered as optional extras on the other models.

Dave Rudge had this hood made up for his Series I roadster using period photographs for reference. The hood is separate from the frame and has no rear quarter windows.

WEATHER EQUIPMENT

It might seem, in these sophisticated times, that windows might be part of the doors, but to Morgan people hoods and side-screens are 'weather equipment'.

The 4-4 two- and four-seater hood have a folding metal frame, which is bolted to the inside of the body with wood screws. Then a totally separate piece of fabric is slung over the top and fastened to the body with various turn-buckles and 'lift-a-dot' fasteners all the way around. The hood itself has one rear window only and is made of close weave cotton or 'duck'. The modern equivalent is mohair or 'riven cloth'.

A separate pair of steel-framed side-screens, trimmed in material to match the hood and with fixed celluloid windows, fastens onto sidescreen brackets on the doors. There is an opening flap to the base of each front sidescreen, allowing the driver to stick an arm out to give hand signals as required. This flap fastens down with a strap to a 'lift-a-dot' inside the car.

The very earliest door brackets were very crude and are elusive nowadays – but John Worrall has found one pair and hopes to make up a batch in stainless steel. These brackets would have been steel, painted body colour. The back plate, which fitted to the door with three wood screws, had a clover-leaf shape and contained a threaded hole in the centre. A $^3/_8$ BSF bolt, with a huge wing nut welded to the top of it, secured the sidescreen.

A flap is provided in the side screen of the two-seater roadster and four-seater to allow the driver to make hand signals. It could be fastened shut with this strap and press stud.

Identifying the original style of side-screens for a particular car, however, is close to impossible. The screens tended to be thrown about, bent or lost, and few cars have the originals (even if the owners believe they do!). As sales brochures hardly ever show the cars with the hoods and screens up, and period photographs are rarely clear enough to show the details, this is one area where it is best either to stick to what you have or aim for something that looks authentic, rather than striving for a totally original look.

Roadsters could have 17in Easiclean wheels or this 16in wheel with a dummy spinner.

The twin spare wheels (above) mounted on the back of two-seater roadsters and coupés are held in place by an alloy bracket shaped like a cartoon seagull, secured by a chromed T-bar. A Morgan wings badge sits on the tip of the rearward 'wing' of the seagull. The bar between the wheels rises up from the trunnion tube between the rear leaf springs.

The four-seater (left) had only one spare wheel – this is the 17in Easiclean type – mounted on the rear.

A two-seater has a half-tonneau which is secured around the back of the car and along the wooden bar supporting the seat back. A four-seater has just a hood frame cover, going around the back of the car – anything else would have been added at extra cost.

The coupé has a folding hood frame and a hood that rolls back fully or just half way. This is secured to the wooden frame of the rear panel with small screws, which are then covered by a chrome strip. Coupé side-screens have sliding glass windows and solid timber frames designed to peg into the tops of the doors. The threaded ends of the pegs emerge into the top of the cutaway armrests where they are secured with $3/8$ BSF nuts.

The standard colour for the weather equipment was black – but any colour was available if a customer was willing to pay for it.

WHEELS & TYRES

Before the war roadsters had 17in wheels while the coupé ran on 16in wheels – but roadster owners could specify 16in wheels at extra cost. The 17in wheels, known as Easiclean wheels, have four studs covered by a plain domed hub-cap, and the solid centre of the wheel is surrounded by a ring of holes (so they resemble the wheels of a sit-up-and-beg Ford Popular). The 16in wheels are solid discs, also with four studs and a chrome hub-cap, this time with an imitation two-eared spinner in the centre. Tyres, which would usually have been Dunlop, were $4^1/2$in wide on 17in wheels and 5in wide on 16in wheels.

Typically, four different types of wheel nut were used on Series I cars, depending on what was available the week the wheels went on. The candidates were the dome wheel nut, the dome with a hexagon, and two types of open nut, one of which was shared with the F-type three-wheeler.

Two spare wheels were mounted in a recess on the tonneau deck of the two-seater and coupé, supported as previously described.

The 'Quick Lift' jacking system was by Stephenson. The long screw pillar jack slipped down through one of the holes provided either side of the floor, and a peg latched onto the rear U-section chassis cross-member. The handle was turned, so winding the peg up the screw and lifting both wheels on one side of the car. This jack has usually been replaced by a scissor jack which can fit under the chassis,

together with a replacement floor without the holes.

LIGHTING

Two large chromed Lucas headlamps are mounted on a bar attached to the cross-frame with a single Lucas FT37 spotlamp, or pass lamp, mounted in the centre below the bar – although the lamp is commonly mounted above the bar nowadays. In those days, if you dipped your lights the head-lamps went out and the central pass lamp came on.

A Lucas sidelight is mounted on the top of each wing. This tiny teardrop-shaped lamp shows white light to the front via a frosted glass lens with a chromed surround, but it has a circle of red glass in the top with the Lucas name stamped into it. This lamp is fortunately now being remanufactured.

The only illumination at the back of the

The central pass lamp, which illuminates on its own for dipped beam, was more usually positioned below the mounting bar.

The coupé has semaphore indicators which are operated by a turn switch on the dash.

The Lucas 'pork pie' light provided the only rearward illumination for the Series I two-seater and four-seater. It has a small Lucas badge on the top and a cut-out in the red lens for its securing screw.

The Beutler-type lamp seen here on a coupé was also made by Lucas, but is now very rare.

car is provided by a single black 'pork pie' light just above the number plate. This has red lenses to the rear, but a clear lens below to light up the number plate. On the coupé, the rear lamp is a 'Beutler' type, which is oval but otherwise like the 'pork pie' light and made by Lucas.

ELECTRICS

The 4-4 has a 12 volt electrical system using two 6 volt batteries in series. On the two-seater, one battery sat at the back either side of the axle. On the four-seater and coupé, the batteries were under the bonnet, sitting against the right-hand side of the bulkhead on right-hand drive models, forward of the full length toolbox.

The coil was a Lucas item and the spark plugs were by KLG or Champion. The earliest cars were fitted with a chain-driven dynamo and distributor unit, but from 1936 the Lucas dynamo was driven by a belt and the separately-mounted distributor was driven independently by skew gears.

ENGINE

The technical specifications of later Morgan engines are easy to find in the manuals of the production cars which shared them. However, information is harder to trace on the early engines, so far more detail, including technical specifications, will be given in this chapter than in those dealing with better documented engines.

Although the prototype had used a Ford 8

Owing to the infamous 'horsepower' tax, the Coventry Climax engine has a bore of 63mm but a gigantic stroke of 90mm. Its thermo-syphon cooling system causes problems in modern traffic. The single carburettor is a Solex 30HBFG with a metal cap over the top, but no air filter.

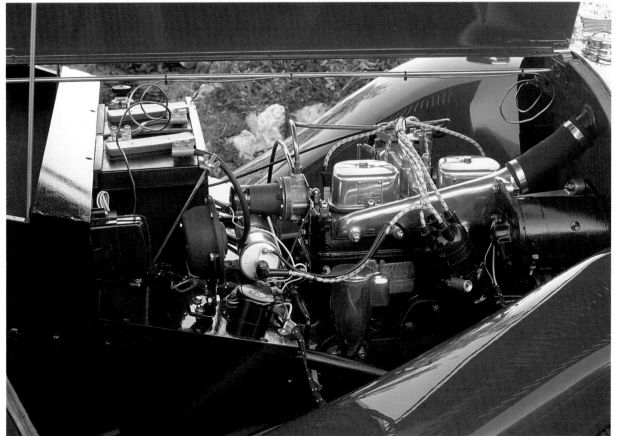

The battery (left) sits beneath the bonnet on this Coventry Climax four-seater, but in two-seaters it sits in the rear luggage compartment. This early car has a wooden bulkhead and full-width tool box. The radiator stay bar beneath the bonnet hinge is bolted through the bulkhead, and the copper capillary tube to the temperature gauge is fastened to it. The stay bar would originally have been painted black. Note the electrical control box and horn at bottom left.

The Standard Special engine has an even more gigantic stroke of 100mm with a bore of 63mm. It has a peculiar convoluted top hose (top right) and the luxury of a twin-blade fan driven by the belt. The single Solex carburettor has a metal cap, but air filters did not become standard until 1969.

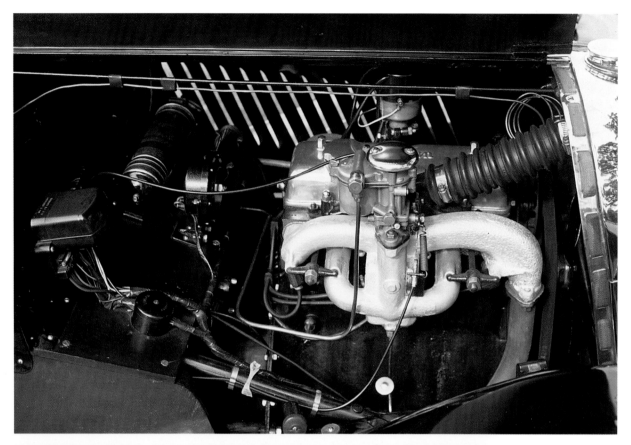

Made for Morgan by Standard, this is the only engine ever to have the Morgan name cast into its rocker cover. The oil filter housing is high up in the centre of the picture. The copper capillary tube still follows the radiator stay bar, note coils on left. The brass fire extinguisher and grease gun are period accessories.

This Coventry Climax engine uses a rare period tuning modification to boost its performance. Instead of the standard Solex carburettor, it has a pair of SU carburettors on a special manifold. Although it is not known who created this set-up, the age of the conversion is indicated by the fact that all the fittings are brass. The grey paint on the block may possibly be authentic; note the rough finish to the alloy rocker covers.

engine, the first production 4-4s were powered by the more sprightly Coventry Climax engine. It is not generally known that the Coventry Climax engine used in Morgans, being similar to that used in the Triumph Gloria, was actually produced under licence for Morgan by Triumph.

It has four cylinders in line, with a pushrod and rocker arrangement operating overhead inlet and side exhaust valves. Its bore and stroke are 63mm by 90mm, the long stroke being forced by the infamous RAC horsepower ratings. Its capacity is 1122cc and it offers 34bhp at 4500rpm. From March 1939, however, there was an option of a lower capacity 1098cc engine to bring the 4-4 under the 1100cc ceiling for racing. Some competition cars had already been produced with this size engine, including Prudence Fawcett's Le Mans car.

The Coventry Climax unit was fitted with a Solex 30HBFG carburettor, with just a metal cap over the top rather than any form of air filter. The mechanical fuel pump was by AC. Cooling is by thermo-syphon action, with no water pump, fan or thermostat. The Coventry Climax engine therefore suffers in modern traffic, so some owners fit an electric fan ahead of the radiator. The radiator itself was made by Morgan and has

a capacity of 16 pints.

Late in 1938, Triumph was having problems and HFS feared that the company might go bankrupt, leaving him without an engine supply. As HFS was friendly with Sir John Black of the Standard Motor Company, which produced a suitable unit (Standard and Triumph were separate companies until 1945), Standard began to produce a version of this engine for Morgan. Christened the 'Standard Special', it had a few minor differences from its Standard brothers, the most noticeable being the name 'Morgan' cast into its rocker cover. The first Standard Special unit was announced in May 1939, the first one having been fitted to Uncle George's Winter Carriage, as mentioned earlier.

However, this does not mean that all cars from May 1939 onwards had this engine. In typical Morgan fashion, the exciting new Standard Special was offered as an option, costing an extra £5, until the supply of Coventry Climax units ran out. However, after the war, all coupés were fitted with the Standard Special engine.

This engine is another very tall long-stroke unit, pulling long, smooth, lazy strokes to avoid the horsepower tax. Its bore is 63.5mm compared to a gigantic 100mm

stroke. Its capacity is rather larger than that of the Coventry Climax at 1267cc, and it has a more modern overhead valve arrangement for both inlet and exhaust valves. Its compression ratio is 6.8:1 and it will rev happily up to 5500rpm, although the 38.8bhp power peak is achieved at 4500rpm.

The combustion chamber is more or less oval, its length being slightly greater than the diameter of the cylinder, while the width is considerably less. The valves are operated by long pushrods and overhead rockers, and they are offset from the centre of the combustion chamber. As the piston reaches the top of the compression stroke, gas is deflected into the combustion chamber from the part of the cylinder blanked off by the head casting. This gives rise to additional turbulence, which is also increased by the sideways flow of air into the ends of the chamber.

Single springs are used on the valves and there is an additional spring at the foot of each pushrod. The overhead rockers are simple forgings and adjustment of the valve is by a ball-ended set-screw in the rocker, the ball fitting into the cupped top of the end of the pushrod. At the bottom, these rods are rounded to fit into the cupped tops of the tappets.

A special cam was designed for the engine, giving a clearance of .015in – this clearance is gradually taken up before the valve starts to open. Owing to the push-rod return springs mentioned above, the valve

clearance must always be at the top end.

To prevent any sort of metallic hammering, oil is fed along the overhead rocker shaft to each rocker bearing and, through it, to passages drilled at each end of every rocker. Consequently there is always a supply of oil in the clearance between the rocker and the valve stem as well as in the cupped top end of the pushrod.

As for the rest of the lubrication system, oil is fed to the three main bearings and through passages drilled in the crankshaft to the big end bearings. The cylinder bores and the small-end bearings receive their lubrication by 'splash', the top of each connecting rod being cupped and drilled.

The oil pump itself is of gear type and is submerged in the sump, which is a large ribbed aluminium casting holding 11 pints. A floating, gauze-covered intake on the pump makes sure the lubricant is drawn from the cleanest oil, close to the surface. The pump is operated by a vertical shaft driven by helical gears near the centre of the camshaft. The shaft then continues upwards to drive the ignition distributor head.

On the other side of the engine is a solitary Solex 30FAI downdraught carburettor mounted on a manifold which combines inlet and exhaust passages, and this is arranged to provide a hot patch near the centre of the inlet portion. An AC mechanical fuel pump is driven by the camshaft.

Cooling is by thermo-syphon action, but is more effective than for the Coventry Climax, thanks to a two-blade fan, belt-

The exhaust exits from the chassis on the driver's side with the Standard Special engine, but on the passenger's side with the Coventry Climax. Morgan is the only car allowed by the MoT regulations to have its wheels rub against part of the chassis, and at the top right of the picture is the aluminium block known as the 'wheel stop'. The front wing stay (top left) fastens through the wooden valance.

driven from the front end of the crankshaft. A water pump was also added on post-war models.

When this engine was introduced, thicker rubber engine mountings were specified to cut down the vibration transmitted into the cabin. The exhaust system for both engines has a 1.5in bore, and on these flat radiator cars consists of a single downpipe from the manifold into a cylindrical silencer and a full length tail pipe. Owing to the different designs of the engines, the tail pipe exits on the nearside (left-hand side) on cars with the Coventry Climax engine, but on the offside (right-hand side) on Standard Special engines.

TECHNICAL DATA

COVENTRY CLIMAX
Firing order: 1-3-4-2. Contact breaker gap: 0.012-0.015in.

Tappet clearances
Inlet: 0.006in. Exhaust: 0.008in. These should be set with the piston at the top of its stroke. Inlet valve head diameter: 1.433in. Exhaust valve head diameter: 1.224in. Face angle for both valves is 45°.

Pistons
Running clearances: at bottom of skirt on thrust side, 0.00–0.0005in; at top of skirt on thrust side, 0.002–0.003in. Gudgeon pin, push-fit in piston when hot. Two compression rings and one scraper ring per piston,

gap 0.015in, free fit without play in the grooves.

Crankshaft
Three main bearings, with bronze-backed white metal-lined shells dowelled in the housing. Running clearance: 0.0015–0.002in. The end float of the crankshaft is controlled by the front main, which has a thrust washer behind the timing gear; float distance, 0.003-0.007in. Flywheel with integral starter gear has 80/10 teeth and is bolted to the crankshaft and locked by tab washers. If removed it is advisable to renew tab washers on assembly. Round felt oil seals are fitted in grooves in the sides of the rear bearing cap. Bearing diameter: two outer mains, $1^3/4$in; centre, 2in; crankpins, $1^1/2$in.

Connecting rods
Running clearance: 0.0015-0.002in. Side clearance: 0.002-0.0055in. Small ends are bronze-bushed. Gudgeon pin thumb push when cold. Big end nuts easily damaged, use $5/16$in ring spanner, chamfered to $1/16$in wide on edge. Tighten nuts to 35lb ft.

Camshaft
Engine must be removed to allow extraction of camshaft. No timing marks are provided, so wheels should be marked before dismantling. Inlet and exhaust closes the same angle either side of dead centre.

Fuel system
Carburettor choke 30–23mm. Jet sizes:

main, 115mm; pilot, 55mm; compensating, 210mm.

STANDARD SPECIAL
Firing order: 1-3-4-2. Running clearance: inlet and exhaust valves, 0.022in. Timing marks are provided, but may be indistinct. Valve timing: inlet opens 10° BTDC; inlet closes 50° ABDC; exhaust opens 50° BBDC; exhaust closes 10° ATDC. Ignition timing: advance is automatic, should be set to fire at top dead centre.

TRANSMISSION

A Borg & Beck single dry-plate, cushion clutch is connected directly to the gearbox (which was set well back in the car, so avoiding the need for remote control) by a short shaft enclosed in a tube (ie, a torque tube).

The first gearboxes were by Meadows of Wolverhampton, and the gears were selected using the short, centrally mounted gearlever. The four-speed Meadows 'box has an 'upside down' selector pattern, with first and second gears on the right-hand plane, third and fourth on the left-hand. Synchromesh is provided on third and top only. Reverse sits to the right of the H, with a lift-up mechanism. The gear ratios are 5.0, 7.0, 12.0 and 17.5:1; reverse is 26:1.

From March 1938, Morgan fitted the Moss gearbox, which was similar in design to the Meadows, with the same gear pattern but no lift-up reverse. The ratios for this

The rear axle was made by Salisbury for Morgan and uses spiral bevel gears in a pressed steel banjo casing. This picture shows the Andre Hartford shock absorber and handbrake compensator rods. Boxes have been added by the owner to cover the two 6 volt batteries which are connected in series to power the 12 volt system.

gearbox are 5.0, 6.7, 11.95 and 19.3:1; reverse is 22.35:1.

The Moss gearbox carried the prefix MGC on the serial number and gave the 4-4 (and 4/4) a top speed of 60mph in third gear and 75mph in top.

The final drive is by an open Hardy-Spicer propeller shaft, with needle-bearing universals, to a conventional rear axle (made for Morgan by Salisbury) with spiral-bevel gears in a pressed-steel banjo casing.

CHASSIS

The Morgan chassis has changed very little since these early days. It may have grown longer and wider, and cross-members have been moved to support different engines and gearboxes, but it remains a simple structure, designed to flex and to support independent front suspension from the beginning.

The 4-4 chassis was made for Morgan by Rubery Owen. It has Z-section steel side

rails, with an underslung chassis frame and open, inverted U-section cross-members cold-riveted and welded to it. The rails curve outwards from the front to make a shape like a rowing boat, and then run back straight and parallel. There is no 'kick-up' at the back, as the rails pass under, not over, the back axle.

A Morgan invention called the 'front cross-frame' is bolted across the front of the chassis to carry the hubs and to support front suspension. This consists of two horizontal tubes with a central X-shaped flat steel structure. There are two $^3/_8$in round tie bars to brace the top outer lug to the lower inner lug.

At this time, the chassis and front cross-frame were given no protection from the weather and so suffer badly from corrosion. However, the silver lining to this cloud is that a new chassis can be ordered from the factory. It is advisable to have a new cross-frame jigged in by the factory, to make sure that everything is square and aligned correctly (see restoration chapter).

SUSPENSION

The front suspension is the one exception to the Morgan rule, in that it is the only feature fitted to all Morgans, be they three- or four-wheelers. When HFS Morgan and Stephenson Peach created the first three-wheeler in 1909, it was one of the first British cars to feature independent front suspension. HFS invented an ingenious sliding pillar arrangement which is still used in much the same form today.

Originally the sliding stub axle assemblies moved on vertical $^3/_4$in diameter steel kingpins. From August 1936, the diameter of the kingpins was increased to 1in and they were inclined slightly to the rear. Two $2^1/_2$in long phosphor bronze bushes were added on each side, one above and one below the stub axle. The kingpin runs directly through the stub axle and the bushes, so the bushes must be reamed to fit the kingpin precisely. As metal is sliding and twisting against metal, this assembly must also be kept well greased. From 1950, incidentally, a foot-operated lubrication system was provided (see Plus 4 and restoration chapters).

A top coil spring $9^1/_4$in long (this grew gradually longer over the years) is provided to give slight relief to a rock hard ride, with a small coil rebound spring below. This was replaced in October 1936 with a rubber bush, as reported by *The Motor* (where it was described as a 'rubber snubber'), but within months the spring returned for good. The front shock absorbers were originally Newton telescopics, but these have often been replaced by more efficient Spax units.

At the rear are a pair of five-leaf (on the two-seater) or six-leaf (on the four-seater) 40in elliptical springs, again with an unusual arrangement. The forward ends of the springs are bolted directly to the chassis, while the rearward ends run through a trunnion tube with a bush at either end. The trunnion tube is also used as the base for the tubular support holding the twin spare wheels in place. The springs are underslung beneath the axle, to which they are located by U-bolts of $^3/_8$in diameter, two each side being anchored by a plate beneath the lowest leaf. The rear shock absorbers were André Hartford scissor-type friction dampers.

STEERING

In the very early cars, a reduction gear is mounted half way down the steering column. From August 1936, however, the steering operated through a Burman-Douglas cam and peg steering box bolted to the chassis and the wooden front inner valance, right down at the far front corner of the car.

A ball-jointed track rod runs across the front of the chassis from steering arms projecting forward from the stub axles, with a drag link running from the drop arm of the steering box to a ball joint mounted via a block on the track rod. A solid steering column is angled back into the car like a spear to the driver's heart, held firm by a small bracket attaching it to the bulkhead. The whole system is quite crude, although typical of the time, and gives only two turns lock to lock. The turning circle is 33ft.

A choice of two steering wheels was offered, both with a Bakelite rim. The standard type was of 16in diameter, and mounted onto the column with a large chromed brass nut; it had three sets of triple round, thin spokes of chromed steel. The optional Brooklands steering wheel was more substantial, and had four sets of spokes. There was no badge or insignia of any kind on show, except for a blue 'Bluemels' badge across one set of spokes on the Brooklands wheel.

BRAKING

Most Series I 4-4s have cable-operated 8in Girling brake drums front and rear, with two leading shoes in the drum. However, in 1949 the drums grew to 9in in diameter. The handbrake is cable-operated and, as with all Morgans, is a 'fly-off' type. The cable from the handbrake mechanism runs to two compensator bars at the rear, working on a fulcrum on the back axle.

The brake pedal itself was mounted on a shaft which was bolted to the flange of the front chassis member with aluminium blocks at each end.

LE MANS & TT REPLICAS

Miss Prudence Fawcett made quite an impact with her only venture into motor sport, driving a Coventry Climax powered Morgan to second place in its class at Le Mans in 1938. At the time, she was 'courting' an Aston Martin agent who was preparing an Aston for himself to enter Le Mans. Prudence fancied a go herself, so he prepared a Morgan for her.

Morgan wanted nothing to do with the car

The famous sliding pillar front suspension is still used today. This early example has the 'rubber snubber' used in place of a rebound spring for a few months from October 1936, as well as the early, smaller Newton telescopic shock absorber (right). The king pin runs through the stub axle and two phosphor bronze bushes which cannot be seen here. The damper blade (centre left) is fixed around the king pin by the 'damper bronze', which can be seen at the base of the large top spring. Note also the early track rod end (bottom left).

before the great race, but after Prudence and her co-driver, one Mr White, had collected their trophies, several Le Mans Replicas were made and went on sale from March 1939 at a cost of £250. The Le Mans Replicas are not quite identical to Miss Fawcett's car, but they are lightweight versions capable of 80mph. Prudence Fawcett, died in 1990, having never competed in another major event.

To reduce weight, the Le Mans Replicas have cycle wings at the front and the rear wings are cut away at their forward edge. At the rear, a single spare wheel is recessed into a slightly different rear panel, and the luggage compartment is panelled over and contains an enlarged long-range fuel tank.

TT Replicas were based on the cars driven by the Morgan TT team which, unlike Miss Fawcett, received some encouragement from the Morgan factory before the event.

Both these replica models are powered by

the 1098cc Coventry Climax engine with a balanced crankshaft and flywheel, and they could be equipped with a four-branch external exhaust manifold, either a Solex or a Zenith carburettor, a Burgess silencer and magneto ignition. Both have twin filler caps and 17in wheels, and were given higher gear ratios in the Moss gearbox and rear axle.

The major difference between the two was that the TT Replica had a solid back panel with a single spare wheel mounted on top of it. In all, eight TT and Le Mans Replicas were produced and are now highly prized.

Production Data

PRODUCTION FIGURES & CHASSIS NUMBERS

Production totals for the 4-4 (1936-39) and 4/4 (1946-50) models are as follows:

Standard cars	1307
Rolling chassis for specials	113
Le Mans and TT Replicas	8
Total	**1428**

Chassis numbers are in the range from 1 to 2081. Before the war, chassis numbers were allocated to orders and many were not met, especially as the war approached. From 1946, chassis numbers were allocated as the cars left the factory, with equally confusing results.

Chassis number 1 was the original four-wheeler prototype, based on an F-type three-wheeler, complete with its 933cc side-valve Ford 8 engine. Chassis numbers 2 and 3 were also prototypes, but both were powered by 1122cc Coventry Climax engines with Meadows gearboxes. Number 3 was later rebuilt and sold as number 11. The factory records state under chassis 3 'See also Number 11', and vice versa. Number 5 was delivered to Maskells (who had been Morgan three-wheeler agents in London for many years) on 27 March 1936. Factory records state by chassis 5 'See also Number 13'.

All the early cars were green until chassis number 32, which was blue. The first car to be exported was chassis number 44.

PRODUCTION CHANGES

1936 (Mar)
Introduction of 4-4. Chassis numbers given to orders. Earliest cars had chain drive for dynamo, then belt drive. Sliding spring bonnet catch soon replaced by circular knob sliding within chromed escutcheon plate. First 50 two-seaters have rear hinged doors, thereafter front hinged.

1936 (Aug)
King pin diameter increased to 1in, and now inclined slightly to the rear. Two $2^{1}/2$in long phospor-bronze bushes added on each side, one above and one below the stub axle. Reduction gear mounted halfway down the steering column replaced by Burman-Douglas cam and peg steering box, bolted to chassis and wooden front inner valance.

1936 (Oct)
Rebound spring on front suspension replaced, for a few months only, with a rubber bush.

1937 (Aug)
Introduction of four-seater.

1938 (Mar)
Meadows gearbox replaced by Moss.

1938 (Aug)
Two-seater coupé introduced. On coupés only initially, mesh over flat radiator replaced with more solid vertical slats fixed to a broad section of chromed brass, which could be screwed top and bottom to the radiator.

1939 (Mar)
Le Mans Replica introduced. Lower capacity 1098cc Coventry Climax engine offered for competition purposes.

1939 (May)
Standard Special engine introduced as optional extra.

1946
Nomenclature changes from 4-4 to 4/4, chassis numbers allocated as cars leave factory.

1949
Brake drums increase to 9in diameter.

DIMENSIONS

Wheelbase, 7ft 8in
Track front and rear, 3ft 9in
Overall length, 11ft 8in
Width, 4ft 6in
Height of two-seater with hood erected, 4ft 4in
Height of four-seater with hood erected, 4ft $6^{1}/2$in
Height of coupé, 4ft 2in
Ground clearance, 6in
Weight with full tank: two-seater, $15^{1}/2$ cwt
four-seater, 16cwt
coupé, $16^{1}/4$cwt

OPTIONAL EXTRAS & SPECIAL EQUIPMENT

Brooklands steering wheel	(1936)
Exterior door handles	(1936)
Full tonneau	(1936)
Chrome strip on coupé painted over	(1938)
16in wheels, standard on coupé	(1938)
Standard Special engine	(May 1939)
Coventry Climax 1098cc engine	(1939)

COLOURS

Black
Green
Red
Nile Blue
White
Other colours were available at extra cost

Plus 4, 1950-69

The Plus in Plus 4 stands for extra power, first provided by the four cylinders of the Standard Vanguard engine and then by the power units of the Triumph TR sports cars.

With the introduction of the Vanguard, Standard-Triumph ceased production of the 4/4's Standard Special engine, so Morgan needed a new engine. Anyway, a bit more 'oomph' was required to stop Morgan lagging behind more modern competitors. The obvious move was to stay with the same supplier and use the Standard Vanguard engine, but there was a potential hitch.

HFS was worried about the re-introduction of some kind of horsepower tax, so he initially sent his son, Peter, on a hunt for an engine of not more than 1750cc. It was only when he was packed off for a test drive in a prototype propelled by a Vanguard engine, but without knowing what was under the bonnet, that HFS came round. He loved the performance, particularly as he did not much like changing gear – this engine had so much torque he did not have to.

The Plus 4 was introduced to the public at the Earls Court Motor Show in 1950, with the first cars reaching their owners (and the journalists) in 1951. The two-seater roadster made it into production first, followed by the four-seater and the coupé within the space of a year.

The era that stretched ahead is one of the most fascinating, and certainly the most active, in Morgan history. The engine changed almost with the seasons, and the look of the car changed more frequently and dramatically at this time than before or since, producing by 1954 the archetypal Morgan profile, still continued today.

This was also an age of experimentation, resulting in some real oddities which included the infamous Plus Four Plus, the four-seater drophead coupé or 'Snob Mog', and the flat radiator Morgan saloon (see sections at the end of this chapter).

BODY

The body changed very significantly during this period, with a series of radical facelifts which were to be the Morgan's last.

Pat Kennett's 'flat-rad' Plus 4 coupé has a chrome strip down the side and no louvres in the bonnet top – this was standard for coupés. The flashing indicators are a later addition for safety. The front crossframe would originally have been painted black rather than red.

At the rear, this 'flat-rad' coupé displays clearly the twin spare disc wheels mounted into the S-shaped tonneau deck. The flashing indicators on the number plate panel are a later addition.

The early Plus 4s have similar styling to the 4/4, but the car is higher and wider than before, while the grille, though still upright and flat, has shorter slats with a deeper half moon at the top. This is a coupé model; note the 'praying hands' action of coupé windscreen wipers.

The early Plus 4s were larger than the old 4/4s (see the dimensions section), but looked very similar in style, featuring the same upright, slatted grille, separately-mounted headlamps and spotlights as on the old 4/4. These first cars also had twin spare wheels and a folding windscreen. As before, the coupé model was produced with larger and higher doors, no scuttle vent or top bonnet louvres unless specified, a rigid windscreen with a wooden frame, and a wooden top to the dash surround.

All cars were now sprayed in ICI cellulose paint rather than being coachpainted. However, they were sprayed in one piece, and the paint was applied over the Rexine or plastic piping between the wings. The restoration chapter describes the problems this caused as the wings flexed, the paint cracked and the water crept down between the wings. It is also believed by some Morgan *aficionados* that Motor Show cars were still coachpainted during the early 1950s.

The first cowled radiator models, now known as the 'interim cowled models', were introduced in December 1953. As usual there was some overlap, and the last 'flat-rad' cars were produced in June 1954. However, several of these last cars were returned to the factory some time later to be rebodied as cowled models, because owners wanted to have the most up-to-date look.

The immediate reasons for this change were that the supply of the big front head-lights was running out, and the whole front end of the car was looking old fashioned — not a good thing in the forward-looking 1950s. So the front end was redesigned. The radiator became a separate item under the bonnet, covered by a curved and more aerodynamic cowl. On the interim-cowled

models the grille is flat, but angled slightly backwards, and the front wings are fuller and more enveloping. The headlights are set in straight tubes on the inner valance, between the cowl and the wings. To this day Peter Morgan still refers to this car when talking to proud owner, Pat Kennett, as the 'bean can model', because the tubes look like catering size baked bean tins with the bottoms cut out.

The change was startling, as the 'flat-rad' cars are so very upright, and their front wheels are almost totally exposed, the shorter, squarer wings just hovering above them. From now on the front of the Morgan sweeps down from the top of the bonnet in a waterfall shape, the wings curling over the wheels from 3 o'clock to almost 9 o'clock, and the inner valances hiding the suspension and 'works' from view. The sides of the bonnet also had to change to accommodate the new angle of the wings as they rose up the side of the car.

However, this model was obsolete almost as soon as it appeared. Peter Morgan disliked the appearance of the flat grille and the low lights and persuaded HFS to change the design, although the changed shape was more expensive to manufacture.

So, in 1954, the lamps were raised, and

the whole 'face' of the Plus 4 was redesigned again as the front of the interim-cowled model had looked rather a mess. The grille became curved and lost its quarter moon at the top, with the top of the slats disappearing up under the cowl instead. The headlamps were set into neater, teardrop-shaped nacelles. The result was a far more integrated and pleasing look for what is now called the 'high cow!' model.

Only 19 interim-cowled models were made, before the introduction of the 'high

The interim cowled model, launched in December 1953, was short-lived because Morgan had failed to notice new lighting regulations, coming into force from January 1954, which dictated that the headlamps should be higher.

Haydn Williams' 1968 Plus 4 two-seater has wire wheels with twin-eared spinners. The flashing indicators were optional from 1954 and standard from 1960.

cowl'. The evidence for this figure comes from John Teague, who wrote in his 'Profile' of the Plus 4 that the man who made grilles for Morgan at the time said that only 20 flat cowls were made, and that an unused one was found in a loft in the factory in 1978. Only two are still known to exist. One car has been rebuilt and campaigned fiercely by Pat Kennett over the years, and has been photographed for this book; the second car belongs to John Smith.

The rear end of the Plus 4 had remained the same throughout this period, but after the 1955 Motor Show the traditional second spare wheel disappeared, to be replaced with a single spare that was set, at an angle, into a recess in the tonneau deck. One of the reasons for this alteration was that Morgan had changed the way the rear springs were mounted, so that the trunnion tube was no longer used – hence there was nowhere to mount the spare wheel support frame. Instead, the spare wheel was fastened by studs onto a bracket, which was screwed,

through the rear panel, onto the wooden frame of the car.

The 'fold-flat' windscreen, which had been a standard fitting on the two-seater roadster since its introduction, disappeared from October 1956. It was no longer even offered as a 'listed' option. A year later, in October 1957 (at chassis number 3790), a new cowl, lower by about 1in, was offered as an option on the two-seater roadster, but this was withdrawn after only a year (at chassis number 3923).

In October 1958 (at chassis number 4023), the tail of the roadster and coupé was changed again and given a more sloping tonneau deck. The filler cap was moved from the centre to the left of the panel. The wing profile also became narrower and neater. Cars from this era can be referred to as 'high cowl, single spare, sloping tail'.

December 1966 (chassis number 6393) saw the last major – and permanent – change in the look of the car as the low body style of the Super Sports was adopted

Roger Jay's Plus 4 four-seater wears standard pierced disc wheels, but the hub caps are not original - the 'M' in the centre stands for Morris Minor, not Morgan.

Plus 4s never wore 'Flying M' mascots. It became fashionable about this time for the 'cross' in the Plus 4 wings badge to be painted body colour.

for all two-seaters. To spot the difference between the high- and low-line bodies, look at the distance between the top edge of the front of the door and the bottom of the windscreen support.

The last four-seater Plus 4 was produced in November 1968, the last two-seater roadster a month later, and the last drophead coupé in January 1969.

BODY TRIM

From the start, 'Morgan wings' badges mounted on the radiator and the spare wheel clamp proclaimed the new name of Plus 4. But there was no Flying M – just a plain chrome radiator cap. The flat radiator grille is slatted as before.

The bonnet is secured by a spring and slider catch with a chromed escutcheon plate and a flat, round knob, decorated with concentric circles. Morgans never had a bonnet stay – you are expected to hold the bonnet up with one arm!

The interim cowled car has its lights mounted in straight tubes. The radiator is covered by a curved, more aerodynamic cowl, but the grille is flat and the wings badge sits on an exposed quarter moon beneath the cowl. Pat Kennett's car has the optional, and rare, square badge bar.

In 1956 the 'high cowl' model completed the transition from 'flat-rad' to the recognisable face of modern Morgan. The ungainly straight tubes housing the headlamps have been replaced by teardrop-shaped nacelles, the grille is curved and the wings badge sits up on the cowl itself. Owned by John Lloyd, this is the 1956 Motor Show car.

Plus 4s built after December 1966 adopted the lower body style of the Super Sports, so the height of the cowl is slightly reduced. The stone guards over the lights of this 1968 car are period accessories.

This is a folding screen from an interim cowled model, but it remained the same on fully cowled cars. This is still an 'eight-point' screen, but the wiper motor is now hidden away on the bulkhead rather than mounted to the screen itself. The wipers are attached by bezels through the scuttle to a rack beneath.

This bonnet knob, (below) decorated with concentric circles and sliding within a chromed brass escutcheon plate, was used from 1936 (some early 4/4s had spring-loaded catches) right up to 1968.

One tread strip is now standard, but the customer could choose two or three at extra cost.

The grille of the interim cowled model is flat and slatted, with a broad base and a quarter moon of chrome across the top, resting inside the cowl. The 'Morgan wings' badge sits in the centre of this quarter moon at the top of the grille. For the first time the car had, as standard, a chrome front bumper with a hole in it for a starting handle. At the rear, a pair of overriders were standard, but a full width bumper was offered as an optional extra.

When the new, curved grille appeared in 1954, the 'Morgan wings' badge moved up, off the grille and onto the cowl. Cars from this time could have overriders fitted to the front bumper, but the back stayed with overriders only as standard and a proper bumper as an option.

In 1958, the word Morgan, in chromed script, was fixed at a jaunty angle on the right-hand corner of the new back panel

This spear only ever appeared on the top of the cowl on the interim cowled model.

The wings badge during this period was a very deep casting. Behind it the brass bonnet end piece can be seen slotted into the end of the centre strip. All Morgans have this piece, but it has usually been painted over.

The Morgan script (above) appeared for the first time in the early 1960s at the top right-hand corner of the tonneau deck.

This very simple chrome filler cap sat at top centre of the tonneau deck until 1958, when it was moved to the top left-hand corner.

and the fuel filler cap was moved from the centre to the top left-hand corner of the tonneau deck, opposite the Morgan script.

INTERIOR, INSTRUMENTS & CONTROLS

The instruments in the early Plus 4s are very attractive and distinctive 'self-lit' cream and brown dials, matched by cream knobs and switches (although the horn and indicator switches could be black).

The main gauges are a speedometer with a small clock inset at the bottom, and a 'quadrant' of the same size, showing fuel, water temperature, oil pressure and amps, and with a Morgan script in the centre. These sit at either end of an elongated metal oval painted in crackle black and fixed into the centre of the dash from the rear with slotted wood screws. In between these large dials are (from left to right) the twin jack plug holes, a knob for the lights with the ignition in the centre, the choke on the bottom, and knobs for the starter, wiper and panel lights on the top. The horn push sits on the centre metal oval on early cars, but from the cowled models onwards it moves onto the wooden dash surround in a 'V' cut into the top centre of the oval.

The coupé from the start also had trafficators, the knob for which is mounted above the horn. Flashing indicators were introduced as an optional extra for all models

The front seat (left) in the Plus 4 is a bench once again, with the seat squabs mounted on loose wooden blocks and 'Float-On-Air' cushions within the seat covers. For warmth, the occupants were offered a 'fug stirrer' heater as an optional extra from 1952.

from 1954, and operated by a large cream switch similar to those fitted to Austin A30s, mounted high up on the dashboard oval. However, indicators became standard in 1960 and from this time (coinciding with a general change of switches) they are operated by a toggle switch mounted sideways in the middle of the dash.

The wiper motor on 'flat-rad' models is as for the 4-4, but with the introduction of the interim cowled model the motor was moved onto the bulkhead and operated a full Lucas wiper rack, mounted under the scuttle. Windscreen washers became an optional extra for all models in 1958.

The roadster has only one glovebox, but the coupé has two. In either case a rev counter, of the same size and colour scheme as the speedometer and quadrant dials, could be specified on the outside of the steering

wheel on the driver's side, replacing the glovebox in the case of the coupé. This was a popular option until a rev counter became standard on TR-engined cars.

For the first time Morgan offered a heater as an optional extra in 1952. The Smiths recirculation heater, better known as the 'fug-stirrer', is attached to the bulkhead above the passenger's feet.

In October 1958, the front seats on the four-seater were widened by 2in, although the basic design remained the same. They could now be moved forwards and backwards as they were mounted on long studs through the floor and fastened by wing nuts.

In September 1960 (chassis number 4650), black toggle switches replaced the cream knobs. Instruments changed to white on black in June 1962, the quadrant still featuring the Morgan script in the centre.

This interior door lock with a top release lever and a lower locking lever was standard in all two-seater roadster and four-seater Morgans from 1936 until 1971. The 'D-rubber' (bottom right) fits into a metal 'dovetail' in the door frame.

Early flat radiator Plus 4s have very attractive brown-on-cream instruments with matching cream knobs set into an elongated oval painted crackle black. The design of the combined headlamp and ignition switch is slightly different from that of the Series I 4/4. The driver's side glovebox has disappeared — this is where the optional rev counter would be set.

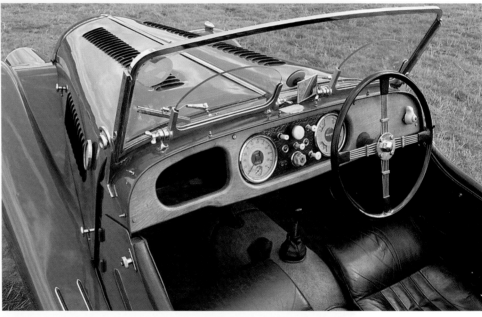

These pedals (above) sit in an interim cowled car, but they are the same to this day, with a roller throttle pedal on the right. The rubbers have 'Morgan' written downwards in the centre.

The interior of Pat Kennett's interim cowled four-seater (above) is similar to that of the flat radiator model. The switch for its optional flashers can be seen to the right of the steering wheel. The flap to the left of the gear lever allows the driver to check the fluid level in the Moss gearbox without removing the tunnel cover.

This 1968 Plus 4 has white-on-black instruments, supplemented by black flick switches and an optional wood rim wheel. The turn switch on the right is for the optional Armstrong Selectaride shock absorbers. Although the windscreen no longer folds, its weather rubber still tucks back beneath the screen and sits directly on top of the bodywork.

The back window of the coupé hood, pictured on Malcolm Lamb's car, was originally a very small rectangular piece of glass held in place by two chrome frames (one inside and one outside) screwed together through the fabric of the hood.

The coupé hood rolls back in coupé de ville fashion as before. This hood frame has been painted red and can be seen clearly through the open roof.

WEATHER EQUIPMENT

The sidescreen brackets are now fixed with a round, knurled knob onto a triangular bracket secured by three screws with a $^3/_8$ BSF stud welded onto it. This is one of the most obvious visible differences between a 'flat-rad' 4/4 and Plus 4! Later on a rivet was banged into the end of the knurled knob to stop it falling off, but at the beginning you could wind it right off – and lose it.

The sidescreens were made of vinyl stretched over a steel frame. They had celluloid windows and a flap which opened at the bottom to allow hand signals.

All coupés have a small glass window in the back of the hood. This is generally a single rectangle with its corners rounded off, and with a chrome surround screwed through the hood material to a matching inner surround. The roadster rear window was slightly bigger and was made from a celluloid-type material called Vybak. Some four-seaters had a split rear window.

WHEELS & TYRES

The standard wheels on early Plus 4s were of 16in diameter and used 5.25in tyres. The wheels were pierced discs (they have little holes all the way round) with a plain chrome hub cap. From the 1959 model year, the wheels changed to 15in, using 5.60/165 section tyres. Offered as an option from the same date were 15in 60-spoke wire wheels with a knock-on twin-eared spinner; from the 1962 model year, coinciding with the arrival of the Super Sports, 72-spoke wire wheels were also available.

LIGHTING

The lights on the 'flat-rad' Plus 4s remained the same as for the 4/4, but a change occurred with the introduction of the interim cowled model in 1953. Now the headlamps were set into straight tubes protruding from the front inner valance (see body section). Smaller Lucas L516 chrome sidelights sat on top of the wings. From 1954

The four-seater soft top is quite ugly, rising up like a pram hood to clear the heads of rear occupants. The four-seater is taller than the two-seater: the extra height can be seen in the gap between the bottom of the windscreen pillar and the top of the door.

Since the Plus 4 was introduced, all Morgan hood frames (below) have been anchored to the wheel arches with straps which match the interior trim and are fastened down with press studs. The separate hoops are linked together by tapes. This view also shows the wooden bar supporting the back of the bench seat in a roadster.

Rearward visibility was improved by the addition of rear quarter windows in the early 1960s – the exact date is unknown. These sliding sidescreen windows became optional on the two-seater roadster and four-seater from 1962. If they were not selected, the driver would have the usual flap for arm signals.

The Plus 4 from 1959 wore 15in pierced disc wheels as standard, but this 60-spoke wire wheel (below) with a knock-on twin-eared spinner was offered as an option.

The Lucas L549 rear lamp used by the Plus 4 was also standard equipment on the 4/4, as well as early TRs and MGAs. The wing piping seen here, between the rear wing and tonneau deck, would originally have been sprayed over in body colour, as the body was sprayed in one piece until 1986.

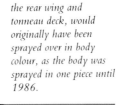

onwards, as previously described, the headlamps were set into teardrop shaped nacelles.

A push/push foot-operated switch on the bulkhead operates a proper dip/full beam function, rather than killing the headlamps and bringing on a passing lamp. A spotlamp and/or fog lamp was an optional extra, together with a square-section badge bar on which to mount them.

The Plus 4's small circular rear lights are similar to those of a Morris Minor and have integral reflectors. They have a chrome surround and are set into the rear wings. A separate chromed clear light is mounted on a plinth above the number plate.

When the flashing indicators were introduced as an option in 1954, the rear indicators were initially operated via the stop/tail lamp units. The small front indicators were round clear glass units surrounded by a chrome bezel, and fitted below the headlamps towards the cowl on the inner wing valance. From 1959, the rear indicators became matching separate units with amber glass lenses and mounted on the rear panel.

ENGINE

The Standard Vanguard engine, the ancestors of which started life in a Ferguson tractor, was fitted to the Morgan from 1950 to 1958, overlapping with the TR2 engine which was introduced in 1953. All 'flat-rad' models were built with the Standard Vanguard engine (although some cars were converted to the TR engine at the factory for competition purposes).

This four-cylinder unit displaced 2088cc, from a bore and stroke of 85mm × 92mm. It was fitted with wet liners, and its overhead valves were operated by pushrods. It used a single Solex downdraught carburettor. With a compression ratio of 6.7:1, it offered 68bhp. This made the Morgan an 85mph car, enabling the company to boast once again that it was 'fastest at the price'.

The exhaust system is a single, flexible down-pipe from the manifold into a bigger cylindrical silencer and a full-length tail pipe. The bore, at 1³/₄in, is slightly bigger than for the Standard Special or Coventry Climax. The same fuel tank was retained – 11 gallons for the two-seater and coupé, 10 gallons for the four-seater – in the same position.

One obvious visual difference between the Vanguard engine and the TR2 unit is

that the Vanguard block was painted black, whereas the Triumph engine was maroon. In both cases, the engines were painted by the supplier. As mentioned before, the engine bay around them would have been finished in a rough layer of chassis black.

The engine number is stamped on the near-side of the block above the petrol pump. Vanguard engine numbers are pre-fixed with a V, earlier TR engines with TS, and the TR4 engine with CT. The number itself is normally stamped on one or both of the bonnet hinge flanges towards the front of the car.

Morgan began to offer the TR2 engine as an option with the introduction of the interim cowled models in 1953. However, a coupé, because it was not considered to be a racing machine, always had a Vanguard engine unless its new owner had very strong views about it, right up until the engine was phased out in 1958.

The TR2 engine was basically a tuned Vanguard unit, but was sleeved down to 1991cc (with a bore of 83mm and a stroke of 92mm) to get it below the 2-litre class ceiling for competition. It offered 90bhp at 4800rpm thanks to two SU carburettors, a new inlet manifold and a higher compression ratio of 8.5:1. John Bolster tested the car for *Autosport* in August 1954 and

This car has twin SU carburettors, but it could also have been fitted with Strombergs, according to what was delivered by Triumph. No air filters were fitted to either sort of carburettor. The electrical control box sits on the bulkhead on the left. The bulkhead and engine bay always would have been painted black, but not as neatly as this.

achieved a maximum speed of 100mph, with a 0-60mph dash in 10sec flat.

Morgan started to offer the TR3 engine as an option throughout the range from late 1955, but continued to use the 'obsolete' TR2 unit until stocks ran out in October 1957. The TR3 unit had the same capacity as its forerunner, but its larger SU H6 carburettors and redesigned intake manifold, coupled to a modified 'high-port' cylinder head, boosted power to 100bhp at 5000rpm. This time, *The Motor* achieved a top speed of 100.3mph and a 0-60mph time of 9.7sec.

The first Morgan to have the TR4 engine was produced in 1961. Again, it was offered at first as an option, but it became standard in June 1962 (chassis number 5155), with the TR3 engine remaining on the books as an option for under 2-litre competition.

The TR4 engine had an increased bore of 86mm, giving a capacity of 2138cc. It was fitted with Stromberg or SU carburettors (according to what came from Triumph) and offered 100bhp at 4600rpm. In 1965, the TR4A engine was introduced with Stromberg carburettors as standard. This unit offered 104bhp at 4700rpm. As this engine was developed, the lubrication system was gradually improved, full-flow oil filtration was adopted and the crankshaft oilways modified.

From the first, the Plus 4 had a proper fan and water cooling system. The only change came in December 1966, when the low-line body was adopted for all two-seaters. As the bonnet and cowl were now lower, a new shorter radiator had to be fitted. This threatened overheating problems on the Super Sports and a header tank was added, but this was not necessary for the ordinary Plus 4s.

For more technical details for all these engines, see the workshop manuals for the Standard Vanguard, or the appropriate TR – or refer to *Original Triumph TR*, published by Bay View Books.

Two long hoses converge on the 'fug stirrer' heater. It is worth noting that all cars with the 'fug stirrer' had a full width metal toolbox. The wiper motor sits on the bulkhead (right). The bonnet prop (right) is not original.

Between 1954–56, Morgan customers were able to buy a four-seater drophead coupé, which became known as the 'Snob Mog'. This example, one of 51 made, is owned by Terry Day.

TRANSMISSION

The new Plus 4 retained the Moss four-speed gearbox, working through the same torque tube arrangement with a Borg & Beck clutch.

Two sets of gear ratios were used, marked on the gearboxes as HR (High Ratio) and LR (Low Ratio). With a 3.73 final drive ratio, the overall gearing is as follows. High: first, 11.1; second, 6.5; third, 4.5; fourth, 3.73. Low: first, 12.8; second, 7.4; third, 5.2; fourth, 3.73. The gearboxes are also numbered, on the front left-hand side of the top surface.

The rear axle remains the same Salisbury unit, but with a final drive ratio of 4:1, and later 3.73:1.

CHASSIS

The Plus 4 chassis is similar in shape, but bigger and beefier than that of the 4/4. Again it featured Z-section members, but it was strengthened by the addition of new box-section crossmembers welded (not riveted) into place. The bulkhead and valances also became steel instead of wood with the introduction of the cowled models.

In early cars, the front cross-frame, rear suspension and trunnion tube supporting the spare wheels are as for the 4/4 Series I. The ash frame was produced in the same way as before, and was still given no treatment against rot throughout this period.

SUSPENSION

The front cross-frame supporting the suspension and the sliding pillar arrangement retain the same design, but the front top springs and the telescopic shock absorbers are longer, giving a slightly softer ride. Shock absorbers were originally by Girling, but are often replaced by Koni or Spax, as Girling telescopics are no longer available.

The introduction of the Plus 4 also heralded the arrival of the 'One Shot Chassis Lubrication System', which has been a standard feature on *all* Morgans ever since. This system of lubricating the front suspension is operated by a foot button, similar in appearance to a dip switch but mounted on the cockpit side of the bulkhead. This opens a valve to allow engine oil to be carried via $^3/_{16}$in diameter pipes to the top of the king pins, which are drilled at the top so that oil dribbles down the outside of the pin and onto the bronze bushes.

This system is better than no lubrication, but the oil does not always hit the required spot. Used engine oil will also be contaminated with hydrocarbons, which have an adverse effect on bronze. So bushes stand a better chance of long life if you are prepared to get under the car every couple of weeks with a grease gun and apply some clean molybdenum-disulphide grease, such as Castrol MS3 (see the restoration chapter).

The rear shock absorbers are Girling lever arms, but Armstrongs later on. In 1955, the rear leaf spring mountings were changed. Instead of running through a trunnion tube, the back ends of the springs are attached to the chassis by shackles; the front ends are bolted through the chassis as before.

STEERING

The Plus 4's steering box is by Cam Gears (the same company as Burman Douglas). It is a similar design to that used by the Series I 4/4, but is slightly bigger and beefier.

In standard form the castor angle is 4°, the camber angle 2° positive. The turning circle is 33ft and two complete turns are needed lock to lock.

The steering wheel is, as before, a 17in sprung wheel, but with three sets of triple spokes. The rim was generally black, but some optional Brooklands wheels were made with a cream Bakelite rim. A wood rim wheel was offered as an optional extra from the early 1960s. This had triple aluminium flat spokes with an elongated centre cut out in each spoke. All steering wheels fastened to the column via a small, round, splined boss and a central chromed brass nut.

BRAKING

The brakes are Girling '2LS' hydraulics using the 9in diameter front drums introduced towards the end of the 4/4's life. The rear drums are also of 9in diameter. Front brake linings were $1^1/_4$in width to 1956,

*Gerry Willburn
owns a one-off 'flat-rad'
Plus 4 saloon, which has
an elegant aluminium
roof inspired by the
Hillman Aero Minx.*

and 1³/₄in thereafter.

In May 1959 (chassis number 4203), 11in front discs became an optional extra, in conjunction with wire wheels. In October 1959 (chassis number 4368), you could have the disc brakes, still as an optional extra, with the pierced disc wheels. From September 1960 (chassis number 4644), disc brakes became standard for all Plus 4s.

FOUR-SEATER COUPÉS

Late in 1951, Morgan began to produce a four-seater drophead coupé, now known by its fans as the 'Snob Mog'. The first two produced were 'flat-rad' models: a prototype in September 1951, and another in September 1953 which was owned and used by HFS. By the time the style was offered to the public from 1954, it had become a high cowl model – and the 1951 prototype was subsequently rebodied as a cowled car.

From the front, this car looked just like another coupé, but the back end was totally different. Apart from the four seats, there was a tall, narrow boot with a lift-down lid, although the luggage space it offered was minimal, thanks to the spare wheel lodged inside. Some also have a split rear window in the hood, with two short rectangular halves with rounded off corners. Two rear axle ratios were offered: 4:1 or 3.73:1.

In all, 51 'Snob Mogs' are known to have been made, the last (chassis number 3428) being produced in February 1956. All the British versions were Vanguard-powered,

but all those exported had TR2 engines. Originally 29 were sold in the UK, 18 went to the USA, two to Spain, and one each to Belgium and Australia. However, in later years they became very popular in the USA, and most have now followed the Pilgrim Fathers across the pond.

PLUS 4 SALOON

Another interesting oddity is the Plus 4 'flat-rad' saloon. This was produced from a rolling chassis sent, at its customer's instruction in 1952, to Cooper Motor Bodies of Putney, who built a saloon body on it along the lines of a Hillman Aero Minx.

At the front it has a flat radiator and standard Morgan wings, but at the rear it has a boot, similar to that of the four-seater coupé, but with a slightly more rounded profile and a single spare wheel taking up most of the space inside. Above the coupé-style doors, the roof, which sweeps down over the back in an elegant curve, is made of a single piece of aluminium. A sunroof was fitted a couple of years after the car was built.

When it appeared in 1953, the car was finished in grey with a dark grey leather interior and it had tiny period interior lights.

This car has recently been purchased and restored from a very dilapidated – even smashed-up – state to concours standard by American Morgan fancier Gerry Willburn from California, who is reputed to have spent a lot of money on the restoration.

Plus 4 Super Sports

The side scoop on the bonnet of the Plus 4 Super Sports, one of only 101 made, gives away the presence of a pair of twin Weber carburettors. As the front bumper was often discarded for competition, registration numbers were frequently fixed to the offside front wing instead.

The Plus 4 Super Sports is one of the rarest Morgans produced, but also one of the most important. It is a high-performance, competition version of the Plus 4, based on Chris Lawrence's competition car 'TOK 258', which eventually won its class against stiff opposition at Le Mans in 1962.

Lawrence bought his Plus 4 in 1957, and so impressed Peter Morgan with his success in tuning its TR2 engine and racing the car that a deal was made for him to tune engines for Morgan customers on a regular basis – quite extraordinary in 1960.

Lawrence decided to enter 'TOK' for Le Mans in 1961, but the French scrutineers took one look at this funny, old-fashioned looking car and turned it down flat, insisting it was a tarted-up pre-war car that would fall apart on the track . . . at least that was the public story at the time. However, it has since been revealed that pressure had been put upon the organisers by Triumph, which was itself entering a team of TRs with the infamous 'Sabrina' twin cam engine . . .

Lawrence was furious, and Peter Morgan joined in the fury since an insult of this kind could hurt his sales as well as his pride. So, for 1962, Morgan offered full works support to Lawrence. This was a far cry indeed from the days when racers spent hours explaining their plans to HFS in the hope of getting sponsorship, but receiving instead a pat on the head and a Woodbine.

'TOK' went back to the factory and was given a lower 4/4-derived aluminium body, which gave it both reduced weight and a lower drag factor. The lower bonnet line was possible because of the use of side-mounted Weber 45 DCOE carburettors on a special pair of twin inlet manifolds, and a four-branch exhaust manifold. Lawrence worked his magic on the car, drove it to Le Mans in 1962, won his class at an average speed of 93.97mph for 2255 miles, and the car was then driven home again, but without Lawrence who went to the South of France to spend his winnings.

The Plus 4 Super Sports model was cata-

logued from 1962. The Super Sports name had been used before on three-wheelers, but only for models which had proved themselves in competition. There were some obvious differences between the model offered and the Le Mans car. For example, Lawrence's car had a 20 gallon fuel tank, a 2.9:1 rear axle ratio and an aluminium hardtop to improve the aerodynamics and protect the drivers from the buffeting of the wind for 24 hours (Lawrence later marketed a glassfibre 'lid' for the car). The total weight of the production car was 1736lb, compared with 1884lb for the normal Plus 4.

The Super Sports model was originally constructed with the standard Plus 4 body style, but with a bonnet scoop. These were the early 'high line' Super Sports models, which also featured a reverse wired lip to the rear of the bonnets. From late 1963, however, the Super Sports models featured the same 'low-line' body as the Le Mans car, and the engine was sent away to be given the 'Lawrence Tune' treatment.

The chassis, running gear and wood frame were put together at the Morgan factory. Then the engine would be taken down to Chris Lawrence at Westerham Motors in Acton, West London. The TR3/3A/4/4A engine would be stripped, and the clutch, flywheel, con rods and crankshaft sent to Jack Brabham Motors to be balanced. The cylinder head was polished and gas-flowed, and the compression ratio was raised to 9:1. A high-lift camshaft was added, along with a cast alloy inlet manifold with either 42 or 45 DCOE Weber carburettors, and a fourbranch exhaust manifold.

As both bonnet and cowl were now lower, the radiator had to be cut shorter. This would have led to overheating problems, so a separate header tank was fitted to the bulkhead with tubes leading back from the radiator. Originally both the header tank and the tubes were brass, but some have now been converted to stainless steel because of constant problems with the joints on the brass tanks. An oil cooler was also

From the rear John Worrall's Super Sports could be any original Plus 4 of the time. The wheel cover, made to match the weather equipment, was a period optional extra. A pair of overriders was standard equipment, a full-width rear bumper optional.

The scoop on the Plus 4 Super Sports is louvred forwards to gulp in plenty of air for the twin Weber carburettors. This picture also shows the bonnet knob, still decorated with concentric circles, and the small Lucas sidelight on top of the front wing.

fitted between the radiator and the grille, below the cowl box.

When the car returned to the factory, it was clad in a lightweight aluminium body – but the scuttle and cowl were steel. A scoop in the bonnet was riveted (with exposed rivets on 'high-line' models, filled and painted over on 'low line' models) over the top of the carburettor trumpets. The scoop was louvred, with the louvres opening forwards to admit air.

At the front, the Super Sports has a bumper with overriders, but just a pair of

overriders are standard at the rear. A number of owners who went racing, however, specified nothing at all front and back. The wheels are 72 spoke wide-rim wires; originally the tyres would have been Dunlop RS5s or Duraband racing tyres. The suspension is as for other Plus 4s of the time, but a few were produced to customer request with double-acting telescopic rear shock absorbers.

Inside, the standard seat was a bench, but a customer could opt for the Super Sports bucket seats. These were fixed, very narrow, enveloping bucket seats, with very little padding. The dashboard is similar to the normal Plus 4's, but it has a big rev counter directly in front of the driver. All Super Sports have toggle switches rather than knobs. The original steering wheel is similar to that of other Plus 4s, with a Bakelite rim and three sets of sprung steel spokes. As an optional extra, you could have a wood rim wheel with three alloy spokes.

There were a number of changes in 1962, mainly tied in to modifications for the rest of the range. The most important was the adoption of the TR4 engine (from chassis number 5155), although the TR3 engine remained available for those wishing to compete in the under 2-litre class. Other

This unique four-seater Plus 4 Super Sports was made in 1966 for Eric White, a Morgan agent in Cranfield. Sold by him when he bought the only Plus 8 four-seater ever made, it now belongs to Allan Cameron.

Although visually like a Super Sports, the Plus 4 Competition has a body made of steel instead of aluminium and its TR4 engine was only mildly tuned with the addition of a four-branch Derrington exhaust manifold. Owned by Andy Biddlecombe, this is a rare survivor of 42 cars made.

changes included the option of Vybak sliding sidescreens on a static base, and in June 1962 the change of the instruments from brown on cream to white on black.

The first Super Sports offered 115bhp at 5500rpm, and a top speed of 122mph. It could sprint to the quarter-mile in 16sec, or from 0-60mph in 7.6sec. With the TR4 engine it boasted 125bhp at the same revs.

In all, 101 Super Sports were produced, including one four-seater made in 1966 for Eric White, a Morgan agent in Cranfield, and another supplied to actress Lynda Baron. The last factory-built Super Sports was built in January 1968, but Plus 4s were subsequently taken to Chris Lawrence to be turned into 'Super Sports'. However, it is a little-known and confusing fact that some of the Super Sports that went to the USA went untuned, and some had steel bodies!

PLUS 4 COMPETITION

The Plus 4 Competition is a kind of 'poor man's Super Sports'. It was produced between October 1965 and April 1967, but only 42 were made, all of them two-seater

The SLR racing Morgan has a lightweight aluminium body designed for aerodynamic efficiency. This car, owned by Bill Fink in California, is one of three SLRs assembled on a Morgan chassis, although a fourth was built around a TR4 chassis.

roasters. The Competition model has a similar low-line body style to the Super Sports, but in steel rather than aluminium. Its wire wheels are the ordinary 60-spoke wheels, not the special 72-spoke versions.

A little extra power was given to its TR4 engine by a four-branch Derrington performance exhaust manifold, and it had Armstrong Selectaride lever arm rear shock absorbers, adjustable by a knob on the dashboard.

SLR MORGANS

Like the Plus 4 Plus covered later, the Sprinzel Lawrence Racing Morgans are another exception to the no-roof-on-a-Morgan rule. After the success of 'TOK' at Le Mans, Chris Lawrence formed Sprinzel Lawrence Racing with John Sprinzel, and decided to produce an aerodynamic body on a Morgan Plus 4 chassis.

So, in 1963, the SLR racing Morgan was born. Its lightweight aluminium body, produced by Williams and Pritchard, looks like the marriage of a mini-Jaguar E-type rear end with an equally miniaturised Corvette bonnet. This body sits on a standard Plus 4 Super Sports chassis, with light subframes beneath to support and protect it. Some straightening was also required to the bulkhead, and the shock absorbers were mounted on subframes.

The power under the bonnet was produced by a TR4 engine, but using cross-flow cylinder heads, with staggered 90° angle valves, produced by Lawrence. Their development was jointly financed by

Morgan and Lawrence Tune, a fact well worth mentioning as this was the only occasion on which Morgan ever put money into engine development. Sadly, the heads suffered too many problems, the major ones concerning the lubrication of the rockers and the constant oiling up of the plugs, so the idea was dropped in 1964.

The SLRs, however, were very successful in competition, and the experience of running such high-powered cars and dealing with the stresses they faced was undoubtedly useful for the development of the Plus 8. For example, the SLRs used bigger stub axles and strong wheel hubs, because 'TOK's standard Plus 4 stub axles were found to be cracked when it returned to the factory after Le Mans. Having proved themselves on the SLRs, these stub axles and hubs were later used by the production Plus 8.

As they were strictly racing cars, the SLRs had plexiglass windows, no lights, and a single, long windscreen wiper. As they were also quite roughly finished, they tend to look better in photographs than in the flesh.

In all, three cars were made on Morgan chassis and one on a Triumph TR4 chassis. One of the three on a Morgan chassis was crashed dramatically by Chris Lawrence, putting him out of action for a considerable time. Another, which carried the well-travelled TOK 258 registraton number at some stage in the 1960s, has been restored and now resides with Morgan agent Bill Fink in the USA, where it is campaigned regularly in historic events. The remaining two are also still in circulation and have both been extensively restored in recent years.

Plus 4 Plus

The Plus 4 Plus could have been the end of Morgan as we know it, but this model instead ended up as a mere aberration in a long history. It's hard to imagine now, but the 1960s were not kind to Morgan. The decade of swinging London was a loud, brash time when everything had to be new. Old buildings were gaily bulldozed to make way for squared-off tower blocks, and car buyers were being offered a bewildering array of new little sports cars by the likes of Triumph, MG and Lotus.

In an age when nostalgia was out of fashion, the traditional looked distinctly out of place. So Peter Morgan wondered whether it was not time to offer a modern Morgan, perhaps utilising the unique prop-

erties of glass-fibre. A car called the EB Debonair, produced by EB (Edward Brothers) Plastics of Tunstall, Stoke-on-Trent, found its way to Morgan's factory in 1962 and was thoroughly inspected. Finally, Peter sent a Plus 4 chassis to EB Plastics, and to ask them to produce a glass-fibre body for a revolutionary new Morgan. The only proviso was that the traditional grille be incorporated into the design.

The result was the Plus 4 Plus, introduced in November 1964. It featured a totally standard Plus 4 chassis, with the same TR4/TR4A engine, exhaust system, gearbox and back axle as the normal Plus 4 of the time. But the body was a fixed-head coupé, with two doors, two seats and an

Leigh Sebba's left-hand drive Plus 4 Plus was originally exported to the USA. Beneath the glass-fibre body is a standard Plus 4 chassis and running gear, but the only external family features are the Morgan-style grille and the wings badge above. Like most surviving examples, this one is missing its Riley-like horizontal side grilles.

The Plus 4 Plus has a large rear window, a boot with a Morgan script on the bottom right-hand corner of its lid, and totally different rear lights from other Plus 4s.

The boot holds the spare wheel, but still offers a reasonable amount of space for luggage. It is uncertain whether a strap would have been provided to stop the wheel rolling around inside the boot. The wheels are 72-spoke wires fitted with twin-eared spinners.

externally opening boot.

To support the body, and to stop it shaking itself apart as the chassis flexed, a pair of sheet steel extensions are bolted to each side of the engine, and then linked through the front suspension mountings to the bulkhead.

The extraordinary roofline is shaped like a wave rolling into shore, and all four windows in the 'bubble' top are picked out with chrome surrounds. The doors have wind-up windows, but because of their almost perfectly round shape the windows will not wind all the way down. As the roof is a permanent fixture, door handles also have to be standard: this sacrilege alone might be enough to call for the car to be burned at the stake . . .

Inside, the Plus 4 Plus usually has bucket seats, although some have a bench seat. Some luggage space is provided behind the seats, but as neither type folds, access is restricted. The dashboard is similar to that of the Plus 4, with white on black dials and toggle switches – but a rev counter was standard and the dash is vinyl covered. The

Bucket seats were standard in the Plus 4 Plus, although some early cars did have bench seats. A useful amount of luggage space is provided behind the seats, but access is not easy as the backs of both bucket and bench are fixed. The instrument layout is similar within a totally redesigned dashboard with a long, thin glove box.

The strangely kicked-up shape of the roof results in an equally strange elliptical side window, which winds only three-quarters of the way down (further than shown) within its fixed chrome frame.

steering wheel is either the standard sprung item or the optional wood rim with three alloy spokes. The windscreen is served by a Lucas windscreen wiper motor and longer wiper blades than usual.

The Plus 4 Plus could be fitted, as an optional extra, with the Armstrong Selectaride lever arm rear shock absorbers also used by the Plus 4 Competition. This enabled the driver to select one of four suspension settings using a knob on the dash in front of the steering wheel. The wheels were 72-spoke wires with twin-eared spin-

ners, and 11in front disc brakes were standard. The spare wheel takes up most of the space in the boot.

As for badging, nothing on the car actually reads Plus 4 Plus – the 'wings' badge on the bonnet reads merely Plus 4. Beneath an arch in the glass-fibre nose, where there would normally have been a cowl, are some curving vertical slats, approximating the usual Morgan grille. They also had some rows of horizontal slats either side of the base of the grille, which look a little like the 'whiskers' of a Riley. The car has a standard

Production Data

PRODUCTION FIGURES & CHASSIS NUMBERS

Plus 4 bumper, without overriders, at the front, while a specially produced bumper wraps around the back and wears a pair of overriders.

The petrol cap sits to the left and behind the rear window, on what would normally be called the tonneau deck, but is perhaps more correctly termed the decker panel. The boot is hinged at the rear edge of this panel by two long, rocket-shaped chrome hinges.

The rear lights look like standard Plus 4 items, but faired onto the car. They have oblong reflectors between them and a Lucas stop tail light at the bottom. At the front, the standard Lucas Plus 4 headlamps are faired into the wings within chrome surrounds, but underneath are two oblong flashers of a type never fitted to any other model.

In fact, no two Plus 4 Plus cars are quite the same in every detail, because the few which were made were spread over three years, and even some details of the glass-fibre bodies may change. In all 26 cars were made, plus two extra bodies which were later used to rebody crashed cars. The last Plus 4 Plus was made in January 1967.

EB Plastics also produced one open-topped car on Morgan 4/4 running gear, known as the EB Morgan. It was powered by the Ford Cortina 1500 engine found in the Series V 4/4. This car is now in Holland in rather 'tatty' condition and fitted with a later cross-flow Ford 1600 engine.

As so few were made, the Plus 4 Plus has become extremely collectible. However, at the time it was a culture shock for Morgan enthusiasts and a very expensive one at £1275. But the real reason for its failure was not the car itself, but the fear among faithful Morgan buyers that it would push out the traditional 'old-fashioned' Morgans.

The Plus 4 Plus did well in both rallies and trials with Peter Morgan behind the wheel. And with such a light body it was extremely fast, returning a maximum speed of 110mph in John Bolster's *Autosport* road test. But this made no difference – the little coupé was doomed.

Production totals for all Plus 4 models break down as follows:

Plus 4, flat radiator	656
Plus 4, interim-cowled	19
Plus 4, cowled	3684
Plus 4, four-seater coupé (Snob Mog)	51
Super Sports (includes 1 four-seater)	101
Plus 4 Competition	42
Plus 4 Plus	26
SLR (excludes 1 on TR chassis)	3
EB Morgan	1
Plus 4 saloon	1
Total	**4584**

When production figures are analysed by engine, the totals are as follows:

Vanguard, flat radiator (1950-53)	656
Vanguard, interim and cowled (1953-58)	143
TR2 (1954-56)	344
TR3/3A (1956-64)	1808
TR4/4A (1962-69)	1582
Plus 4 Lawrencetune (non Super Sports)	9
Plus 4 Competition	42

The chassis number on two-seater cars can be found stamped on a chassis cross-member on the off-side behind the gearbox. On four-seaters the number is usually stamped on the cross-member behind the front seats. The Standard Vanguard engined Plus 4s carry the prefix 'P' to the chassis number, and they run from P2100 to P2756, plus the usual rogue – P2761.

The Triumph engined Plus 4s, introduced from 1953, were initially prefixed 'T' and start with chassis number T3000 (remembering that the Ps stopped at P2761). This prefix only covered the interim-cowled models, which were dropped in mid-1954. The chassis of the Plus 4 Plus, produced 1964-67, are numbered in series, as if they were ordinary Plus 4s, but they carry the prefix 'A'.

PRODUCTION CHANGES

1950
Chassis number 2038 is first Plus 4 prototype, later rebuilt with cowled radiator. Chassis number 2100 is prototype registered HUY 982.

1950 (Oct)
Plus 4 introduced to the public at Earls Court Motor Show.

1951
First cars reach their owners – and the press. All cars are now sprayed rather than coachpainted. One-Shot lubrication system introduced for sliding pillar front suspension.

1951 (Sep)
First four-seater coupé (Snob Mog) prototype produced.

1952
Smiths recirculating heater introduced as an optional extra. Plus 4 saloon produced.

1953 (Sep)
Second four-seater coupé prototype produced.

1953 (Dec)
Introduction of interim-cowled model, also first TR2-engined car at chassis number 2750.

1954 (Jun)
Last 'flat-rad' cars and last interim-cowled models produced; 'high-cowled' model introduced. Four-seater coupé offered. Flashing indicators introduced.

1954
Chassis number 3421 is first TR3-engined car.

1955 (Oct)
Rear springs fixed by shackles instead of trunnion tube. As a result, only a single spare wheel is recessed into sloping rear panel.

1956 (Feb)
Last 'Snob Mog' delivered, chassis number 3428.

1956 (Oct)
Fold-flat windscreen disappears.

1957 (Oct)
From chassis number 3790, a new, lower cowl offered as an option on two-seater roadster. This was withdrawn after a year, the last one being chassis number 4023. Last TR2-engined car produced.

1958 (Oct)
From chassis number 4023, tail of two-seater and coupé changed, given a more sloping tonneau deck. Filler cap moves from centre, to left of top edge of back panel. Wing profile becomes narrower and neater. Windscreen washers become an optional extra. Front seats on four-seater widened by 2in, and can now be moved backwards and forwards. Wheels change to 15in, with 60-spoke wire wheels as an optional extra. Last Vanguard-engined car, chassis number 3922.

1959 (May)
From chassis number 4203, 11in front disc brakes optional with wire wheels.

1959 (Oct)
From chassis number 4368, front disc brakes optional with pierced disc wheels.

1960 (Sep)
From chassis number 4650, black toggle switches replace cream knobs. From chassis number 4644, front disc brakes standard.

1961 (Feb)
TR4 engine offered as an optional extra.

1961 (Mar)
First Super Sports delivered, chassis number 4749.

1962 (Jun)
Instruments change from brown on cream to white on black. From chassis number 5155, TR4 engine becomes standard, TR3 engine remains on the books as an option.

1964 (Nov)
Plus 4 Plus introduced.

1965
TR4A engine offered as an option.

1965 (Oct)
Chassis number 6079 is first Competition model.

1966
Single four-seater Super Sports produced.

1966 (Nov)
Competition model discontinued, last one is chassis number 6387.

1966 (Dec)
From chassis number 6393, all two-seaters fitted with 'low line' body as standard

1968 (May)
Last Super Sports delivered, chassis number 6656.

1968 (Nov)
Last four-seater delivered, chassis number 6833.

1968 (Dec)
Last two-seater delivered, chassis number 6850.

1969 (Jan)
Last two-seater coupé delivered, chassis number 6853.

DIMENSIONS

Flat-Rad Plus 4
Wheelbase, 8ft 0in
Track, 3ft 11in
Length, 11ft 8in
Width, 4ft 8in
Height to top of windscreen, 3ft 10in; coupé height, 4ft 2in
Ground clearance, 6in
Weight with full tanks: two-seater, 15$\frac{1}{2}$cwt; four-seater, 16cwt; coupé, 16$\frac{1}{2}$ cwt

Interim-Cowled Plus 4
Wheelbase, 8ft 0in
Track, 3ft 11in
Length, 11ft 8in
Width, 4ft 8in
Weight, 16cwt

High-Cowl Plus 4
Wheelbase, 8ft 0in
Track (front), 3ft 11in
Length, 12ft 5$\frac{1}{4}$in
Width, 4ft 8in
Height to top of windscreen pillar, 4ft 3in
Ground clearance, 6in
Weight, 16cwt

OPTIONAL EXTRAS & SPECIAL EQUIPMENT

As for 4-4 model, plus the following:

Rear bumper
Flashing indicators (1954-60)
Windscreen washers (1958-69)
Rev counter (standard on TR-engined cars and Plus 4 Plus)
60-spoke wire wheels with twin-eared spinners (1958–69)
72-spoke wire wheels with twin-eared spinners (1962–69)

COLOURS

Blue
Red
Green
Ivory
Or any colour to suit at extra cost. Standard colour shades varied according to fashion and customer requirements.

4/4 Series II-V, 1955-68

This car, owned by Cecily Jelliman, is a 'Series III bodied Series II', still powered by its original 1172cc Ford sidevalve engine. The rear wings overhang the wheels, with a massive gap to the wheelarches. This picture shows the car with only its sidescreens in place. The hole in the front bumper is for the starting handle.

The spare wheel of the Series II 4/4 roadster completely fills the well in the back panel. The plain twist-on filler cap was used in all Series II to V cars and early 1600s.

In 1954, Morgan decided that it would be prudent to build a lower powered, more economical version of its product. As this car was not going to have the extra power that gave the Plus 4 its name, it had to be a 4/4. After a gap of four years, therefore, the 4/4 was reborn, but it was a very different car from the one that had last worn the badge.

For a start, it was by this time a fully cowled model, whereas the last 4/4 had been a 'flat-rad'. The engine was also a surprise. It was not a Standard Triumph product, but a Ford, so reviving ties that went back to the days of the three-wheelers. The first engine, the 100E sidevalve unit, went into a car that was christened the 4/4 Series II, although it never wore a badge to say it was a 'Series II' – just a 4/4 'wings' badge on the cowl. The two-seater roadster launched at the Earls Court Motor Show in 1955 was referred to as a 'tourer', presumably to indicate that it was slow and steady rather than fast and ferocious.

As Ford changed its engines, Morgan had to follow. The 4/4 became gradually nippier as it went through the 105E Anglia engine (Series III), followed by the 109E Classic 315 engine (Series IV), and finally the 116E Cortina engine (Series V) before moving onto the 1600 Kent and CVH engines to be covered in the next chapter.

Nevertheless, the Plus 4 remained the most popular choice with customers, so very few Series II to V cars were built. And, as already noted, Morgan owners tend not to keep cars slow and standard when they can stick a faster engine under the bonnet. So a large number of the earlier engines have been replaced by 1600 or 1600 GT engines.

BODY

The Series II 4/4 was a two-seater roadster, but because its engine was so tiny it did not need such a high bonnet as the Plus 4. So it was given a smaller body, and this generally lower outline was used by the Super Sports

Anthony Lo Pinto's rare Series IV 4/4 two-seater roadster would originally have been powered by a 1340cc Ford Classic 109E engine, but like most Series II to V cars it has had its engine replaced with a faster Cortina unit. There is no badging to identify the 'Series', or which engine it has.

The dashboard of Cecily Jelliman's Series II is a remarkable combination of the original and the personal. The radio and the mascots are anything but standard, yet all the switches and instruments are totally original. The glovebox is longer than on a Series I and the switches are housed in a rounded-off square in the centre. The 'quadrant' (visible through the left-hand side of the steering wheel) houses only three gauges.

These beautifully preserved cream knobs are still marked with clear black lettering, and the change pattern can be seen clearly on top of the original gear knob. Once again, the optional Brooklands steering wheel was chosen.

and later by the 'low-line' Plus 4s.

The windscreen does not fold, and it has a windscreen wiper motor attached to the bulkhead under the bonnet, as for the Plus 4 of the time. The car had no top bonnet louvres as standard, but these were available as an optional extra. The tonneau deck (or rear panel) was a simpler shape than before, sloping back at an angle of almost 45° from the rear hood fastenings. Beneath the bonnet is a full-width tool box in steel, but it still contained no tools – except for a jack and wheelbrace.

The Series III body is 1$^{1}/_{2}$-2in wider than that of the Series II, but overall width is the same because the wings are narrower, giving more room in the body and less overhang in the wings. A strange point to note, however, is that this body was being produced before the last of the 100E engines had been used up, and before the Series III, with its smaller diameter wheels and slightly wider tyres, had gone into production. So some of the last Series II cars have Series III bodies: their wings appear to overhang the wheels just a bit too much. To the few who have heard about this aberration, these cars are known as Series III-bodied Series IIs.

Fuel tank capacity on Series II and III models was 8 gallons, but from the Series IV onwards the factory quoted an 8$^{1}/_{2}$ gallon tank.

This Series IV uses modern radial tyres on its correct 15in pierced disc wheels.

This Series II still runs on cross-ply tyres; this picture shows how much wider the wing is than the wheel.

BODY TRIM

The 'wings' badge of this model simply reads 4/4 and is mounted on the cowl. The running boards have two rubber strips with aluminium surrounds. The petrol cap sits on the left-hand top portion of the rear panel; and from the Series IV the rear panel also has a Morgan script fixed at an angle on the right-hand top corner.

The front of the 4/4 has a bumper with a hole for the starter handle, but the handle was an optional extra, as was a set of over-riders. The rear has overriders only, a full width bumper being an optional extra.

INTERIOR, INSTRUMENTS & CONTROLS

All Series II to V cars have a bench seat with an adjustable back rest and 'Float-on-Air' cushions, but they offer a little more space in the footwells than a Plus 4 because the gearbox is set further forward in the car. The standard upholstery was PVC, with leather as an optional extra. The floor covering is flat, fluted rubber.

The dashboard itself is wood, as before, but the glovebox is much longer than on the Plus 4 and the instrument panel is a small black square housing the knobs and switches in the centre of the dash. Directly in front of the steering wheel are the 'quadrant' gauge (on the left on a right-hand drive car) and the speedometer (on the right).

The 'quadrant' only has three dials, for fuel, oil and amps, losing the temperature gauge – but as we are dealing with Morgan, it is still described as a quadrant. The ignition switch sits at the bottom in the centre panel, but the rest of the cream knobs and inspection lamp sockets are placed in the same pattern as on a Plus 4. Flashing indicators, offered as an optional extra from the outset, were operated by a switch similar to that found in the A35 at the time, as on the Plus 4. The horn push sits on the extreme right. No obvious space is left for a rev counter, but one was listed as an optional extra in *The Motor* road test of 8 August 1956. The 'fug-stirrer' heater and screen washer were optional extras.

From September 1960, black toggle switches replaced the cream knobs. From June 1962, the dials became white on black

WEATHER EQUIPMENT

The hood is separate from the frame as before and has a single small window in the back. The hoops of the frame itself are joined together to create a single folding structure in Series II and III cars, but the Series IV has three completely separate 'hood irons'. In all cars the hoops are loosely joined by tapes to ensure that they are evenly spaced when the hood is raised.

A half tonneau was provided, stretching between the back of the car and the back of the front bench seat. It fastens to studs on the inner rear panel and around the wooden rail supporting the seat backrest. A full tonneau cover was an optional extra.

Series II sidescreen brackets are fixed inside the door, but those on Series III and later models fix outside. Both have the knurled knobs described for the Plus 4.

WHEELS & TYRES

The 4/4 uses the same 16in x 5in pierced disc wheels with a plain hub cap as the Plus 4. 'Hervel' wheel trims were offered as optional extras. The single spare wheel is mounted in a recess in the tonneau deck, sitting at the same angle as the deck as though it had half sunk into sand.

From the Series III onwards, the wheels are of 15in diameter but still of 5in width; they use a wider 5.20 tyre. From the Series V's introduction in 1963, wire wheels became an option.

ENGINE

The Series II 4/4 kept its name as its four wheels were still powered by four cylinders, this time from a sidevalve Ford 100E unit serviced by a single Solex carburettor. This engine has a bore and stroke of 63.5mm × 92.5mm, giving a capacity of 1172cc. Its

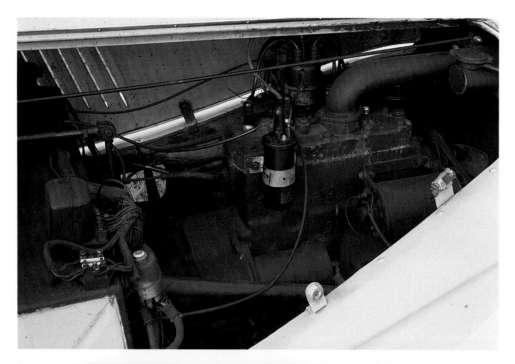

The tiny 1172cc sidevalve engine from the 100E Ford has acres of room around it in the Morgan Series II engine bay. The top of the remote gear linkage can be seen on the left.

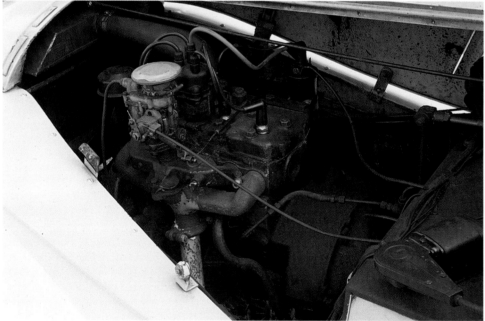

The Ford sidevalve engine's single Solex carburettor has this metal cap as standard, but a pancake air filter was available as an optional extra. The wiper motor (bottom right) is the same unit as in the Plus 4.

compression ratio is 7.0:1. It offers just 36bhp at 4400rpm, as in the standard Ford.

The standard 4/4 Series II was very slow, *The Motor* in 1956 recording a maximum speed of 76.3mph and a 0–60mph stroll in 26.9sec. As a result, many owners changed the engines as soon as faster ones became available, or added period bolt-on tuning accessories designed for this engine. However, the car achieved the economy which Morgan had sought: overall fuel consumption recorded in the same road test was 35.1mpg.

The Series III has the 105E Anglia's 997cc engine, which delivers 39bhp at 5000rpm and has overhead valves. When launched, it had great potential for racing in the under 1-litre class. Bore and stroke are 80.97mm × 48.41mm.

Series IV models have the 109E Classic's 1340cc engine, which produced a considerable power jump to 62bhp at 5000rpm. Again this is an overhead valve unit, with a single carburettor and a bore and stroke of 80.97mm × 65.07mm. Performance was up to 92mph and 0–60mph in 16.5sec.

From a Series V owned by Roger Curtis, this pre-crossflow 1498cc engine has a four-branch competition exhaust manifold. The top hose can be seen snaking across the top left-hand corner. Two long hoses feed the 'fug stirrer' heater (right). The carburettor is a single Zenith and would have had a metal cover. The washer bottle is a period accessory, the horn a later addition.

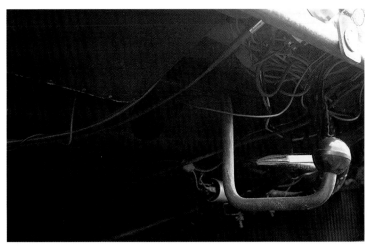

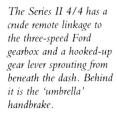

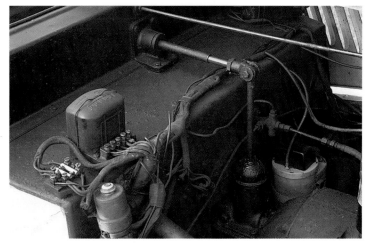

The Series II 4/4 has a crude remote linkage to the three-speed Ford gearbox and a hooked-up gear lever sprouting from beneath the dash. Behind it is the 'umbrella' handbrake.

The remote gear linkage for Series II 4/4s emerges through the bulkhead from behind the dashboard and an arm beneath the right angled joint descends into the top of the gearbox. The electric control box sits on the bulkhead (left), with the solenoid beneath.

The Series V was considerably faster than the previous models as it was powered by the 116E Cortina's 1498cc engine. This unit has a bore and stroke of 80.97mm × 72.74mm. The standard model, which produces 65bhp, has a single Zenith carburettor and a compression ratio of 8.3:1,

For further technical details of these engines, refer to the workshop manual for the appropriate Ford models.

TRANSMISSION

Series II 4/4s had a Ford three-speed gearbox with synchromesh on second and top, although most cars have had their engines and gearboxes changed. Because the engine and gearbox were fitted as a unit, the previous torque tube arrangement was not possible. Instead, the gears have to be changed using a crude remote linkage.

A straight shaft rises up from a swivelling ball on top of the gearbox. This is linked to a horizontal bar, which runs backwards through the bulkhead and emerges beneath the dashboard, much like the gear lever of a classic Citroën. The gate is down-and-right for first, up-and-left for second, down-and-left for third, and up-and-right (using the lift mechanism) for reverse.

Series III and IV models have a four-speed gearbox without synchromesh on first gear. It is mounted in the same way as the three-speed, through the same remote linkage. A 'Wooller' remote change, which was also marketed as an 'after-market' fitting for Cortinas of the time, was offered as an option on Series V cars. However, the

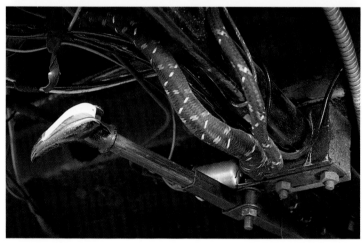

The 'Wooller' remote change, using the normal four-speed 'H' pattern, was offered as an option on Series V 4/4s. Some Morgan drivers had this fitted as an aftermarket option, but factory-fitted conversions are easy to spot, as Morgan machined the 'Wooller' name off the casing.

The 'umbrella' handbrake with its attractive cream handle works on a ratchet. It pulls on and must be twisted to release. The fabric-covered wiring is completely original.

factory machined off the Wooller name from the casing! The last Series V cars use Ford's Lotus Cortina gearbox, which is longer, reaches much further back into the car, and allows the use of a proper 'four-on-the-floor' gearshift.

The final drive is a Hardy Spicer open propshaft to a Salisbury 3HA hypoid-bevel axle unit with a ratio of 4.1:1 or 4.56:1. The differential often broke, especially when owners fitted 1600 engines!

CHASSIS

Using Z-section chassis rails, the chassis was unaltered from the Plus 4.

SUSPENSION

As always, the front suspension is independent with sliding pillars, coil springs and Armstrong telescopic shock absorbers, all as for the Plus 4. At the rear, the 4/4 uses a live axle with semi-elliptic springs and Armstrong lever arm shock absorbers. 'Selectaride' shock absorbers were an optional extra for the Series V, but standard on the competition model.

STEERING

The 4/4's Cam Gears steering is as for the Plus 4. The steering wheel has three sets of sprung steel spokes and a Bakelite rim. A Brooklands wheel – with a black or cream rim – was an optional extra on the Series II and III, while a wood rim wheel was optional on the Series IV and V.

BRAKING

These are 9in diameter drums at front and rear. Except for the Series V, the 4/4 has an umbrella handbrake, with a Ford handle, mounted under the dash; the handbrake became a fly-off type on the Series V. With the introduction of the 62bhp Series IV, 11in diameter front brake discs and 9in rear drums became standard.

COMPETITION MODELS

In September 1957, Morgan introduced a Series II competition model. It still used the 100E sidevalve engine, but was fitted with an Aquaplane aluminium cylinder head and inlet manifold, a copper/asbestos cylinder head gasket, twin SU carburettors, a four-branch exhaust manifold, and a compression ratio of 8:1 – all of which boosted power from 36bhp to 40bhp at 5100rpm.

The Series V competition model has the Cortina GT engine, which shares the standard unit's capacity, but is boosted by a twin-choke Weber carburettor, a higher compression cylinder head, a high-lift camshaft and a four-branch exhaust manifold. This engine produced 83.5bhp and offered a top speed of 95mph and a 0-60mph time of 11.9sec. This model has a rev counter and Armstrong Selectaride shock absorbers as standard.

Production Data

PRODUCTION FIGURES & CHASSIS NUMBERS

Production figures for the low-powered 4/4 models manufactured 1955-68 are as follows, the chassis number ranges (now with no numbers missed out) and production dates being given in brackets:

Series II (A200-A586, Oct 1955 to Nov 1960)
387
Series III (A590-A648, Oct 1960 to Nov 1961)
59
Series IV (B650-B849, Oct 1961 to Mar 1963)
206
Series V (B850-B1495, Feb 1963 to Mar 1968)
646

Total   **1298**

Series II production includes one coupé, chassis number A553 and registration 380 AAB, made for Miss Skinner (a relative of HFS) and delivered on 1 February 1960. There were also 38 Series II Competition models (seven with the Aquaplane head) and a single four-seater (chassis number A296). Series III-V cars were all two-seater roadsters, with no specials or one-offs.

PRODUCTION CHANGES

1955 (Oct)
4/4 Series II launched with Ford 100E sidevalve engine and three-speed gearbox.

1957 (Sep)
Series II Competition model introduced.

1960 (Sep)
Black toggle switches replace cream knobs.

1960 (Oct)
Series III launched, using 105E Anglia engine. Body becomes $1^1/2$-2in wider, but wings narrow by equal amount (some new bodies are fitted to the last Series II cars). Sidescreen brackets fixed to outside of door. Wheels change to 15in, using wider, 5.20in tyre. Four-speed gearbox introduced.

1961 (Oct)
Series IV introduced using 109E Classic 315 engine. Brakes uprated to 11in discs at front and 9in drums at rear. Fuel tank capacity reduced from 9 to $8^1/2$ gallons. Morgan script added to top right-hand corner of tonneau deck. Fixed hoops of hood become three separate items joined only by tapes.

1962 (Jun)
Instruments become white on black.

1963 (Feb)
Series V introduced using 116E Cortina engine. Rev counter becomes standard. Wire wheels, Wooller gearshift, Selectaride shock absorbers become optional. Competition model uses Cortina GT engine.

1968
Last Series V cars adopt Lotus Cortina gearbox.

DIMENSIONS

Wheelbase, 8ft 0in
Track, 3ft 11in
Overall length, 12ft 0in
Height, 4ft 2in
Width, 4ft 8in
Turning circle, 33ft (16in wheels), 31ft (15in wheels).
Weight, 1568lb with 5 gallons of fuel

Series III as above
Series IV as above except for: weight, dry 1456lb
Series V as above except for: rear track at 4ft 1in, weight dry 1848lb

OPTIONAL EXTRAS & SPECIAL EQUIPMENT

Bonnet louvres
Full tonneau
Door handles
Starter handle
Rear bumper
Leather upholstery
Flashing indicators
Rev counter (Series II-IV)
Brooklands wheel (Series II/III only)
Wood rim wheel (Series IV/V only)
Recirculating heater
Screen wash
Hervel wheel trims
Wire wheels (Series V only)
Wooller remote gearshift (Series V only)
Selectaride shock absorbers (Series V only)

COLOURS

Blue
Red
Green
Ivory
Or any colour to suit at extra cost. Standard colour shades varied according to fashion and customer requirements.

4/4 from 1969

Bob Williams' 1982 four-seater is one of the last 4/4 1600s made. It wears wire wheels and aluminium bumpers, without overriders front and rear. The flashing indicators were standard equipment.

Although the 4/4 1600 followed directly on from the Series V, it would be wrong simply to tack it onto the end of the previous chapter, as it marked the beginning of a new era for the 4/4. The Series II to V cars always played second fiddle to the Triumph-engined Plus 4s and very few were made. However, just a few months after the 4/4 received the punchy 1600 MkII Cortina engine in February 1968, the Plus 4 disappeared in the wake of the new and far more powerful Plus 8, leaving the 4/4 1600 with the lower-powered field to itself.

As a result, the Kent-engined 4/4 became a very long-running and successful model, its total sales challenged only by those of the Plus 8. When it was introduced, this new 4/4 was available in two forms, standard and competition, both cars being offered as two- or four-seaters - the coupé had disappeared by this time. As the competition models outnumbered the standard ones by around four to one, all 4/4s were given competition specification from May 1971.

The Kent engine finally met its end in March 1982, when Ford introduced its new CVH engine. Morgan had been forewarned that this engine would be designed for transverse location in a front-wheel drive car, and so not immediately suitable for use in a rear-wheel drive sports car. Having looked around at various options, therefore, Morgan made an astonishing announcement at the 1981 Motor Show. The 4/4 was to be offered with an Italian engine - the lusty Fiat twin-cam 1600 unit similar to that of the old Mirafiori, linked to a five-speed Abarth gearbox.

Morgan lore has it that a Ford executive came onto the stand at this show and was horrified by the news, especially as he had a 4/4 on order and knew he would never be allowed to run it if it had a Fiat engine. He persuaded Ford to allow Morgan to work on the CVH engine of the XR3, to turn it longways, and to mate it to the Cortina four-speed gearbox.

For the next few months, Morgan pro-

duced cars powered by the Fiat twin-cam engine *and* the Ford Kent engine, using up the last few crossflow engines Ford could supply. For the following two years, customers then had the choice between the Fiat and Ford CVH engines.

The correct nomenclature of the Fiat-engined car is 4/4 Twin-Cam, although this title is not often used. The car was offered on the price list until 1984, but most people chose the cheaper Kent-engined car and only 92 were produced. The 2-litre Fiat Twin-Cam model is described in a later chapter on the recent Plus 4 models.

In 1987, Ford introduced the 'lean-burn' version of the CVH engine, which Morgan put in the 4/4. And in October 1991, the 4/4 adopted the new catalysed Ford XR3i CVH engine, becoming the first Morgan ever to be offered with a catalytic converter as standard equipment, without a 'delete option'. The change to the fuel-injected and catalysed engine at this precise moment was the result of the non-availability of the pre-

vious unit from Ford, but a further 35 lean-burn carburettor engines arrived at the Morgan factory two weeks after the change-over. They will, no doubt, confuse and bewilder some restorers 20 years hence.

BODY

The body is as for the late Series V car. The first four-seater model, chassis number B1732, was made in January 1969 and was powered by a standard 1600 engine.

From the 1971 Motor Show, a number of changes were introduced. New EEC safety regulations dictated the introduction of 'anti-burst' door locks, taken from the Land Rover. These were fastened by four dome nuts to studs which were fixed into the wooden door frame. The outer door handles remained optional, but inside a 'dog's ear' handle was introduced with the usual pip to lock the door. Larger steel hinges held by $1/4$in screws replaced the previous brass ones, but they are still externally mounted.

This rare Fiat-engined 4/4, owned by Brian Cowell, has many options, including a headrest, spare wheel cover and weather equipment in the colour of the interior trim. Yet it lacks the most popular option – it has standard Rostyle wheels instead of the usual optional wires. Note the exhaust tail pipe emerging on the driver's side.

At the rear, this four-seater has stop/tail lights and reflectors on the rear wings, flashing indicators on the rear panel and twin fog guard lights mounted on the bumper. The number plate has a light above it and the optional reversing lights either side. This car has the optional locking filler cap. The rear bumper replaced a set of chrome overriders as standard equipment in 1977.

An aluminium body and wings were offered as a 'standard' optional extra from January 1977 (chassis number B3905). However, some may have been produced by special request before this.

From the launch of the Plus 4 in October 1985, the 4/4 was also available with the Plus 4's wider body. This is referred to as the 'wide-body' style, although the extra width is actually in the wings, which were extended to cover the Plus 4's wider wheels.

Significant anti-rot and rust measures were introduced for the whole Morgan range in 1986, and have been continued ever since. Now the chassis is powder-coated or, as an optional extra, galvanised. The completed ash frame is dipped in Cuprisol wood preservative for 40 minutes. The body says 'goodbye' to good old cellulose and 'hello' to ICI 2K, a modern two-pack synthetic paint. The body, wings and doors are also now painted separately, so every inch of the car is protected (the cowl and bonnet were always sprayed separately). As the external piping is now fitted after the wings have been sprayed, it is no longer painted.

A powder coating plant was installed soon after these measures arrived, so the bulkheads, valances, brackets and small fittings also have an epoxy powder coating. It is rumoured that the man with the chassis black paint pot and chewed-up paint brush liberated his old equipment from a cupboard and continued to splash chassis black over the newly powder-coated metal for

some hours before someone noticed . . .

In 1987, these protective measures were extended as Morgan began to use zinc-plated and passivated nuts, bolts and fasteners. It is to these standards, rather than a car's original state, that most Morgan owners aspire when they restore their cars.

BODY TRIM

The external door handles, an optional extra, are Land Rover type small chrome door handles. The bonnet knobs are slightly smaller and plain in style, without concentric circles. They are surrounded by a chromed escutcheon plate fastening with two chrome screws through the bonnet to an inner plate.

In January 1977, the chrome bumpers were replaced by semi-square section aluminium equivalents. The overriders disappeared from the front and rear, while a rear bumper became standard for the first time. The bumper brackets also changed from black-painted steel to a similar style in aluminium.

There was never any difference in badging during this time to indicate which cars had the Ford engines and which the Fiat twin-cam engines. All wore the same 4/4 wings badge. So, the only way to tell without sneaking a look under the bonnet is to check the exhaust pipe, which emerges on

The exhaust of the Kent-engined car exits on the passenger side. From 1976 it had a mild steel rear resonator box similar to the stainless steel one in the picture. The 'rear chassis sweeps' (the brackets which hold the bumper on) are also visible here.

The bonnet knob with concentric circles was replaced by this plain item in 1969.

the passenger's side from a Ford engine and the driver's side from a twin-cam.

INTERIOR, INSTRUMENTS & CONTROLS

The first cars have the same dashboard as the late Series V, but it was redesigned in October 1969. From this time, a rev counter, half the size of the other instruments, is set on the right-hand side of the steering wheel (assuming right-hand drive). The glovebox remains ahead of the passenger and the white-on-black instruments are contained in a central metal panel shaped like an elongated oblong.

A quadrant (this time with all four gauges and a Morgan script in the centre) sits in the right of this panel, the speedometer in the left, and two rows of black rocker switches are set in between. The top row has four switches controlling the screenwash, two-speed wipers, lights and two-speed heater fan. The three switches along the bottom control the spotlamps (if fitted), hazard flashers and parking lights (or other auxiliary fittings). In between the two rows are three warning lights for the indicators and handbrake. There are no jack plug points.

In a few early cars with this layout, the ignition switch is on the dashboard above the steering column. From November 1970, when a collapsible steering column was introduced, the switch moved onto the column. The windscreen wiper motor sits below the bonnet on the bulkhead nearside top, and operates two windscreen wipers until 1977, three wipers thereafter.

Some crash padding was put on top of the steel scuttle for the first time from October 1971, and the whole dashboard was covered with vinyl or leather to match the interior trim of the car unless the customer asked for a different colour. Bucket seats were also offered as a new option, the standard item being a bench seat as on the Series V. Their frames were mounted on wooden blocks

This dashboard is completely original – apart from the plaque. The dash on all Morgans in this period was covered to match the interior trim. Four dials replace the quadrant and the flick switches have been replaced by rockers. The warning light cluster between the speedometer and rev counter comes from a Jaguar XJ-S. The black wheel centre has 'MORGAN' moulded into it in capital letters.

This 1991 dashboard belongs to the last official CVH-engined car (built before another 35 CVH engines unexpectedly turned up from Ford). The steering wheel has a Morgan script in red beneath a plastic bubble. The separate warning lights are arranged in a T shape, and in this case an extra light has been added at the bottom for the repeater indicators connected to a factory-fitted tow-bar.

which were bolted directly through the floor and chassis of the car. The frames have built-in runners which allow the seats to slide backwards and forwards. An order for bucket seats was accompanied by a full tonneau, as the half tonneau had fixed on the wooden rail at the back of the bench seat – with bucket seats there was nothing to fix it to.

The optional 'fug-stirrer' recirculating heater was replaced by a standard equipment Smiths fresh air heater in May 1972.

Whereas the 'fug-stirrer' sat at the end of the passenger's footwell, the box which blows air in from the Smiths heater is situated above the transmission tunnel, and has two small flaps, one on either side, to allow the heat to be directed to one or both sides. The front of the box has two open tubes which were later used for the demister, but no demist function was offered until 1975.

The heater has a radiator (fed with hot water from the inlet manifold) and a fan (driven by an electric motor) housed in a

Folding and reclining seats were standard in the four-seater, but optional in the roadster. The front seat belts are fixed to the top of the rear wheelarches. Fittings for optional head rests are provided on the front seats.

box and attached to the bulkhead under the bonnet. An air duct to the heater opens from the top to a metal scoop pushed up against the louvres in the bonnet to suck in fresh air.

The problem with this early Smiths heater is that there is no mechanism to turn it off. The only solution in summer is to shut both flaps and stuff some rags into the open tubes at the front! Demisters were introduced in November 1974 (chassis number B3367) and consist of two convoluted plastic tubes, running from the front of the heater box up to a housing beneath slots in the scuttle and its padding. Where they emerge on top of the dash, each slot is finished with a thin metal surround held down with two self-tapping screws. At the same time, a valve was introduced into the heater outlet/inlet water pipes to allow the heater to be turned off. The valve was operated by a knob situated on the left-hand side of the steering column.

It became a legal requirement in mid-1975 for the driver's seat of a new car to be adjustable independently of the passenger seat, so the traditional bench seat disappeared forever. Bucket seats became standard, and folding/reclining bucket seats became an optional extra. Door pockets

were also introduced in late 1975.

The dashboard changed again in 1977. The rev counter, now the same size as the speedometer, sits on the right of the steering column and the speedometer to the left, while there is a T-shaped warning light cluster (borrowed from an early Jaguar XJ-S) in between.

The rest of the instruments are placed in the centre of the dash in a rectangular recess, with rounded corners. Instead of the previous quadrant, four small gauges line up at the top of this rectangle to show fuel, water temperature, oil and volts. These gauges do not have any Morgan scripts or other labels to help you at an autojumble. Below them, five smaller Lucas rocker switches operate the lights, spotlamps (where fitted), hazard flashers, rear fog guard lights and two-speed heater fan. These switches contain tiny bulbs which light up when they are switched on. The windscreen wipers (including a single-wipe function) and washers are operated by a stalk on the left of the column, the indicators, horn and headlamp dip/main beam by a stalk on the right.

From 1986, the warning light arrangement changed from one single cluster to separate coloured lamps arranged in the same pattern. At the same time, the seat

The hood's window area has increased considerably since the early days, but the basic design remains the same, still with the 'pram' shape at the rear on the four-seater. This car has the optional external door handles.

The four-seater still has four separate sidescreens; sliding windows became standard in 1969.

belts were changed to modern inertia reel belts – and four-seaters were available with static rear lap belts.

The heater changed again in 1988. This one is larger, and the heat can be switched off or cold air pumped in. But when you need heat, it is not actually as effective as its predecessor. It sits under the dashboard and has a fibreboard cover instead of a metal box. First cold, then hot, air wells up as you pull out a knob on the dashboard - the further you pull the knob the warmer the car gets. Another knob on the heater itself directs the heat onto feet or screen, and the two-speed fan is operated by a rocker switch on the dashboard.

From this time the switches themselves were changed to more solid Italian-made rockers. The black on white dials now say 'Tudor' in the centre, as this company had taken over Smiths Industries. From the 1988 motor show, a walnut veneer dashboard with a lockable glovebox, still with a padded top covered in vinyl or leather, could be specified.

WHEELS & TYRES

The standard wheels are the same pierced disc ones worn by the Series V, but the

The 72-spoke 15in wire wheel (left), with this octagonal 'continental' spinner, was optional from 1969 and standard on all 4/4s from 1990.

The side light has reverted to a very similar style to the earliest small Lucas lamp, but with a plastic lens and no red circle in the top.

optional wire wheels have 72 spokes, rather than 60. They are 15in × 5.6in wheels on 4J rims, or 4¹/₂J in the case of the wire wheels.

Early wire wheels at first had twin-eared spinners, but these were outlawed by new EEC safety regulations. So from October 1971 they wear octagonal 'continental' spinners, which presumably do less damage to your ankles if you happen to get in the way. These screw on and off and have little arrows engraved in them to show which way they must be turned to be removed. From 1977, customers could specify chrome wire wheels, still with 72 spokes.

During 1980 Dunlop stopped making the 15in pierced disc wheel, so Morgan bought up the old stock of four-stud, Rostyle-type wheels used by VW on various export model Beetles. These are 15in steel wheels with a silver rim and a spoked effect, the spokes in silver, the background in black. The centre is a small chromed metal cap. Most customers, however opted for the wires. The tyres were 175 HR 15 on 'Rostyle' wheels or 165 HR 15 on wire wheels; originally these were Pirelli Cinturato, but Michelins were offered as an optional extra. Stocks of Rostyle type wheels ran out in 1990 and wire wheels

became standard. Tyres on the 4/4 have been Pirelli Cinturato, Michelin and Uniroyal (in that order), but 'Plus 4 Body Style' cars had Avon 195/60 HR 15 tyres fitted to their centre-laced 6in wide wire wheels.

LIGHTING

From October 1971, the rear light assemblies are larger and housed in tubular 'torpedo plinths' made out of plastic and painted body colour. The lights have chrome surrounds and Lucas lenses. The plinths for the rear lights protrude from the wings and those for the flashers from the bottom corners of the tonneau deck – but a legal requirement caused the positions to reverse from 1988.

Separate oblong reflectors with a chrome surround are mounted on plastic plinths, again painted body colour, below the stop lights or flashers on each rear wing. The chrome surround was deleted from June 1990 in order to increase the visible reflector area. Reversing lamps are optional and mounted on the number plate panel.

From June 1990, the earlier type of single number plate lamp, mounted on a separate plinth above the number plate, was replaced

Morgan bought up unused stock of Rostyle wheels made by Lemmerz in Germany for VW and offered them as standard equipment for 4/4s. The wheel has a spun metal centre cap.

A single Lucas number plate light with a chrome surround was fitted above the number plate from the 1950s.

by two similar chromed Lucas units mounted on the panel either side of the number plate.

In 1988, the fuse box, which had always sat on the bulkhead, moved to a new position beneath the dashboard to the left of the driver. From this point on, it uses modern pull-out fuses.

ENGINE

The standard 4/4 was launched with a 1600 Cortina engine, known as the 'Kent' engine (Ford designation 2737E). It has four cylinders in line, a bore and stroke of 81mm × 77.7mm, a capacity of 1599cc, and two overhead valves per cylinder. It delivers 70bhp at 4750rpm. The single Zenith carburettor and intake manifold are mounted

on the left-hand side of the engine (viewed from the front), while the exhaust manifold sits to the right and the gases are transferred across the top of the cylinder head. So the Kent is also known as the Ford 'crossflow' engine.

The competition model of the 4/4 has the Cortina GT engine (Ford designation is 2737 GT). Basically the same unit as the Kent, this uses a twin-choke Weber carburettor with a four-branch manifold to improve its breathing, a lightened flywheel and, in the Morgan, a plastic fan to reduce weight and a rev counter as standard equipment. The difference in performance was striking as this version delivers 95.5bhp at 5500rpm – as a result, most customers opted for the competition model.

In May 1971 (chassis number B2381), all

Two number plate lights, still in chrome surrounds, are positioned to either side of the number plate from June 1990.

This Kent engine, from the Cortina GT, has 'Morgan' cast into the top of the air filter box. The collapsible steering column with UJs (bottom left) became standard from November 1970. The earliest Kent engines had a single Zenith carburettor, but from 1971 all cars adopted 'Competition' spec and gained a twin-choke Weber.

From 1971, all Kent-engined cars had a Morgan-designed tubular exhaust manifold. From 1975, an airbox was added into the manifold, as seen here, with trunking from the air filter system to help the engine warm up more quickly and therefore reduce carbon output. The washer bottle (bottom right) is made by Lucas.

The Fiat 1600 (Mirafiori) engine has the same air filter box, marked with the Morgan name, as the Kent-engined car. This car also has the original foam around the heater radiator air inlet.

The Fiat twin-cam has a non-standard tubular exhaust manifold for increased performance – the correct item would be shorter and cast. The toolbox (top left) on all models became shorter when the fresh air heater was introduced in 1971.

When the 'fug stirrer' was replaced by this Smiths recirculating heater in 1971, the tool box had to be reduced in size to make room for it. The air inlet for the heater radiator (top right) used to have foam around the edges to stop it denting the underside of the bonnet. However, the foam tends to collect water and causes rust instead.

4/4s adopted this specification and the name 'Competition' was dropped. Two months later, Ford made some slight changes to the engine to refine the oilways, assigning a new designation of 2265E. The first Morgan to receive this revised engine was chassis number B3540.

The last Kent-engined Morgans left the factory in March 1982, as Ford was changing over to the new CVH (compound valve-angle hemispherical chamber) engine for the Escort. At first it looked as if this power unit would not be suitable for use by Morgan as it was designed for transverse location and front-wheel drive, so Morgan adopted the Fiat 1600 twin overhead cam engine and offered it alongside the Kent from October 1981. The Fiat engine is a four-cylinder 1584cc unit, with a bore and stroke of 84mm x 71.50mm. It delivers 98bhp at 6000rpm.

Meanwhile Ford and Morgan had been working on the CVH engine, mainly at the insistence of that Ford executive who saw his 4/4 in jeopardy. It was given a more tapered Cortina sump, a special Morgan-designed flywheel and a Capri bellhousing. To make it fit into the 4/4, the car's bulkhead was re-shaped, new engine mountings were designed and a larger radiator was installed. It worked, and so was offered alongside the Fiat engine, but at a slightly lower price.

The CVH is another four-cylinder unit, with a bore and stroke of 79.96mm × 79.52mm and a capacity of 1597cc. It oper-

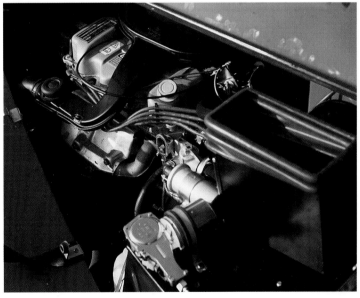

ates its valves through a centrally mounted single overhead camshaft and hydraulic tappets, has a compression ratio of 9.5:1, and uses a single Weber 32/34 DFT twin-choke carburettor. It delivers 96bhp at 6000rpm.

Ford introduced the lean-burn version of the CVH engine, with a 28/32 TLDM twin-choke carburettor, in 1987. The easiest way to identify this engine is by its big, flat air filter, which is painted black instead of the previous grey. The later carburettor also has a more rounded base.

In October 1991, Ford replaced the carburettor with fully mappable fuel injection and a three-way catalytic converter with a

The heater used from 1988 (in this case fitted to a 1991 'lean-burn' CVH engine) has a large rubber surround on top of the air inlet. Its efficiency is questionable as it does not sit below the bonnet louvres.

Ford's 1597cc CVH engine, with a single overhead camshaft and hydraulic tappets, was designed for transverse application in the front-drive Escort. To fit into the Morgan, it needed a more tapered Cortina sump, a Morgan-designed flywheel and a Capri bellhousing. Morgan also had to reshape the bulkhead and fit a larger radiator. The pre 'lean-burn' CVH engine is recognisable only by its grey air filter box, just visible here.

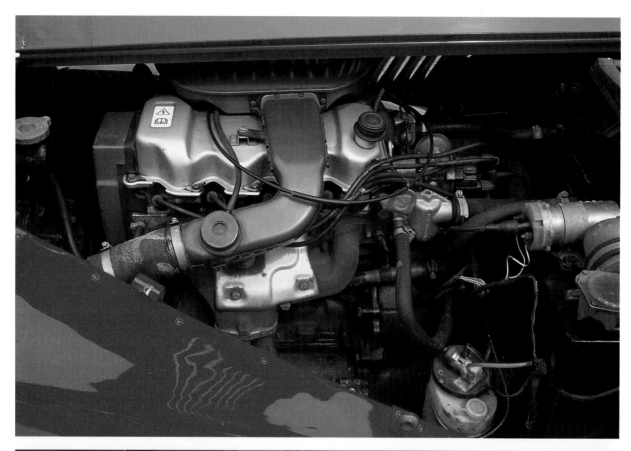

The CVH 'lean-burn' engine, with its W28/32 TLDM twin-choke carburettor, has a black, oval air filter box. The original factory tool roll – a brown paper wrapping! – is still in place in the toolbox. The optional bonnet strap attaches to the bonnet rubber buffer stop, just left of centre on the wing. The bonnet tape would have been painted over up until 1986; the side repeater flasher was standard from 1988.

From November 1991, 4/4 models gained the CVH EFI engine fitted with fully mappable fuel injection and a three-way catalytic converter. Maximum power is 100bhp.

The fuel tank sits behind the rear axle (below), and the handbrake compensators run between the tank and the axle. The ends of the lever arm shock absorbers are just visible. The surround to support this car's rear seat is metal, but a wooden surround would support the rear load floor on a two-seater.

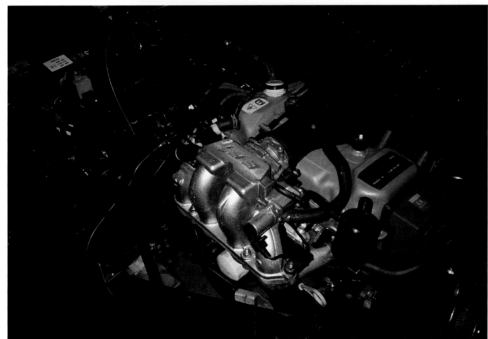

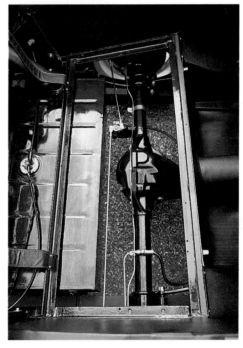

Apart from its Weber/Marelli indirect multi-point fuel injection and distributorless ignition, the CVH EFI engine remains similar to previous carburettor versions.

Hego/lambda sensor. This engine, known as the CVH EFI, is similar to the previous CVH carburettor engine, but with Weber/Marelli indirect multi-point injection using a programmed twin-spark ignition system without a conventional distributor, ignition timing being pre-set and not adjustable. This engine delivers 100bhp at 6000rpm and 102lb ft of torque at 2800rpm. Used for the Escort, Orion and Fiesta XR2i, it became standard in the Morgan 4/4 from November 1991.

TRANSMISSION

The early 1600 and 1600GT 4/4s both use the four-speed, full synchromesh Ford 1600 GT gearbox, operated through a remote linkage. The 4/4 Twin-Cam uses the five-speed Abarth rally gearbox, whose ratios are as follows: top, 0.87; fourth, 1.1; third, 1.36; second, 2.05; first, 3.61; reverse, 3.24:1.

The CVH engine was at first mated to a four-speed Cortina gearbox, but this was replaced in 1983 by the newly-developed

This type of steering column lock has been fitted since 1971. The CVH gear lever still has its label on from Morgan's supplier. The speedometer drive exits through the hole in the tunnel, which would normally be covered by a leather or vinyl cover.

The Fiat-engined car has an Abarth gearbox (below). The gear knob has a change pattern which states 'lift for reverse', but the handbook points out that you do not have to in a Morgan.

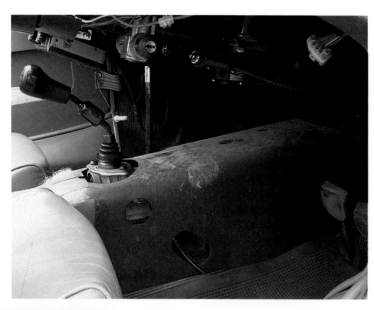

five-speed transmission of the Capri and Sierra. Its ratios are: top, 0.83; fourth, 1:1; third, 1.37; second, 1.97; first, 3.65; reverse, 3.66:1. The ratios for the four-speed gearbox are the same apart from the lack of fifth gear.

In all cases the clutch is of $7^{1}/_{2}$in diameter and operated by diaphragm spring. As for the Series II to V models, the final drive ratio is 4.1:1.

CHASSIS

The chassis is as for the Series V, but detail changes were made with the introduction of each new engine and gearbox. As with other Morgan models, since 1986 the chassis has been powder coated black, or galvanised at extra cost, and the complete ash frame has been dipped in Cuprisol for 40 minutes.

STEERING

The 4/4 1600 began life using the Cam Gears steering box, until Gemmer in France began to produce a recirculating ball type steering system. As this steering box was very similar in design to the original Burman Douglas box, Morgan fitted it as standard from October 1986. It gives a turning circle of 32ft, and takes $2^{1}/_{4}$ turns lock to lock with the 15in steering wheel or $2^{1}/_{2}$ with the 14in wheel.

The steering wheel on early cars has three aluminium spokes with holes drilled in them, and the centre is a plain black plastic plug. The rim was covered in black vinyl as standard, but it could be sent back to Astrali to be retrimmed in any colour if a customer wished it.

In November 1970, a collapsible steering column with a steering lock was installed, and the ignition was moved onto the column. In 1973, the plain centre of the steering wheel was replaced by a larger, soft rubber bung embossed with Morgan script.

There was another minor change in 1987, when the rubber steering wheel centre was given a new Morgan script, written in red on a black background and covered by a clear plastic dome. The spokes are still aluminium, but now without holes.

BRAKING

The brakes are 11in discs at the front and 9in × 1.75in drums at the rear. A Girling dual circuit hydraulic system became standard in October 1971 to conform with EEC safety regulations.

Production Data

PRODUCTION FIGURES & CHASSIS NUMBERS

Production totals for the 4/4 with Ford 'Kent', Fiat twin-cam and Ford CVH engines are as follows:

Ford 1600/1600GT	3513
Twin-Cam 1600 (Fiat)	92
Ford CVH 1600 (to July 1991)	1900
Total (to July 1991)	**5505**

The chassis number prefix depends upon the engine fitted: Kent, B; Fiat, F; CVH, C. The first car, in February 1968, was chassis number B1600. During the confusing period of engine changes, chassis numbers remained consecutive, only the prefix altering. In 1600 Competition models, engine numbers are prefixed A; from chassis number B2381, all Kent-engined cars had Competition specification.

PRODUCTION CHANGES

1968 (Feb)
4/4 1600 and 1600GT launched using Ford, 2737E and 2737GT engines.

1969 (Oct)
Dashboard redesigned; a rev counter, half the size of the speedometer and quadrant, is set to the right of the driver; instruments are set in oval-shaped panel in the centre; jack plug deleted.

1970 (Nov)
Collapsible steering column with steering lock introduced, and ignition switch moves from dashboard to steering column. Indicators, horn and dip switch now worked by a black plastic-covered stalk to right-hand side of steering column (on RHD cars).

1971 (May)
From chassis number B2381, all cars adopt Competition specification and Competition designation dropped.

1971 (Jul)
From chassis number B3540, Ford makes slight changes to engine and designation changes to 2265E.

1971

EEC safety regulations lead to the introduction of anti-burst door locks; external door handles remain optional. Crash padding for top of the scuttle, whole dashboard covered in vinyl or leather to match interior of car. Bucket seats offered as an option. Twin-eared spinners on wire wheels replaced by octagonal 'continental' spinners. Brakes become dual circuit Girling hydraulics. Rear light assemblies become larger and housed in tubular 'torpedo plinths' of painted plastic.

1972 (May)

Optional recirculating 'fug-stirrer' heater is replaced by standard Smiths fresh air heater.

1973

Hard plastic centre of steering wheel replaced by rubber centre with 'Morgan' embossed.

1974 (Nov)

Demisters introduced from chassis number B3367.

1975

Bench seat replaced by bucket seats, folding and reclining seats become optional. Door pockets introduced.

1977

Aluminium body and wings officially offered as optional extras. Chrome bumpers replaced by semi-square section aluminium, overriders deleted; rear bumper becomes standard; bumper brackets altered in style, and made from aluminium rather than black-painted steel. Dashboard redesigned: rev counter increased to same size as the speedometer, and quadrant is replaced by four separate dials. Rocker switches sit in a central rectangle with rounded corners. Windscreen wash/wipe operated by left-hand stalk; indicators, horn and headlamp main/dip by right-hand stalk. Chrome wire wheels officially offered as an option.

1980

Dunlop pierced disc wheels replaced by Rostyle type.

1981 (Oct)

4/4 Twin-Cam launched using Fiat 1600 engine and five-speed Abarth gearbox.

1982 (Mar)

Kent engine replaced by CVH.

1983

Transmission of CVH-engined car changes from Cortina four-speed to Capri/Sierra five-speed.

1985 (Oct)

'Wide body' style offered, using body of newly launched Plus 4.

1986

Weather protection measures introduced. Chassis is powder coated, or galvanised at extra cost; ash frame is Cuprinol-dipped. Body is sprayed 'wings off' using ICI 2K two-pack synthetic paint. Bulkheads, valances, brackets and small fittings epoxy powder coated in black. Cam Gears steering box replaced by Gemmer recirculating ball system. Warning light arrangment ahead of steering wheel changes from single cluster to individual coloured lamps. Inertia reel seat belts introduced.

1987

Introduction of 'lean burn' CVH engine. Zinc-plated and passivated nuts, bolts and fasteners introduced. Steering wheel centre gains Morgan script in red on a black background, beneath a clear plastic dome.

1988

Larger heater installed. Rocker switches replaced by larger Italian made rockers. Smiths Industries taken over by Tudor, so instruments now have Tudor legend in centre. Walnut veneer dash with lockable glovebox offered as optional extra. Fuse box moved from bulkhead to beneath dashboard.

1990

Wire wheels become standard. Number plate lamps now dual, fitting directly onto number plate panel either side of number plate.

1991 (Nov)

Introduction of catalysed XR2i engine with fully mappable fuel injection. Fuel filler cap is now on right-hand side of rear panel, beneath a lockable flap; script badge moves to left-hand side. In order to accommodate the filler cap 'box', spare wheel aperture is now cut closer to edge of spare wheel.

DIMENSIONS

4/4 1600 Kent & Twin Cam
Wheelbase, 8ft 0in
Overall length, 12ft 0in
Width, 4ft 8in
Front track, 3ft 11in
Rear track, 4ft 1in
Dry weight, 1624lb (two-seater), 1680 lb (four-seater)

4/4 1600 CVH
Wheelbase, 8ft 0in
Overall length, 12ft 9in (with aluminium bumpers)
Width, 4ft 9in
Front track, 4ft 0in
Rear track, 4ft 1in
Ground clearance, 6in
Height, 4ft 4in (two-seater), 4ft 6in (four-seater)
Dry weight, 1912lb (two-seater), 2024lb (four-seater)

OPTIONAL EXTRAS & SPECIAL EQUIPMENT

Competition specification (1969-71)
Two-seater or four-seater (1969 to date)
Recirculating heater (1969-72)
Door handles (1969 to date)
Aluminium body and wings (1977 to date)
'Wide body' (1985 to date)
Underseal (1969 to date) NB: wings are under-sealed as standard from 1988
Rear bumper (1969-77, then standard)
Full tonneau for two-seater (1969-75)
Bucket seats with full tonneau (1971-75, then standard)
Folding and reclining seats (1975 to date)
Walnut veneer dash (1988 to date)
Wire wheels, 72 spoke (1969-90, then standard)
Reversing lamp (1969 to date)
Galvanised chassis (1986 to date)
Connolly leather (1969 to date)
Bonnet strap (1969 to date)
Door mirror (1977-84, then standard)

COLOURS

1969-86
Brunswick Green
Signal Red
Dark Blue
Royal Ivory
Plus one other colour which varied year on year.

From 1986
Connaught Green
Rosso Red
Indigo Blue
Black
Royal Ivory
Any other colour/two-tone colour scheme at extra cost. Black vinyl is standard interior trim, but other colours/materials at extra cost. Wing beading (from 1986) available in black, red or cream.

Plus 4 from 1985

The Plus 4 has wider wings to cover the 6in wide wheels, so the body of this 1991 Rover-engined Plus 4 is slightly wider than its bumpers, which come directly from the 4/4. This car has factory-fitted mirrors and repeaters on the side. Like all post-1986 Morgans, it was painted at the factory in separate pieces and then put together with contrasting wing piping.

The Plus 4 name disappeared in 1969 with the demise of the TR4A engine and the adoption of the Rover V8. However, in early 1985 Fiat offered Morgan its 2-litre twin-cam engine, and Maurice Owen felt that this would be a great opportunity to enlarge the range and offer a car in between the 4/4 and the Plus 8.

In retrospect, this seems a logical move as the Fiat 1600 twin-cam had been used in the 4/4, but in fact the two cars were never on sale at the same time, the 1600 having been discontinued in 1984. It should also be noted that this 2-litre engine was never used in the same guise by any Fiat sold in the UK – a fact which most owners find out only when they start searching for spares. The 2-litre Fiat engine is fuel-injected, but around nine cars were produced with a twin-choke Weber carburettor. No-one knows whether to call them Plus 4s or 4/4s - including the factory. The cowl badges on some say 4/4, while others say Plus 4!

The Rover M16 engine was introduced to replace the Fiat unit in 1988. The first

prototype was chassis number 7300, later registered as D955 AWP. Its aluminium body was a cross between a two-seater and a four-seater 4/4 body. From the front, up to the modified scuttle, was a two-seater body with a Plus 8 cowl, but behind this was a modified four-seater rear end. This car was painted opalescent white and trimmed in pale blue with a dark blue tonneau and a walnut dashboard. The steel body of the second prototype, chassis number 7400, registered E766 FUY, was very similar to that of the 4/4, with only minor modifications. It was painted dark blue, with a contrasting red interior and tonneau, and red wheels.

The new Plus 4 was first seen at Brands Hatch in May 1988, but thanks to various hold-ups associated with type approval (in particular noise emissions regulations), cars did not reach customers until October. The first production car, chassis number 7494, was sprayed British Racing Green and had a cream interior, chrome wheels and walnut dashboard.

All later Plus 4s have 'Cobra-style' centre-laced wire wheels painted as standard, or chromed as an optional extra. The tyres are Avon low profiles with specially-imported inner tubes; wire wheels are not airtight.

BODY & BODY TRIM

The production body is basically the same as the 4/4's, but the wings are 1in wider either side to cover the wider wheels. Both the Fiat- and Rover-engined cars were always offered as two- or four-seaters.

At the end of 1990, the four-seater was given a slightly lower body style. To accommodate it, the battery was moved from the engine bay to beneath the rear seat, ahead of the rear axle.

Body trim is as for the 4/4, but the cowl badge always reads Plus 4 – except on a few early Fiat-engined cars.

INTERIOR, INSTRUMENTS & CONTROLS

In every respect, specification is as for the 4/4 of the same period.

WHEELS & TYRES

As standard, the Plus 4 has 15in x 6in wide wire wheels which are epoxy powder coated in silver, or chromed at extra cost. In both cases they are 'Cobra style' – they are centre-laced wire wheels with low profile

Avon Turbospeed 195/60 R15 tyres. As wire wheels cannot be air-tight, the tyres must be fitted with tubes, which have to be imported specially from Scandinavia, because a tube for a low profile tyre is an unusual request.

The cowl badge reads 'Plus 4' whether the car has a Fiat or Rover engine, but is thinner than the earlier Plus 4 badge.

LIGHTING & ELECTRICS

All external lights and items of electrical equipment are identical to those used on contemporary 4/4 models.

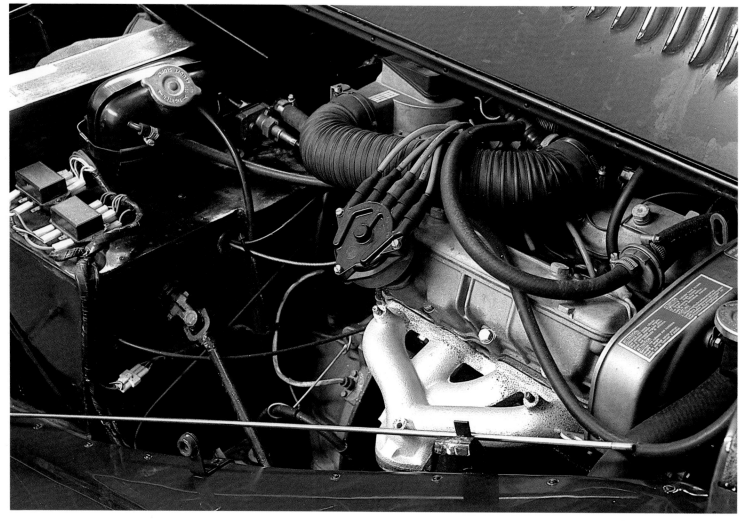

ENGINE

The 2-litre Fiat engine has a Marelli multi-point distributor positioned beneath the top bonnet louvres, where it frequently gets wet. It has a cast manifold and the same sealed cooling system as the 4/4.

The 2-litre Fiat engine may break with tradition in its country of origin, but it allowed the familiar Plus 4 tag to be revived because it has four cylinders.

It has a bore and stroke of 84mm x 90mm and a capacity of 1995cc. Its twin overhead camshafts are belt-driven and operate two valves per cylinder. The compression ratio is 9.0:1. A Bosch LE Jetronic fuel injection system with Digiplex ignition control is fitted to all cars except the nine with a single Weber DCOE twin-choke carburettor. The sump requires 9 pints of oil (including the oil filter), while the fuel tank developed for the Plus 8 sits beneath the tonneau deck and holds 12½ gallons

This engine offers 122bhp at 5300rpm and 129lb ft of torque at 3500rpm. When *Autocar* drove it for the 7 May 1986 issue, the testers achieved 109mph, 0-60mph in 9.5sec, and a fuel consumption figure of 25.9mpg.

Morgan's engine supply dried up in 1987 when Fiat changed to a transverse engine for front-wheel drive, so the foreign invader was replaced by a British engine – the new M16 engine from the Rover 820. After a slight gap in Plus 4 production, this unit was introduced from October 1988 and remains under the Plus 4's bonnet in 1992. Boldly announcing 'TWIN CAM 16 VALVE' and 'ROVER' on its top, this engine looks much tidier in the Morgan engine bay than the previous Fiat occupant.

It is a 2-litre, 16-valve engine with multi-point fuel injection. The dimensions are 84.5mm x 89mm bore and stroke, a capacity of 1994cc, and a compression ratio of 10:1. The combustion chambers in the aluminium alloy cylinder head are shaped to produce a 'swirl effect', which maximises the amount of fuel burned. The twin overhead camshafts are belt driven, and the fuel injection system is the Lucas L hot wire injection with digital ignition control, as used in the Montego.

This is a free-revving unit which delivers 138bhp at 6000rpm and 131lb ft of torque at 4500rpm. *Autocar's* test of 25 May 1988 recorded a top speed of 109mph with a 0-60mph sprint of 7.7sec. The fuel tank holds 12.5 gallons in the two-seater or 10 gallons in the four-seater. Cars with the Rover engine can run on unleaded fuel.

A large-bore exhaust for the Rover M16 engine is manufactured and finished specially for Morgan. It uses aluminised silencer components to comply with the strictest noise emissions regulations in Europe. An extremely efficient four-branch manifold feeds into twin connecting pipes, then into a large oval centre silencer with a further connecting pipe to the rear resonator box which is mounted, curiously, at 45 degrees into the rear section of the nearside back wing.

For more detail, refer to the workshop manuals for the Fiat Argenta (its engine is slightly different, but as close as you can get) and Rover 820.

TRANSMISSION

The ratios of the Fiat gearbox, from the 125 Special, are as follows: fifth, 0.83; fourth, 1.00; third, 1.36; second, 2.05; first, 3.6; reverse, 3.24:1.

The M16-engined car uses the same five-speed Rover gearbox as the Plus 8, since this engine is normally mated to front-wheel drive transmission. Mounted end-on to the engine, it requires modifications to the bellhousing, bulkhead and chassis cross-member to accommodate it, plus a special back plate made up from Sherpa van parts. Its ratios are: top, 0.792; fourth, 1.0; third, 1.396; second, 2.087; first, 3.321; reverse, 3.42:1.

Fiat- and Rover-powered cars both use a $7^{1}/_{2}$in single dry plate clutch with hydraulic operation, but produced by the appropriate company. As before, the propshaft, with needle roller universal joints, transmits power to a Salisbury rear axle, fitted with hypoid gears. The final drive ratio is 4.1:1 for the Twin-Cam and 3.73:1 for the M16.

The Fiat engine's air filter box is similar to that of the 3.5-litre V8. The injection system is by Marelli. The air intake for the Smiths recirculating heater is at the top right.

The Rover M16 engine has a four-branch manifold as standard, and the ancillaries have to be shielded as the tight fit means they run close to its hot branches.

The rocker cover announces the Rover four-cylinder engine's technical modernity. The spark plugs are beneath the cover in the centre, so the Morgan bonnet has to be removed and a special spanner is needed to reach them. The 'elephant's trunk' from the air filter runs down to pick up warm air from the manifold. The tools are in their factory brown paper in the tool box.

CHASSIS & SUSPENSION

The chassis and suspension were as for the 4/4 until December 1991, when the Plus 4 adopted the Plus 8 chassis. Suspension details are still as for the 4/4.

STEERING

Fiat- and Rover-engined Plus 4s both use the Gemmer recirculating ball system as standard equipment, but rack and pinion was offered as a no-cost option from December 1991. The Gemmer box gives a turning circle of 32ft and requires $2^1/4$ turns lock to lock.

BRAKING

The brakes operate via a Girling dual-circuit hydraulic system. The front discs are of 11in diameter and the rear drums are 9in $\times$ $1^3/4$in. A 'fly-off' handbrake operates on the rear drums.

Production Data

PRODUCTION FIGURES & CHASSIS NUMBERS

Production totals for the two recent Plus 4 models are as follows:

Plus 4 Twin Cam (Fiat, 1985-88)	122
Plus 4 M16 (Rover, 1988 to date)	120
Total (to July 1991)	**242**

The chassis numbers of Plus 4s with Fiat engines have the prefix 'F', while those with Rover M16 engines have the prefix 'M'. The first prototype with the Rover M16 engine was M7300, registered D955 AWP; the second prototype was M7400, registered E766 FUY. The first production car was M7494.

PRODUCTION CHANGES

1985 (Oct)
Plus 4 Twin Cam introduced.

1986 (Oct)
Weather protection measures introduced. Chassis is powder coated, or galvanised at extra cost; ash frame is Cuprinol-dipped. Body is sprayed 'wings off', using ICI 2K two-pack synthetic paint. Bulkheads, valances, brackets and small fittings epoxy powder coated in black. Warning light arrangement ahead of steering wheel changes from single cluster to individual coloured lamps. Inertia reel seat belts introduced.

1987
Zinc-plated and passivated nuts, bolts and fasteners introduced. Steering wheel centre gains Morgan script in red on a black background, beneath a clear plastic dome.

1988
Larger heater installed. Rocker switches replaced by larger Italian made rockers. Smiths Industries taken over by Tudor, so instruments now have Tudor legend in centre. Walnut veneer dash with lockable glovebox offered as optional extra. Fuse box moved from bulkhead to beneath dashboard, now with modern type fuses.

1988 (May)
M16 engine with Rover five-speed gearbox introduced, final drive reduced from 4.1:1 to 3.73:1.

1989
Battery on four-seater is moved from engine bay to beneath rear seat.

1991 (Dec)
Plus 4 now built on Plus 8 chassis for ease of production, resulting in increased track. Rack and pinion steering available as no cost option.

DIMENSIONS

Wheelbase, 8ft 0in
Overall length, 12ft 9in
Width, 4ft 9in
Front track, 3ft 11in (4ft 2$^{1}/_{2}$in from Dec 1991)
Rear track, 4ft 1in (4ft 3$^{1}/_{2}$in from Dec 1991)
Ground clearance, 6in (5in from Dec 1991)
Height (two-seater), 4ft 2in
Weight (two-seater), Fiat 1785lb, Rover 1984lb

OPTIONAL EXTRAS & SPECIAL EQUIPMENT

Two-seater or four-seater
Rack and pinion steering (1992 onwards)
Galvanised chassis (from 1986)
Underseal
Folding and reclining seats
Walnut veneer dash (from 1988)
Reversing lamps
Aluminium body and wings
Connolly leather trim
Bonnet strap
Door mirror
Exterior door handles

COLOURS

1969–86
Brunswick Green
Signal Red
Dark Blue
Royal Ivory
Plus one other colour which varied year on year.

From 1986
Connaught Green
Rosso Red
Indigo Blue
Black
Royal Ivory
Any other colour/two-tone scheme at extra cost. Black vinyl is standard interior trim, but other colours/materials at extra cost. Wing beading (from 1986) available in black, red or cream.

Plus 8

Allan Cameron's 1969 Plus 8 is one of the first 50 cars built, so its Rover V8 is linked to a Moss gearbox. The car is wider than the Plus 4 and, like all Plus 8s, has three windscreen wipers.

Tim Ot's 1976 Plus 8 has the V8 engine and four-speed gearbox from the Rover 3500S P6. At the front it wears Lucas driving lamps with red lion badges on the tops. The bumper irons hold the front bumper out from the car to give reasonable clearance between its curved ends and the forwards curvature of the wings.

Jim Robinson's 1979 Plus 8, photographed at MOG '91, has a Rover SD1 engine with twin SU carburettors and a Rover five-speed gearbox.

This 1983 Plus 8 (below) owned by David Moss shows the alloy wheels made specially for Morgan, and have 'The Morgan Motor Company Ltd' cast into them. The torpedo light plinths are chromed plastic, but were painted body colour from 1987.

Now owned by Bill Fink in California, the prototype Buick-powered Plus 8 (below), registered OUY 200E, looks just like a Plus 4 with wire wheels at first glance, but notice that two bonnet humps have been added to clear the V8 engine's twin carburettors. Some trim details are missing because the car is being used for competition in the USA.

By 1965, both Standard Triumph and Morgan were aware that the four-cylinder Triumph engine and its power output were too small for the demands of the sporting customer. Triumph's answer was the TR5's straight-six engine, but it was too long and too high to fit into a Morgan. So Morgan was forced to search for another engine to fit into its high-powered model. The Lotus twin-cam was considered, but proved to be too fragile for use in a Morgan. The Ford V6, again, was too tall and too heavy.

However, in May 1966 Peter Wilkes, a director of Rover Cars, visited Peter Morgan. On the surface it was a social call, but he was fishing to see if Morgan would consider a takeover. The approach was politely refused, but during the course of the conversation Wilkes also raised the subject of Rover's new engine: a lightweight V8 that was being adapted from the Buick/Oldsmobile unit used in Buick's 'compact' cars from 1960–3. He wondered whether Morgan might be interested in using it; and Peter Morgan, who already knew a great

This 1969 Plus 8 is only 4ft 9in wide, and the headlamp nacelles are positioned close in to the cowl. Rear-mounted Lucas LR6 driving lamps and the plain chrome bumper were standard. The wheels are 15in x 5.5in.

Compared with the 1969 car, the headlamp nacelles of this 1976 example are set further from the cowl. The bumper is unchanged but the wings are slightly wider, bringing overall width to 4ft 11in.

deal about this engine, snapped up the chance.

Morgan's development work was carried out by Maurice Owen, a race engineer who had approached Morgan previously to offer his services, should anything 'special' be required. He worked in total secrecy in a small brick workshop, and at first he had to make do with drawings as Rover could not spare a working engine. Maurice Owen found a Buick engine, which he sent to Rover to be modified as far as possible to resemble the new unit in size and

specification.

This engine was shoe-horned into a Plus 4 chassis which was subsequently designated chassis number R7000. Rumbling its way out into the factory yard in February 1967, this first prototype looked just like a Plus 4 with wire wheels, but it had two little humps in the bonnet covering the twin carburettors. These were necessary because the Buick engine had an Oldsmobile Offenhauser manifold designed to carry Holley carburettors, and this held the twin SU carburettors higher in the air than the

This 1979 Plus 8 is wider still, at 5ft 2in, with even more space between the headlamps and the cowl. However, the bumper is now wider to fit the car. This Plus 8 runs on the 14in x 6in Milrace wheels introduced for 1977 – by now the steering is becoming seriously heavy.

This 1983 Plus 8 is wider again (at 5ft 3in) because the wings have to house new 15in x 6¹/₂in wheels. From 1984, Morgan offered rack and pinion steering as an optional extra, but this feature was standardized from August 1986.

cast alloy inlet manifold used by Rover.

This car was registered OUY 200E, and was used by Maurice Owen for many years, but now resides in the USA. The second prototype, using a Rover engine and adapted chassis, was chassis number R7001, registered MMC 11. This was tested by *Autocar* in September 1968, and achieved a maximum speed of 124mph, 0-60mph in 6.7sec and the standing ¹/₄-mile in 15.1sec. A third prototype was given chassis number R7002 and registered AB 16. This registration number was later transferred to Peter

Morgan's Ferrari, while the car was sold to his son-in-law, Lord Colwyn.

After a good start, the Plus 8 project was held up by the Leyland buy-out of Rover in 1967. Leyland dithered for so long, making difficulties, that Morgan missed the hoped-for launch at the 1967 Motor Show. Harry Webster, technical director of Standard-Triumph (which had been part of Leyland since 1961), approached Morgan offering the V8 being developed for the Stag instead. Eventually, Peter Morgan invited Webster and George Turnbull of Rover Triumph

over to drive the prototype, and assurances, at last, were given that deliveries of the engines would begin immediately after the launch of the Rover 3500 in April 1968.

So, two Morgan Plus 8s were displayed at the 1968 Motor Show, and the car was offered for sale immediately. About 20 cars were delivered in 1968.

BODY

The Plus 8 has only ever been made in one body style – the two-seater open tourer.

The single exhaust marks this car out as one of the first 50 Plus 8s. On these very early cars, a wheel fouled the exhaust during hard cornering. As there are twin filler caps at the top corners of the rear panel, there is no room for a Morgan script. The rear lights are similar to those of a Spitfire.

The 1976 Plus 8 has twin exhausts. The rear lights have separate reflectors and are mounted in torpedo-style plinths. The reversing lights either side of the number plate were optional.

The coupé was complicated, and not economical to build, so just one was produced, on chassis number R7317 – this was the drophead coupé automatic produced for Peter Morgan's wife (see below).

A four-seater version would probably have faced severe handling problems. However, just one four-seater Plus 8 was made for a Morgan agent, Eric White of Cranfield, who promised he would never sell it – and so far he has not.

The Plus 8 has a wider, squatter, more purposeful stance than its predecessors. In early cars the overall width is 4ft 9in, with a track of 4ft 1in at the front and 4ft 3in at the rear. But most of the extra width is in the wings, which spread over the years to cover the ever wider wheels. The bonnet has louvres in the top and the sides. The fixed windscreen is laminated.

In August 1973, the track was widened to 4ft 3in at the front and 4ft 4in at the rear, and the wings and running boards grew a little wider, making the width 4ft 11in.

The lights on this 1979 car are the same as those on the 1976 model, but the reversing lamps either side of the number plate are now standard. A plain bumper has replaced the rear overriders; the two fog guard lights are later additions. The aluminium spacer on the spare wheel securing bracket allows the fitting of a luggage rack.

The 1983 model has smaller bore twin exhausts and the fog guard lamps are bolted through the back panel. From 1986, only one fog guard lamp was fitted to the bumper.

From 1977, these wings were replaced by wings of the same width and profile as the lightweight, but in steel. However, customers could specify an aluminium body, or individual aluminium panels; the scuttle and cowl were always steel, for strength and rigidity. Overall width was now 5ft 2in, track was 4ft 5in front and 4ft 6in rear, and length was 12ft 3in.

A final 1in increase in overall width, to 5ft 3in, occurred for the 1981 Motor show (but into production in early 1982) when the wings had to be widened to suit new alloy wheels of 15in diameter and 16^1/2in width.

BODY TRIM

The Plus 8 wears a 'wings' badge on its cowl of the same design as previous cars, but stating simply '+8'. On the back it has twin chrome filler caps leading to a single fuel tank; as these fillers sit in each top corner of the square sloping tonneau deck, there is no room for the familiar Morgan script.

These overriders appeared on 4/4s, Plus 4s and Plus 8s. The reversing light was also used by the 4/4.

The Plus 8 wings badge is not as deep a casting as the badge of the Plus 4.

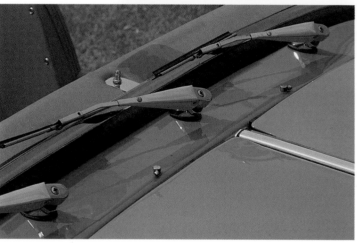

All Plus 8s had three windscreen wipers, as did the 4/4s from 1979. Up until 1989 the wipers pushed onto splines, then they were fastened with steel screws. Early screws rusted, so now they are stainless steel. Jeremy Harrison's car, in a one-off shade of mauve, has the latest tiny twin washer jets.

The Plus 8 has a single rubber strip with an aluminium surround on each running board, but more could always be specified at extra cost – it is quite common to see two. At the front is a plain chromed bumper with no overriders, while a pair of overriders is fitted at the back. A chromed rear bumper was offered as the usual optional extra. From 1977, the chrome bumpers were replaced with aluminium alloy, like those of the 4/4 but wider, and a rear bumper became standard.

A tubular, grey, plastic-coated luggage rack was also offered as an option. This fixes over the spare wheel via a chromed T-bar and an aluminium spacer through the wheel hub centre, together with fixing brackets to the lower bumper spring bracket bolts.

INTERIOR, INSTRUMENTS & CONTROLS

The cabin of the Plus 8 is wider and more spacious than that of the earlier cars.

However, the footwells lose space, first to the four-speed Rover gearbox and then again to the five-speed one.

For the first time, adjustable (fore and aft) bucket seats became standard equipment. Designed specially by Maurice Owen (calling on his racing experience), they were made by Restall. The standard covering is vinyl, although leather was offered as an option. Folding and reclining seats were also offered as an optional extra.

The doors always had the anti-burst door locks provided for other cars from 1971, and they were supported by sturdy steel hinges with three $1/4$in diameter machine screws through each hinge face. Door pockets were also provided; that is, a hole was cut in the casing board of the doors and the inside of the door skin was covered in matching trim, so that maps and sweeties actually sat within the door frame.

The dashboard is wood as before, with a vinyl covering. From 1971 the scuttle top also carried crash padding with matching covering. In a right-hand drive car, an open

This is a pre-1989 push-on wiper arm and the earlier solitary washer with twin jets in the head.

The bucket seats of the early Plus 8 are mainly vinyl, although leather trim was optional. The dash top is still plain painted metal.

The frames of these seats in a 1976 car are of the same design as those of the 1969 car, but these have the optional pleated leather trim. The top of the dash was padded for safety from 1971 .

This 1976 dashboard shares the same layout as the 1969 car, but the gear lever is now for a Rover 'box. The steering wheel is a non-standard Motolita one. Originally the wheel would have had a large rubber centre.

The early Astrali steering wheel has four holes in the spokes and a plain plastic dome in the centre – the small green disc beneath is the original Astrali label. A rev counter sits to the right of the wheel.

glovebox is provided on the left-hand side, while a recessed, elongated oval takes up most of the space between the glovebox and the steering wheel. The speedometer fits snugly into the left-hand curve of the oval, the quadrant into the right, and two rows of large black rocker switches lie between.

The four switches on the top row operate the screen wash, two-speed wipers, spotlamps and two-speed heater fan. The three switches on the bottom row operate the lights, hazard flashers and parking lamps. Three warning lights line up horizontally between the two rows of switches: an outer red light for the handbrake, a central large red light for the hazard flasher and a chromed bezel with a green arrow for the indicators. The other warning lights are of the small 'jewel' type and are in the speed-

ometer face: red for ignition and blue for headlamp main beam. A rev counter smaller than the quadrant and speedometer sits on the right-hand side of the steering wheel on right-hand drive cars. All the dials are white on black with thin black metal surrounds, and the oval recess is crackle black.

The ignition switch is on the steering column and incorporates a column lock. One stalk to the right of the column controls the indicators, headlamp flash and horn. A windscreen wiper motor sits on the bulkhead below the scuttle as before, but now operates three windscreen wipers, as demanded by US safety regulations.

In March 1973, at chassis number R7602, the old recirculating 'fug stirrer' was replaced by a fresh air heater. From 1974, wool/nylon mixture carpets became stan-

The dashboard was totally redesigned for 1977, with two large dials now ahead of the driver. The five rocker switches have integral warning lights, while more warning lights from the Jaguar XJ-S sit ahead of the wheel. The gear knob displays the change pattern of the Rover five-speed gearbox. The steering wheel spokes are no longer drilled. The rubber wheel centre has 'MORGAN' in capitals across the centre.

This 1989 dashboard is different in detail from the 1977 one. New Italian switches have larger panels for their integral warning lights, while the warning lights ahead of the steering wheel are separate rectangular lamps. The steering wheel centre now has a Morgan script beneath a clear plastic dome. The seats in this car are the optional folding and reclining seats, with thicker backrests. The handbrake light will be upside down on all cars produced before the day, in 1991, when the fitter learned that the lens motif is an exclamation mark and not, as he had always thought, a handbrake.

This car has the optional burr walnut dashboard with a lockable glovebox lid introduced in 1989. It also has one extra warning light, for failure of the lambda sensor on the optional catalytic converter. These seats are the standard buckets, with relatively thin backrests.

dard in the footwells and in loose strips beneath the seats, replacing flat fluted rubber.

From 1977, all models had a new fascia and instrument panel. The open glovebox sits to the extreme left of the dashboard as before. The rev counter sits to the right of the steering wheel and the speedometer to the left of it, with a single T-shaped stack of warning lights in between. In the centre of the dashboard is a recessed rectangle with rounded corners. Four small circular dials

along the top show (from left to right) fuel, water temperature, oil pressure and volts. Below these, five Lucas rocker switches – now internally lit – operate the lights, hazard warning flashers and other ancillary controls. In 1981, the loose strips of carpet beneath the seats gave way to a one-piece carpet each side, with the seats bolted directly through the carpet.

In 1986, the warning light cluster ahead of the steering wheel was changed to separate rectangular light units arranged in a T-

shape, with each lens pushing into the wooden dashboard by means of two rear lugs. The separate bulb to each lens is passed through a central hole behind each lens from the rear of the dashboard.

Instrument, switch, trim and dashboard details changed in line with the equivalent 4/4 models from the mid-1980s, as described in the 4/4 chapter. A walnut veneer dashboard with a lockable glovebox was offered as an optional extra from 1989.

The wheel used from 1968 to 1976 was rough cast alloy (left). The centre disc, in black with a raised silver circle, is secured by a steel clip which can rust badly and break; consequently these centre pieces are often missing.

These 14in alloy wheels (below) were produced by Milrace and used from 1977 to early 1982. The centre is like an upturned beaker made from polished aluminium. All the different Plus 8 wheels use the same wheel nuts.

WHEELS & TYRES

The biggest development cost in producing the Plus 8 was having the casting made for its alloy wheels! Wire wheels were never offered on production Plus 8s because the hubs were not considered strong enough – the prototype and the Traco Plus 8 are exceptions to this rule.

A single spare wheel is mounted in a recess in the tonneau deck by three nuts fixed to studs on a metal cradle. A scissor jack is provided, and can be fixed under any convenient part of the chassis or front frame.

The first wheels are of 15in diameter and 5.5in rim width, with a five-stud pattern. Each stud hole is lined with a push-in steel insert. The wheel nuts are a chromed steel elongated hexagon design with a neatly domed blind end. These wheels are made of magnesium alloy painted silver and the casting is very rough, usually with plenty of blow holes in the metal. The centre cap is a piece of round, black-painted steel with a silver circle standing slightly proud of the surface. This cap was clipped in and frequently fell out if the clip broke. The original car would have worn Dunlop SP Sport 185 VR 15 tyres as standard.

These specially cast magnesium alloy wheels have been used since 1982 and have the words 'Morgan Motor Company Ltd' in the casting. The wheel centre is chromed plastic and has the 'Morgan + 8' logo from the centre of a wings badge photo etched onto it.

This Lucas LR6 rear-mounted spotlight (left) is a halogen long-range, sealed-beam lamp. It was fitted from 1968 to 1974, but is difficult to find now. Plus 8 spotlamps could also be fitted to the 4/4 at extra cost.

with Uniroyals of the same size. The 3.9 Plus 8, introduced in June 1990, was fitted with Pirelli P600 tyres of the same size and speed rating.

LIGHTING

The Plus 8's headlamps are set into teardrop shaped nacelles protruding from the front inner wings. The headlights themselves are all by Lucas, with the exception of late 1981 to late 1983 cars, which used Cibié lights for certain markets. The Plus 8's lights are of the same size as the Plus 4's, but halogen headlamps became standard from 1977.

Two spotlamps, classed as long-range driving lights, are also standard equipment. These are 'rear-mounted Lucas LR6' lamps: that is, their mountings run through the front valance and are secured from behind the panel. Most of these lights carried the word 'Lucas' on a raised portion of the outer rim, although cars from 1975 and 1976 could have the Lucas 'Lion' motif on a red or green background instead. From 1977, these lights changed to Lumax units, although Marchal units were used for a short period in 1984–5.

Two small circular Lucas L691 flashers, with chromed metal surrounds, sit between the headlamps and spotlamps. The teardrop-shaped sidelights mounted on top of the wings are Lucas L516 to 1976, and Lucas 1130 thereafter.

The rear lights complete the bottom corners of a square formed with the twin filler caps around the spare wheel. Although they look similar to the light clusters on the Plus 4, they are completely different units – and bigger and bulkier. The large red stop light has an integral reflector and a chrome surround. Big Lucas flashers are bolted to the rear panel. The reversing lights, mounted either side of and into the number plate panel, were an optional extra until they became standard in 1983.

From October 1971, the rear lights are larger, from the Lucas L691 range. These

From October 1976, 14 × 6in Milrace wheels were adopted. These are alloy and look much like the previous Sports Lightweight wheels, but the squares have raised edges and they have proper wheel stud centres with inserts, enabling the standard Plus 8 wheel nuts to be used. The entire wheel was painted in silver. These wear 195 VR 14 or occasionally 205 VR 14 (post-1980) Dunlop sports tyres; Michelin XWXs were optional.

From the 1981 Motor Show, the wheels changed back to 15in diameter, 6½in wide alloys. These were produced using a far superior special casting, so they are smoother, of better quality, and have the Morgan name on them for the first time ever. They also have a push-in chrome plastic centre, with the Morgan script printed on a cross in the centre; post-1987 wheel centres are of the same appearance but are ½in shallower. These wheels wear low-profile Pirelli P6 205/60 VR 15 tyres. It should be noted that although the wheel diameter increased, the profile of the tyres went down, leaving the rolling radius about the same.

The 1986–88 cars have 205/60 VR 15 Avon tyres, but 1988–90 cars were fitted

The Lumax lamp was the third, and returned to be the fifth, type of foglamp used by the Plus 8. It was fitted as standard from 1977 to 1982 and from 1986 to the present, appearing occasionally in between. These are of poor quality and corrode quickly.

The Marchal lamp fitted from late 1982 to late 1985 is identified by the cat's head sticker in the centre.

This peculiar lamp (above), fitted to the rear wings of the Plus 8 from 1968 up to 1971, is like an upturned clog with a pronounced 'heel'. The flasher sits on the rear tonneau deck.

From 1971, the rear lamp and flasher (above) sit in torpedo-style plinths made of chromed plastic. The 'corned beef tin' plinth of the reflector is also plastic, but painted body colour. The torpedos were also painted body colour from 1987, and in 1989 new regulations caused the rear lamps and flashers to change places.

This Lucas sidelight (above) was used from the mid-1950s up to 1977. It sits on a rubber plinth on top of the front wing.

The front flasher (right) sits in a shaped rubber gasket to follow the curve of the front wing. It has been standard equipment since 1969.

lights and the flashers are mounted into torpedo-shaped plastic plinths, which were chromed until 1987 and painted body colour thereafter. The indicator light torpedos sit on the bottom corners of the tonneau deck, while the rear lights are on the wings – but these positions had to swop in 1989.

A rectangular reflector with a chromed surround was positioned below the torpedo on each rear wing, and mounted onto a small plastic plinth painted body colour. The chromed surround disappeared in 1990 in order for the reflector area to be increased. A pair of rear fog guard lamps was mounted through the lower portion of the rear tonneau deck panel from 1983 to 1986, after which just one lamp of this type was attached to the offside of the rear bumper.

A chromed Lucas L467 number plate lamp is mounted on a flat metal plinth fixed between the number plate panel and lower rear panel, in the centre above the number plate. From 1990, two of these lamps were used, but were positioned either side of the number plate. To accommodate this change, the reversing lights became smaller.

When the Plus 8 was launched, a far more complex electrical system had to be installed to deal with the likes of twin spotlamps, triple windscreen wipers and hazard warning lights demanded by American safety regula-

tions. The 12 volt Lucas battery sits under the rear wooden panel behind the seats, and the Plus 8 has an alternator rather than a dynamo for the first time ever in a Morgan.

With the SD1 engine in 1977 came another Morgan first: electronic ignition. From the introduction of the fuel injection models, there was also a Lucas electronic engine management system.

The fuse box (two boxes from 1982) is situated on the right-hand side of the bulkhead until 1989, when the system changed to 'Continental/European' type fuses set into a long box beneath the dashboard just forward of the heater. Also in 1989, a battery isolator system was introduced in case of fire, and for added security.

ENGINE

Again, the engine gives this model its name, the Plus being the 'oomph' on offer and the 8 referring to the eight cylinders arranged in a 90 degree V. Rover developed this lightweight engine with its light alloy block and cylinder heads for the 3500 and $3\frac{1}{2}$-litre P6, and the Plus 8 runs the engine in exactly the same tune.

Bore and stoke are 88.90mm × 71.12mm and the capacity is 3528cc. Someone at Morgan, incidentally, wrote 3532cc on

The pre-SD1 Rover V8 has a deliberate dent in the black air filter box (top right) to allow clearance for the bonnet hinge. At bottom left is the filter between the mechanical fuel pump and the HS6 carburettors. On the right are the pipes to the 'fug stirrer' heater.

The Girling 'Powerstop' brake servo (deleted from Motor Show 1981) is attached to a panel at the front of the tool box. Two relays are bolted to the toolbox (top left), and the fuse box sits on the bulkhead.

This view shows the 'bite' taken out of the front wing to make room for the alternator, and the swirl pot for the radiator above it. The bonnet catch is to the left of the alternator. The dent in the air filter can be seen clearly.

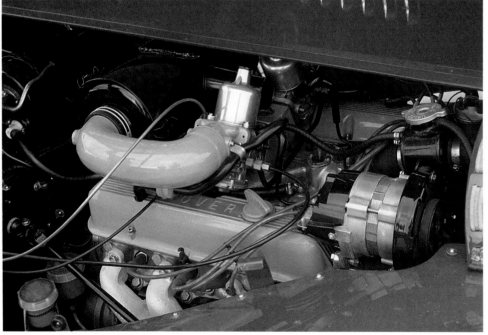

some certificates of newness, and this passed through onto some V5 registration documents. If your V5 says this, ignore it.

The light alloy block is combined with the crankcase and carries steel 'dry' cylinder liners. The cast iron crankshaft, carried in five main bearings, is fully counterweighted and balanced, and has a torsional vibration damper fitted to the nose. The cross-flow cylinder heads have individual inlet and exhaust ports, and part-spherical combustion chambers. The two valves per cylinder are inclined inwards towards the centre of the engine at 20 degrees. A single camshaft in the centre of the V is driven from the nose of the crankshaft by a chain and operates the valves by hydraulic tappets, pushrods and rockers. The compression ratio is 10.5:1. The pistons are also light alloy, with two compression rings and one oil scraper ring.

The twin carburettors are semi-downdraught constant-vacuum SU HS6s (1.75in). Their dashpots lean inwards as though whispering to each other over the top of the

The SD1 engine has squared-off rocker covers and a smaller air filter without a dent in the top, as the bonnet hinge already has good clearance (although in this case the top does appear to be dented!). From 1977, an electric fuel pump is mounted behind the spare wheel at the rear.

The SD1 engine still has a 'bite' out of the wing for the alternator, but the radiator no longer has a remote swirl pot. The black 'hot spot' trunking travels down the centre of the picture to pick up hot air from the exhaust manifold and carry it to the automatic choke. The HT leads have quite a journey from the distributor to the plugs.

engine. However, as they are mounted on the Land Rover manifold, there were never any humps in the bonnets of production V8s. The engine is lubricated through a wet sump system with a capacity of eight pints of oil, plus one pint for the new oil filter. The fuel tank holds 14 gallons and is mounted beneath the tonneau deck. The tank was supported on the chassis by two steel plates until 1986, when a thick wooden board was substituted because the metal plates had been known to corrode badly, leaving the tank poorly supported.

Getting this engine into the Morgan's engine bay was a tight squeeze and required certain modifications. For a start, the cylindrical air filter box was carefully reconstructed by putting a piece of wood on top of it and whacking it with a hammer, thereby making a trough just big enough to accommodate the central bonnet hinge. At least one reputable restoration company has been known to bash the dent out again painstakingly, only to find that the bonnet

The oil filler for the SD1 engined Plus 8 has a stand-up neck and an orange cap.

will not shut.

The inner wing has a recess to clear the alternator, with a corresponding curve in the outer wing. The resulting impression is that something with a big mouth must have taken a bite out of the side of the engine bay. The fan also had to be replaced (as described later), but somehow the full-width toolbox was retained against the bulkhead under the bonnet.

Rover claimed a power output of 160.5bhp (net), which became 151bhp (DIN) according to the new European standard. But perhaps more important was the torque peak of 210lb ft offered at 2750rpm. As five-star petrol was phased out and more emissions regulations loomed, the compression ratio was reduced to 9.35:1 in 1973 (from chassis number R7716) and the power went down to a mere 143bhp (DIN) at 5000rpm, with a maximum torque of 202lb ft at 2700rpm. The carburettors became SU type HI F6.

At the 1976 Motor Show, the first V8 was

replaced by the SD1 3500 engine, distinguishable immediately because the air filter box was smaller and did not require the previous bash-it-with-a-lump-of-wood surgery. This unit is very similar in design and identical in capacity, but it is more flexible and powerful, offering 155bhp (DIN). It keeps twin SU carburettors and has a compression ratio of 9.25:1. From the 1981 Motor Show (chassis number R9067), the carburettors were changed to Strombergs and an automatic choke was added.

At the end of 1983, Rover moved to fuel injection for the SD1 Vitesse, so Morgan built a fuel-injected prototype. This car had a 'clover leaf' shaped air vent cut out of the offside of the bonnet, but this was not carried into production. However, this engine has a large plenum chamber, so this time part of the hinge was cut away to accommodate it! The capacity of the fuel-injected engine remains the same, but it has re-profiled inlet ports for improved gas flow, plus a higher compression ratio of 9.75:1. It

offers 190bhp at 5280rpm and 220lb ft of torque at 4000rpm..

Autocar achieved a mean maximum speed of 122mph in fourth gear and a 0-60mph figure of 5.6sec in its Plus 8 road test of March 1987. As usual the new engines were first introduced at extra cost, the first production one being delivered to Mr John Donovan in June 1984. Most cars were fuel injected by 1986, and all were by 1987.

From June 1990, the Plus 8 received the 3946cc Range Rover engine with fully-mappable 'hot wire' fuel injection and a Land Rover air filter box, still wearing its Land Rover label. This engine's interior dimension are 94mm × 71.1mm, and it delivers 190.4bhp at 4750rpm and 219.6lb ft at 2600rpm.

Since this date, a three-way catalytic converter has also been offered as an option, promising to make Morgan truly a British Racing Green. However, at the time of writing in November 1991, the take-up has been slow. The compression ratio with the

On fuel-injected cars, the bonnet hinge itself has been cut away to clear the plenum chamber of the Rover Vitesse engine. The air flow meter is centre right. The manifolds were cast from 1968 to 1977, tubular from 1977 to 1986, and cast again (taken straight from the Land Rover) from 1986. The manifold comes in a rusty finish straight from Rover. . .

The rocker covers of the 3.5-litre engine are bare aluminium, but wear a Rover badge. The fuel rail with the injectors coming from it can be seen above the rocker cover, with the plenum chamber above. The standard air filter box (left) is now plastic.

'cat' is 9.35:1, the power remains at 190bhp at 4750rpm, but the torque goes up by 7 per cent to 235lb ft at only 2600rpm. Several changes are made to the fuel system with the addition of the 'cat'. A lambda sensor is connected with the engine management system to control the amount of fuel delivered to the engine, and non-evaporative fuel lines with special clips prevent pollution from fuel leakage and evaporation. The fuel tank capacity is reduced to 12 gallons.

Autocar & Motor gave the car an enthusiastic report on 15 May 1991, stating that if anything the car had more 'get up and go', because of all that torque at low revs, than the 3.5 V8 car they had previously tested. The magazine's testers achieved a mean maximum speed of 121mph and a 0–60mph time of 6.1sec although the writer recorded that the test car seemed to have a fuel delivery fault. In fact, Morgan had been supplied with a number of ECUs meant for Land Rovers, and these had a built in cut-out due to the unsuitability of Land Rover tyres for

With the bonnet completely removed, this 1983 car displays the head to head position of the Plus 8 carburettors, originally SU HS6s, but Strombergs from 1981. The sealed cooling system has an overflow bottle bolted to the bulkhead on the right. As this car has a Smiths heater, its toolbox stretches across only half the bulkhead.

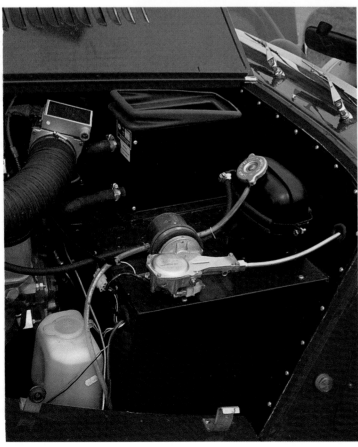

The 3.9-litre engine has a metal overflow bottle for the sealed cooling system; it is taken from a Land Rover and sits on top of the bulkhead. The air flow meter for the fuel injection can be seen to the left of the rubber-topped heater radiator air scoop. At the bottom left is a larger windscreen washer bottle.

speeds above 120mph! Despite this hitch, the test car's in-gear acceleration figures up to the speed limit were rather better than those for a Porsche 911 Turbo.

COOLING SYSTEM

The first engines had a tall radiator which left no room for a filler beneath the cowl, so a remote swirl pot was positioned between the radiator and inlet manifold. To get the engine to clear the Morgan's front cross-frame, the boss sticking out from the front of the water pump was machined off, a different pulley was put on and a Wood Jefferies electric fan fitted between the front cross-frame and the radiator. This fan is sensitised by an 'Otter' switch on the inlet manifold.

The radiator core increased in size at the same time as the new four-speed gearbox's introduction in 1972, because Plus 8s were overheating in hot climates. From 1976, the engine was moved further back and was given a larger capacity radiator with a direct filler neck, so the swirl pot was removed. The 'Otter' switch was also now positioned in the radiator header tank.

The 3.9-litre fuel injected engine has a larger cylindrical air filter box connected directly to the air flow meter. This one still has a tell-tale Land Rover sticker on the top. The wiring loom, direct from a Range Rover, is looped around and secured (left). The bonnet hinge is still cut away.

The air flow meter (below) can be seen at top right, at the rear of the air filter, and the trunking is more tightly curled than in the 3.5-litre car. This car, which had covered only 60 miles when the photograph was taken, still has packing material in the top of the heater air intake. The plenum chamber has '3.9' cast into the top.

EXHAUST SYSTEM

The exhaust system of the first 50 Plus 8s is a single pipe, but was to change frequently. In early cars two downpipes emerge from the cast manifolds and join, via a balance pipe at the back of the engine, to feed into the single exhaust pipe.

In 1971, the design of the manifold flange was changed, and the car went to a dual exhaust system. From this time, the down-pipes were joined by a balance pipe (with 'flexi' centre) around the front of the engine and run into two long, round silencers and straight-through tailpipes, which have 'flats' in them where they run behind the wheels.

From 1977, a four-branch tubular manifold on each side runs into twin downpipes with two silencers either side, the forward one being oval and the rear resonator box being round.

The exhaust remained unaltered when fuel injection was introduced. Then, in late 1986, the exhaust became a single system again, using three silencer boxes in line, Land Rover cast iron manifolds, and a twin tubular balance pipe arrangement around the front of the engine, feeding through the left-hand inner wing to a ball joint secured with twin springs (similar to bonnet catch

springs) to keep it taught yet flexible. The front and rear silencers are round with the central one being a long oval unit. This system makes no difference to the performance, but was designed to help the Plus 8 pass ever stricter noise regulations.

When fully-mappable fuel injection was introduced in 1990, the dual exhaust was

reintroduced for cars without a catalytic converter. There are two silencers on either side – the front ones are long oval units while the rear resonator boxes are round – and a single balance pipe going into link pipes, which exit via holes in the chassis sides. The cast iron manifolds are to the same design as the right-hand manifold of

The Moss gearbox lever (left) in the Plus 8 sits very close to the bottom of the dash. There is still a flap in the tunnel to allow the gearbox oil to be topped up.

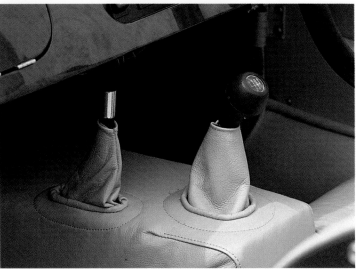

The gear lever from the Rover Vitesse 'box kinks towards the driver, while the handbrake sits ahead of it.

The Salisbury 7HA hypoid bevel rear axle (above) in Tim Ot's Plus 8 has a Powr-Lok limited slip differential produced for Morgan by Salisbury. The shock absorbers are still lever arms and a single 12 volt battery sits to one side. The hoops for the separate hood are stowed as before.

the previous model.

The three-way catalytic converter offered from 1990 uses an auto catalyst produced by the British specialists Johnson Matthey. Two dual-loop catalytic converters sit in the link pipes between the manifold and the oval centre box. This is, again, a 'single-side' system similar to the 1986-90 arrangement previously described.

TRANSMISSION

When Rover introduced the V8 to its own range, the engine was offered only with a Borg Warner automatic transmission. Since neither the Rover P5 3-litre nor the P6 Rover 2000 manual gearboxes were strong enough to deal with the V8's torque, the first 484 Plus 8s have the faithful Moss gearbox connected to the engine by torque tube.

In October 1971, Rover introduced an all-synchromesh four-speed manual gearbox for the 3500S saloon. From April 1972, Morgan customers were offered the same new gearbox, which was a distinct improvement on the imperfect synchromesh of the slow old Moss gearbox. The first car to have a Rover gearbox was chassis number R7475 – but thanks to the usual Morganesque peculiarities the last car to have a Moss gearbox was R7494.

The new gearbox was based on the design of the Rover 2000 unit, but it had a stiffer casing (incorporating a finned sump), an integral oil pump driven through the back of the layshaft, taper-roller layshaft bearings and shot-peened gear teeth. Its oil capacity is 3.75/2.1 litres and its ratios are: top, 1.000:1; third, 1.391:1; second, 2.133:1; first, 3.625:1; reverse, 3.43:1. It operated as before, with a single plate diaphragm spring clutch. However, as the Rover gearbox is mounted in unit with the engine, the torque tube was replaced by a remote linkage. As this gearbox is so wide, room in the footwells is reduced.

A total of 702 cars were produced with the four-speed gearbox, the last being chassis number R8186. Then another gear was added and some more foot space lost in October 1976 with the introduction of the five-speed gearbox, now produced by the merged BL/Rover group. The ratios are: top, 0.79:1; fourth 1.00:1; third, 1.39:1; second, 2.08:1; first, 3.32:1; reverse, 3.42:1.

Drive is transmitted through an open propellor shaft to the Salisbury 7HA hypoid bevel rear axle with a Powr-Lok limited slip differential, produced specially by Salisbury for Morgan. Like all LSDs, it needs special oil (Castrol B373 or equivalent) which should always be changed completely, never topped up. The final drive ratio changed from 3.73:1 in the Plus 4 to 3.58:1 at the introduction of the Plus 8, changing again in August 1973 (chassis R7659) to 3.31:1.

CHASSIS

The Plus 8's chassis has the familiar layout of the Plus 4, but it had to be substantially strengthened at the points where it meets the front crossframe. This was because of the engine's power rather than its weight; in fact the V8 weighed very little more than the Triumph four-cylinder engine it replaced, because it was made of aluminium instead of cast iron.

The track was widened from the Plus 4's 3ft 11in to 4ft 1in. Then, in late 1969, after the first few Plus 8s had been produced, the main side members of the chassis were set 2in further apart, although the track stayed at 4ft 1in. As Rubery Owen demanded £1500 for the retooling, Morgan decided to put in some extra length at the same time, increasing the wheelbase by 2in ahead of the scuttle. A few examples of the first 'narrow' Plus 8s exist, but the exhaust tailpipe rubs against the tyre during hard cornering!

The first Plus 8s also had a steel floor beneath the footwells. The idea was to add extra strength but the steel rotted badly, and some of these cars also suffered radial cracking around the engine mounts. So Morgan returned to wood in 1970, instead providing a triangular gusset plate in between the crossmembers and chassis by the bulkhead.

When the new four-speed Rover gearbox, mounted in unit with the engine, was introduced in 1972, the gearbox mounting rails had to be moved further

The front suspension on a modern Morgan is the same as it has always been. The bottom rebound spring (centre left) and the damper blade (centre) are seen clearly from this low angle. This car has a Gemmer steering box (top right).

apart. In August 1973 (chassis number R7659), the Z-section side members were spaced further apart, and the track was increased again from 4ft 1in to 4ft 3in at the front and 4ft 4in in the rear.

From the 1976 Motor Show, when the SD1 3500 engine and five-speed gearbox were introduced, the chassis was widened yet again by 2in, the gearbox mounting rails were moved further apart, and the bulkhead and crossmember were moved back, allowing the engine to be mounted further back to give more clearance and better weight distribution. By this stage, the track had grown to 4ft 5in at the front and 4ft 6in at the rear. The steering in cars from this time is very heavy.

Rubery Owen closed its chassis plant in the late 1970s, but Rockwell Thompson bought the tooling and took over the job of producing Morgan chassis immediately, with no delay in deliveries during the changeover. Rockwell Thompson refused to renew the contract for 1992 due to Morgan's requirement for a substantial price reduction, so production was moved to a small local Worcestershire specialist.

SUSPENSION

The Plus 8's front suspension is still Morgan's famous sliding pillar system. However, taking note of the experience of cracked stub axles in the SLR Morgans, the factory gave the Plus 8 much sturdier stub axles than those fitted to the Plus 4 or 4/4. The same Armstrong telescopic front and lever arm rear shock absorbers are used, but the top springs at the front are one coil shorter than the 4/4's and

a bit more chunky; the rebound springs are as for the Plus 4.

At the rear, the front anchorage points of the leaf springs were dropped by 2½in, so the springs lean forward by 7°. As standard, the springs on most cars have five leaves, but some cars have six as this became standard for a short time and was then offered as an option. A deeper dip in the frame side members, as they pass under the line of the axle, allows more rebound movement; the total axle movement is 4.5in.

STEERING

All Plus 8s have an extruded mesh AC Delco type collapsible steering column, which had to be carefully re-aligned to thread its way down through the crowded engine bay to the steering box. This was still the old cam and peg Cam Gears steering box. As the body and wheels became wider, the steering became progressively heavier, until this small car was almost impossible to park.

The standard steering wheel is an Astrali 15in wheel with three black alloy drilled spokes (with four round holes of decreasing size in each spoke) and a rim covering in leather or vinyl. At the Plus 8's launch, the centre of the wheel was a plain hard plastic button, but in 1971 it changed to a large, soft rubber, push-in centre pad with the word 'Morgan' embossed boldly across the centre. From 1977, the steering wheel is supported on three alloy black spokes without holes. The steering is geared at 3.25 turns lock to lock.

In 1983, it looked as though Cam Gears were about to go out of business, so Jack

Knight was approached to supply a rack and pinion system for the Plus 8. This great improvement was offered first as an optional extra in 1984, costing £1100, but became standard in August 1986 unless a customer was crazy enough to specify otherwise.

In 1986, a sporty little 14in steering wheel was introduced as an option – this requires 3.5 turns lock to lock. The wheel boss changed to a more collapsible type in 1987: the centre pad after this date has a black plastic surround housing a plastic centre badge, featuring red Morgan script on a black background.

BRAKING

The Plus 8's thunderous performance required much better stopping power than ever before. So dual circuit Girling brakes were fitted, using 11.0in diameter discs at the front and 9.0in × 1.75in drums at the rear.

A single Girling 'Powerstop' brake servo – or two servos on certain export cars – was mounted on the bulkhead in front of the toolbox, but deleted after the 1981 Motor Show. The handbrake, working on the rear drums, is a fly-off type, operated by a vertical lever mounted on the passenger side of the transmission tunnel.

PLUS 8 DHC AUTOMATIC

This unique car, chassis number R7317, registered JM 53, was built in 1971 for Mrs Jane Morgan, mother of Charles. A drophead coupé, it has rearward hinged doors, the earlier specification engine and automatic transmission from the Rover 3500 of the time. It is the *only* Morgan automatic ever built at the factory. Mrs Morgan still has the car, although the colour has been changed from its original dark green to metallic blue, and 14in wheels have replaced the early 15in ones.

PLUS 8 SPORTS LIGHTWEIGHT

This limited edition special was introduced at the Earls Court Motor Show in 1975. Although mechanically similar to the contemporary Plus 8, it has a light gauge (18g) aluminium body, and both the body and wings are the 5ft 2in width of the later five-speed car. As a result the chrome bumpers are 4in too narrow for the car! The rear bumper was an optional extra, standard equipment being a pair of overriders.

The sporty wheels are Millrace alloys of 14in diameter and 6in width, decorated with oval slots. They are painted black, but the rim and slots are outlined in silver. The wheel cap is a spun aluminium conical tube like an upturned beaker. The wheel nuts are blind tubular and tube-threaded with a separate washer, like an AC Cobra wheel nut.

Only 19 Sports Lightweight models were made from late 1975 to early 1977. One of them, chassis number R8111, was left-hand drive – and this also happened to be the last four-speed Rover Plus 8 to be made.

TRACO PLUS 8

The most extraordinary Sports Lightweight is the Traco Plus 8, registered OTN 4, with which Derek Day and John McDonald hoped to enter Le Mans in 1976, aiming for the Thermal Efficiency award.

This fearsome beast is powered by a 3.5-litre Traco Oldsmobile V8 with quadruple Weber 48IDA carburettors, driving through a Triumph TR8 rally gearbox to a conventional rear differential. The engine has a special split manifold which requires two large bonnet cut-outs, straddled by a separate scoop which is secured by Dzus fasteners and covers the carburettor trumpets. As the scoop fits over the bonnet hinge, it has to be removed before the bonnet can be opened!

The Traco is the widest Morgan ever built, and wears centre-laced, 72-spoke wire wheels, 7in wide at the front and 9in wide at the rear. Their hubs were made specially by Rudge Whitworth and have triple-eared chrome spinners.

Just to add the final racing touch, this car dispenses with bumpers and gains an upturned trials number plate and a full roll bar. Built in 1976, the Traco Plus 8 left the factory with a coat of black paint, a red leather interior, and black weather equipment piped in red.

In an echo of Le Mans in 1961, when Chris Lawrence's car, 'TOK', was refused entry, the French changed the formula for the Thermal Efficiency award – so the Traco had no hope. It languished, and got knocked about for years, until John Worrall bought it in 1987. It now belongs to Leif Barryd in Sweden, and enthusiasts may get the chance to feel the ground shake once again as it rumbles past at European Morgan events.

Production Data

PRODUCTION FIGURES & CHASSIS NUMBERS

Production figures for the Plus 8, manufactured 1968 to date, are as follows:

Moss four-speed gearbox (1968-72)	484
Rover four-speed gearbox (1972-77)	702
Rover five-speed gearbox (1977 to date)	2320
Total (to June 1991)	**3506**

Among individual cars worthy of mention are the three works prototypes, numbered R7000, R7001 and R7002. The Plus 8 drophead coupé made for Peter Morgan's wife was R7317. The 19 Sports Lightweight Plus 8s have these chassis numbers: R7983, R8035, R8044, R8050, R8052, R8059, R8066, R8069, R8094, R8102, R8103, R8104, R8111 (the only left-hand drive model), R8124, R8125, R8138, R8140, R8170 and R8186 (the last four-speed Plus 8). R8186 has added interest: it was first owned by Jack Brabham's brother, based in Jersey, and was distinguished by its chromed cowl. The car has a different owner and its cowl has now been painted, but it still lives in Jersey.

Plus 8s with the Rover four-speed gearbox, built from May 1972 to January 1977, fall in these chassis number ranges: R7475, R7478, R7482-7485, R7487-7488, R7490-7491 and R7495-8151.

PRODUCTION CHANGES

1968 (Oct)
Plus 8 launched at Motor Show.

1969
Z-section chassis rails moved 2in further apart.

1970
Metal floor of footwells replaced by wood, with a triangular gusset plate between the cross-members and chassis, by the bulkhead on either side.

1971
Scuttle top given crash padding with covering to match interior. Centre of steering wheel changes from plain hard plastic to soft rubber embossed with Morgan script.

1971 (Oct)
Rear lights enlarged (Lucas L691), and these and flashers set in chromed plastic torpedo plinths. Wheels change to 15in x 6½in alloys, with better quality casting. Dual exhaust introduced.

1972 (Apr)
Rover four-speed gearbox introduced at R7475. Gearbox mounting rails moved further apart. Radiator increases in size. Last Moss gearbox in R7494.

1973 (Mar)
Recirculating 'fug stirrer' heater replaced by fresh air heater at R7602.

1973 (Aug)
Wide track cars with 3.31:1 rear axle phased in, wings and running boards widened. At R7716: compression ratio to 9.35 to 1, carburettors become HI F6, power reduced to 143bhp at 5000rpm, torque to 202lb ft at 2700rpm.

1974
Wool/nylon mix carpets become standard.

1976 (Oct)
SD1 3500 V8 introduced, with compression ratio of 9.25 to 1 and 155bhp. Five-speed gearbox introduced at R8151. Z-section chassis rails set 2in wider apart, gearbox mounting rails also moved further apart (lengthways) and cross-member moved back. Engine moved further back and given deeper radiator without swirl pot. Revised exhaust has four-branch manifold on each side running into twin downpipes with two silencers either side. Track becomes 4ft 4in (front) and 4ft 5in (rear).

1977
Wings now of same width and profile as Plus 8 Sports Lightweight. Chrome bumpers and over-riders become aluminium and rear bumper becomes standard. 14in x 6in Milrace wheels

introduced. Front spotlamps became Lumax, sidelights change from Lucus L516 to Lucas 1130; halogen headlamps now standard. New fascia and instrument panel. R8186 is last Rover four-speed car (R8187-R8199 never used).

1981 (Oct)
Stromberg carburettors and auto choke introduced at R9067. Servo deleted. Loose strips of carpet give way to one-piece carpet either side. Seats bolted directly through carpet.

1982 (Feb)
At R9067, 15in wheels and low profile tyres reintroduced (Pirelli P6 205/60 15). Two fuse-boxes replace single box.

1983 (Oct)
Fuel-injected SD1 Vitesse engine announced as option (first delivery in June 1984) compression ratio 9.75 to 1, 190bhp at 5280rpm, 220lb ft of torque at 4000rpm. Reversing light becomes standard. Twin rear fog guard lamps mounted through lower portion of rear tonneau deck. Rack and pinion steering introduced as option.

1986 (Oct)
Single exhaust system with three silencer boxes and Land Rover cast iron manifold. 14in steering wheel optional.

1986
Wood frame now dipped in Cuprinol and chassis painted. Body panels sprayed separately before assembly. Avon 205/60 VR 15 Turbospeed tyres adopted. Single fog guard lamp attaches to offside of rear bumper (replaces two mounted on tonneau deck). Thick wood board replaces metal plates supporting fuel tank.

1987
Fuel injection becomes standard. Steering wheel boss changes to more collapsible type; centre pad now has black plastic surround housing plastic centre badge with red Morgan script on black background. Rear· light torpedos painted body colour.

1988
Wheel centres ½in shallower. Tyres become Uniroyal 205/60 VR 15.

1989
Battery isolator switch set on heelboard between the seats. Walnut veneer dashboard with lockable glovebox offered as an option. Rear lights and flashers change places. Continental/European style fuses set in long box under dashboard.

1990 (Jun)
Range Rover 3946cc V8 with fully mappable hot wire fuel injection introduced. Dual exhaust with two silencers each side, single balancer pipe and cast iron manifold. Catalytic converter offered as a no-cost option. Pirelli P600 tyres

adopted. Two chromed Lucas L467 number plate lights mounted on each side of number plate. Reversing lights become smaller.

1991 (Feb)
Rear suspension changes to telescopic dampers for the first time ever on a standard Morgan. A round cross-tube is now affixed across the rear part of the chassis, forward of the axle. Bolting through the chassis side members, this carries the top fixings of the Gabriel telescopic dampers, which are anchored at their lower points to triangular plates welded onto the outboard section of the underside of the axle casing, just inboard of the rear wheels.

DIMENSIONS

From Oct 1968
Wheelbase, 8ft 2in
Front track, 4ft 1in
Rear track, 4ft 3in
Overall length, 12ft 8in
Width, 4ft 9in
Height, 4ft 2in
Ground clearance, 6in
Turning circle, 40ft
Unladen weight, 1900lb

From Aug 1973 (R7659)
Front track, 4ft 3in
Rear track, 4ft 4in
Overall width, 4ft 11in
Unladen weight, 1884lb

From Sep 1976 (R8200)
Wheelbase, 8ft 2in
Front track, 4ft 5in
Rear track, 4ft 6in
Overall length, 13ft 0in
Overall width, 5ft 2in
Height, 4ft 0in
Ground clearance, 5.5in
Turning circle, 38ft
Unladen weight, 2068lb

From early 1982
Overall width, 5ft 3in

From Feb 1991
Unladen weight, 2059lb

COLOURS

Connaught Green
Rosso Red
Indigo Blue
Black
Royal Ivory

Any other colours were, and continue to be, available at extra cost. Black, red or cream wing beading can be specified.

Restoration

A Morgan may be simply constructed, but it is quite fiendish to maintain and restore. If you are thinking of buying one, it is vital to consider whether or not you want to face a full restoration – because it is not practical only to do 'some restoration' on a classic Morgan. Once you have disturbed the rot and the rust, 'some restoration' can only mean a 'bodged' job.

That said, Morgans have one major advantage over other classic cars – the factory is still in existence. It still makes the cars in just the same way, still uses many of the same agents, and still produces batches of old-style parts.

Now, as always, each car produced has a ticket listing the customer's individual specifications. As each car is tested, given a chassis number and driven away, its details are entered in a ledger and kept. No matter where you find your car, or what state it is in, you can call the factory and look up exactly what equipment, what engine and even what paint it originally had – if you have the chassis number.

CHASSIS

Until 1986, the steel chassis of a Morgan had no protection at all from the weather. If the chassis has not been replaced it is bound to be rusty – or *very* rusty on an older model. In particular, you should look for rust in the side members, around the holes which support engine mounting brackets, and at the junctions where the cross-members meet the main Z-section side members. Check also for cracking where the front cross tubes pass through the main structure.

The simplest way to check for rust in the chassis is to tap along it with a screwdriver. A different note, or a dull thunk, indicates rust, or a place where a plate has been welded on. A 'patch' repair is not ideal; it is far better to replace a whole chassis member than to plate an existing length. As you can order a new length or a whole new chassis from the factory, there is no excuse for not doing the work properly. It is advisable to have the front cross frame jigged in by the factory to make sure it is square and properly fitted.

Nowadays a chassis is powder-coated, or galvanised as an option, but even this is not ideal. Galvanising is basically a plating process; when the Morgan chassis flexes, as it was designed to do, the plating will eventually crack. In addition, holes are drilled in a chassis as soon as it has been galvanised, negating the whole process.

A more durable solution is to have a chassis shot-blasted and metallised. In this process, aluminium or zinc wire is heated until it is molten, passed through an atomising head and sprayed onto the receiving metal, so the spray of tiny particles seizes to the metal to form a dense corrosion-resistant coating. This process is more usually seen on exhaust manifolds and the finish is quite rough, so it will need some rubbing down. If you want to use your car every day, it is best to rub down the chassis a little and have it epoxy powder coated. But if you are aiming for concours standard, it can be flatted down and sprayed with black enamel for a really smooth finish. Painting the chassis with Hammerite is definitely out.

This Plus 8 chassis (left) has had its front cross frame jigged in by the factory (top). Note that a Morgan chassis has no 'kick up' at the back as it runs beneath the back axle.

The finish is brittle, and it 'pinholes', so moisture can still get through, particularly if you do not use primer.

To try to protect the chassis a little further, it is a good idea to drill a couple of holes in each of the cross-members and fill them with Waxoyl. Some people also put Waxoyl under the wings, but this leaves a sticky finish which attracts dirt. And, of course, if you do any work on the car you get covered in it! A stone chip paint applied beneath the wings will be just as good.

ASH FRAME

The condition of the ash frame depends upon how a car has been used and where it has been kept. If it has been subjected to water and not dried off properly, it will certainly be rotten by the time it is 10 years old.

Rot is easy to spot if you can see the wood. If the end of a section looks 'nibbled', or if you can press your fingernail into the wood, then it is rotten. But most of the wood is covered by trim or panels; if you are looking at a car to buy, the owner will not be keen to start taking it apart.

The worst areas for rot are those where water penetrates, that is around the base of the wheel arches, along the sill boards and around the doors. If you open a door and lift it up, watch the hinge pillar: if it tries to twist or move with the door, the wood behind it is rotten. If a sill board is rotten it may start bending and distort the body, so beware if the doors are difficult to shut; if

A new ash frame and bulkhead fitted to a Plus 8 chassis. The darker areas of timber are those which have already been treated with preservative.

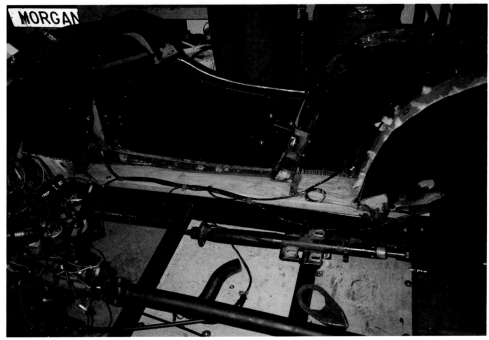

A new sill board fitted. The door rocker on this car, adjoining the sill board, was, unusually, still sound.

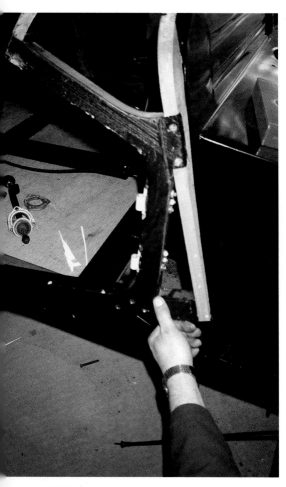

The thumb points to the front end of the door rocker where it joins the scuttle down board – both liable to be rotten on older cars.

the sill board is sound, the chassis could be cracked.

If there is any sort of rot in a piece of wood, that whole section must be replaced. Cutting out and replacing a lump will not help, as the rot will still be there, working its way along the older wood. The timber itself is cheap to buy, and can be bought in cut sections, but fitting it means the time consuming and costly business of taking the car to pieces.

If you do need a part or whole new body frame, there are several suppliers, but it is vital to get one made up to the right pattern as the profile of the car has changed substantially over the years. The factory can provide one, but with a wait up to one or two years. One company which can be recommended is Black Phey, near Bishops Stortford, whose proprietor, Vic Champness, has patterns for all four-wheeled Morgans. His body frames are of very good quality, although you should therefore expect to pay a realistic price for them.

Any new wood should be soaked in Cuprinol. A good method is to brush it on until the wood will not take any more, and then leave it to dry for two to three weeks. Once it has dried, a coat of yacht paint will finish the job. After all, a layer which is good enough to withstand the sea ought to be good enough for a Morgan.

In between the wood and the panels is a damp course of felt, but water can still seep down through the holes around the fastenings. Nowadays the Morgan factory also applies a layer of mastik which will squeeze right up to the nuts and bolts.

BODY

The steel body rusts with the same vigour with which the wood rots. In fact, one of the major causes of rust on older cars was the way the steel panels were simply tacked onto the wood with steel pins. The wood would absorb water and retain it, allowing the pins to rust and transmit the corrosion back into the body work. Check the side panels under the doors, the door skins, the base of the scuttle, the bottom edges of all body panels, the rear tonneau deck and the junctions between the headlamp pods and front wings.

Another classic rust spot is the tool box, which collects rainwater seeping in beneath the back of the bonnet. Once the tool box itself has rusted, water can penetrate beneath it to rust out the back of the bulkhead. During restoration, the bulkhead is one area which should be saved, if possible, by welding in a new section, as it is so difficult to fit a new one. The inner wings (valances) are also prone to rust caused by water getting in under the bonnet. However, there is no strict pattern of corrosion and you will only find out the extent of sound metal when you remove the paint.

Sandblasting will ripple body panels, so it is advisable to take the bonnet, cowl and wings to a metal reclamation specialist and have them dipped in caustic vats. This does not cause any damage, but takes off all the paint, corrosion and filler. Unfortunately, what comes out may sometimes resemble a lace doily, but if that is the state of your car it is better to know. The rest of the paint

The new metal welded into the bulkhead of this 1978 four-seater shows where severe corrosion can be expected on all Morgans with metal bulkheads and valances. Also vulnerable is the lower part of the scuttle, known as the 'fishtail', in front of the door.

must be scraped off carefully with Nitromors, using gloves and goggles for safety, and plenty of patience.

If you need new panels or even an entirely new body, you can buy them in steel or aluminium. Some people prefer aluminium because it is lighter and does not rust, but it creates other problems. It cracks and flexes, and stones thrown up beneath the wings can cause dents which show right through as a 'starring' effect. The wings are held in shape and strengthened by a flange rolled around steel wire, so electrolysis between steel and aluminium can cause bubbling and corrosion; as the steel wire is unprotected, it also rusts badly. However, if your car originally had aluminium wings then, for authenticity's sake, it should retain them. Glass-fibre wings are a good idea if you want to go circuit racing as they are light and easy to replace if you have a crunch, but these should be replaced with metal if you decide to sell.

PAINT

The first four-wheeled Morgans (and all three-wheelers) were brush painted, and will require a trip to a coach painter for total authenticity. However, most Morgans were sprayed and, unfortunately, painted in one piece up to 1986. So, as the car flexes, the line of paint between the body and the wing cracks, allowing water to feast on metal surfaces which never saw the paint gun. If you are unlucky this could mean taking a wing off and finding nothing but a saw tooth edge

of rust hidden behind the body.

Nowadays the factory sprays all the panels separately, and this is the only sensible way to rebuild a car, regardless of originality. The only visible difference when the car is finished is that the plastic piping between the panels will have been sprayed over. Nowadays Morgan uses plastic piping in black, ivory or red, but most restorers use Everflex, a piping specially made up from ICI vinyl wrapped around waterproof Neoprene cord. Of much better quality, Everflex is available in a wide range of colours. Another benefit of Everflex is that it has two flaps on the 'tail', so when you tack the piping into the body frame, you can insert the tacks just through the lower half and then cover the heads with the second flap so they do not dig into the wing.

Post-war models up to 1986 would have been painted in ICI cellulose. From October 1986, the paint was ICI 2K two-pack acrylic, which does not crack as easily as cellulose. However, if you want to restore a car to show condition, cellulose will give you a much better finish – and you can use it easily at home, without breathing equipment.

It is a good idea to use a high-build, surface-etch primer, which is important as most Morgans will have some aluminium on them, and it is vital to etch the metal. This will also fill any tiny surface imperfections. Some filler or lead loading will still be required for larger marks. Morgans used to emerge from the factory with plenty of filler on the front wings, so over the years it cracks and begins to lift off, particularly

around the headlamps.

The easiest way to spray a Morgan is to hang up the bonnet and wings so you can apply paint along the bottom edges. It is best to hang the wings with the short edge at the top and spray them 'uphill'. The bonnet is quite a task because of the louvres, which must be masked up to stop the paint dribbling through. It is advisable to spray the inside of the bonnet first, so any runs that come through can be taken off before you paint the top.

NUTS & BOLTS

Half the problem with working on any car is struggling with rusty nuts and bolts, so you can save yourself a great deal of work in the future by replacing them all with stainless steel as you go along. Matching nuts and bolts can also be a problem, but Heart of England Morgans offers around 70 different kits for different jobs, both directly to the public and to other specialists. For anyone concerned about the tensile strength of stainless steel, forged stainless steel has a higher tensile strength than mild steel, particularly rusty steel . . .

UPHOLSTERY

The best advice for anyone considering a retrim is simple: go to a trimmer! Every Morgan is individual, so you cannot buy a trim kit. You can buy a hood and tonneau, but it will lack fasteners because every one will fasten on differently.

The factory will do the work, but there is a long waiting list. Other specialists include Harpers in Hertfordshire, Melvyn Rutter and Brands Hatch Morgans, while most Morgan agents and specialists will have a trimmer. The ideal material is dyed hide; three hides should cover a two-seater, or perhaps five for a four-seater.

Weather equipment consists of two or four separate side screens according to model, a hood with a separate frame, a full tonneau cover (top right) for a two-seater roadster, or a hood cover (top left) for a four-seater. The standard colour has always been black, but other colours could be specified at extra cost.

ENGINES

Morgans have been through many engines over the years, and the availability of parts depends on whether these engines were ever used in other cars. But keeping the original engine is vital to the value of the car.

Parts for Coventry Climax and Standard Special engines (the latter basically a Standard Ten engine block with an overhead-valve head made for the Series I 4/4) are extremely difficult to find. The Morgan Sports Car Club has some, but a whole engine really would be elusive.

Throughout the 1960s, Morgans used Ford or Triumph running gear. Because of the number of Triumph cars and specialists around, a lot of the parts for these engines are easily available and the spares back-up is very good. Parts are becoming difficult for all the Ford engines used by the Series II to V cars, which have frequently, and sadly, been converted to 1600s in the 1970s anyway. The Ford Sidevalve Owners' Club may be able to help with some parts, and exchange 1172cc sidevalve engines are available from Belcher Engineering of Bury St Edmunds. Some of the Series II engines had bolt-on tuning accessories and this will increase the value of the car slightly, but finding parts would be tricky.

From 1969 onwards, engines are from Ford, Fiat or Rover. Parts for the Ford engines from this time are plentiful. The 2-litre Fiat engine is a problem as it was never fitted in any Fiat car in this country. Rover has a poor record for spares back-up. The company destroyed castings for many old parts and to get a casting made up is extremely expensive.

Plus 8s from 1969-76 (about 1100 cars) had the Rover 3500S manual engine and, remarkably, some parts peculiar to this engine are almost unobtainable, including the cast exhaust manifold. The only other car to share this engine is the Rover P6. A Morgan would be worth more than a Rover, but there is quite an active following for the P6 who might disagree! Even the cars produced after 1976 are not in a rosy position, as the SD1 V8 is now only produced by Land Rover. The engine fitted in the current Land Rover and Range Rover is different again from the V8 used in 1982-3. The person who buys a 1960s Plus 4 with the Triumph engine is possibly in a better position than someone with an early Plus 8.

On the other side of the coin, the Rover V8 engine and the TR engine are extremely strong. A Plus 8 engine will run to 100,000 miles in most cases if it has been well maintained. Ford engines may not have the same lifespan but are inexpensive to replace.

GEARBOXES

Gearboxes cause the most severe problems when it comes to finding spares for Morgans, but people with Ford running gear can breath a sigh of relief. The parts are available and the company has a reputation for sympathy with the old car movement in general.

Things are not so simple for Triumph and Rover engined cars. Parts for the old Meadows and Moss gearboxes are totally unobtainable, so they would need to be specially made – but there are specialists who will do the job. Luckily Moss also made gearboxes for early Jaguars; although their parts are not interchangeable, this does at least mean that expertise exists about this gearbox. A legendary figure called Norton Gabb (known as 'Harry' Gabb), who worked for Moss, carried on rebuilding the gearboxes for many years after Moss went out of business. When he died in the 1980s a specialist called John Smith in Colchester bought his tools to carry on the work. Again, you must be willing to pay a realistic price for such rare skills.

The first Plus 8s had a Moss gearbox, but from 1972 this model acquired the Rover 3500S's four-speed gearbox, for which parts are not available. From 1977, the SD1 engine was fitted with its own five-speed 'box, for which parts are already becoming scarce. When Morgan went to fuel injection in 1985 they introduced the Vitesse 'box, which is different again; none of its internals are interchangeable with the SD1 'box and parts are also becoming difficult to obtain. The 2-litre Fiat owner can also be faced with real problems as this car's gearbox is simply not available.

That said, all the different gearboxes used by Morgan over the years are good, strong units which do not tend to fall apart. The best answer is to treat them with respect, and change the transmission oil every 2000-3000 miles, certainly on the Moss gearbox. If a car is not used, still change the oil every year. Rover used to recommend using automatic transmission fluid, even in manual 'boxes. The Moss 'boxes take a hypoid gear oil, but Molyslip is quite acceptable.

STEERING

The early steering column (this one is from a Series V 4/4) is a solid shaft from the Burman Douglas box at the lower front of the car up to the steering wheel (in this case the standard pre-1969 factory item). On the left is the later steering box with the split column.

Until 1985, Morgan steering was by various methods of cam and peg with a Burman steering box (the very early ones were from a German milk float). These boxes wear out, they are difficult to adjust, and the play, which is always there, becomes worse. Finding someone who can rebuild them is also virtually impossible.

Luckily for Morgan owners, Burman stopped making the steering box in 1985. The Plus 8 gained a superb rack and pinion system, while the other models went to a French steering box by Gemmer, which is similar to the Burman in design but of much better quality. Since the Gemmer box will bolt straight on, a number of owners have changed over from the Burman box, in particular those with Plus 8s from the early 1980s. As the wheels of the Plus 8 widened over the years, the car became heavier to steer; the Gemmer box makes life easier because it is lighter and self-centring. Changing the steering box has now become accepted, so this modification will not detract from the value of a car.

Whatever the steering box, the steering track rod ends will have grease nipples and will wear and rust if they are not greased. A sign that the track rods ends are running dry is that the steering becomes heavier than usual.

REAR AXLE

Morgan 4/4s from Series I to Series V have a Salisbury (now GKN) rear axle. Parts are not available, but the axle can be rebuilt by GKN or an axle specialist. Plus 4s also have Salisbury rear axles, but problems do not arise because the axle from a current Plus 4 is the same width and the ratios are correct.

Plus 8s raise more problems because of their special limited slip differentials. Salisbury will rebuild one of these axles, but can only put modern internals in the old axle casing because modern casings have changed from imperial to metric. If you are shopping for a Plus 8, listen carefully for any signs of trouble. If the axle whines badly, it probably needs a rebuild. If it clonks, then it may just be that the UJs and 'U' bolts need tightening. If the diff is beginning to wear, the car will pull to one side (although you should check this is not being caused by worn or uneven tyres). Check also for leaks around the casing.

Careful maintenance will help you to avoid problems. The proper limited slip diff oil is Castrol B373 and it must be changed every 4000-5000 miles; never simply top up the level as the used oil will contaminate the new.

SUSPENSION

Engines may come and go or the number of wheels may vary, but the Morgan's unique sliding pillar front suspension has hardly changed since 1911.

The suspension consists of long steel kingpins sliding through two phosphor-bronze bushes. To keep it working well, it needs to be regularly and properly lubricated. From 1950, an oil button was provided on the top of the transmission tunnel, allowing oil from the engine to dribble down the kingpin. This is better than no lubrication at all, but this oil will have been contaminated by hydrocarbons, which have an adverse effect on phosphor-bronze. The brake discs are also just behind the kingpin and can pick up oil if you use the oil button too much!

Bushes will last longer if you are willing to crawl under the car with a grease gun every couple of weeks and lubricate the front suspension with a clean molybdenum disulphide-based grease like Castrol MS3. The bushes will eventually wear with the constant friction of moving up and down, the increased play in the front wheels causing the car to waver in a straight line and clunk over pot holes. They will need to be changed every 15,000-25,000 miles using one of the suspension kits available.

When assessing a car to buy, you should check for breakage of the cross-tube lugs at the bottom of the suspension pillar mounts.

Look also for sagging leaf springs, sometimes with broken leaves in the rear. The front and rear damper settings are so firm that some people convert to telescopic rear dampers. This helps axle control, but is not original.

CONCLUSION

Apart from the problems already listed, make sure an early Morgan has all its instruments. Broken instruments can be reconditioned, but missing ones are almost impossible to replace. Brightwork can also be a difficulty as it becomes pitted and corrodes, and some Mazak fittings are too delicate to be re-chromed. Others, such as the 'Flying M', tend to break, and are quite irreplaceable. However, some brass-based fittings are available from the factory.

The first rule for any rebuild is that it will end up costing twice as much and taking twice as long as you expected. If you are not prepared to contemplate this, don't start.

The front suspension never changed after the 'rubber snubber' was replaced by a small rebound spring in 1937. The damper blade and its fittings can be seen clearly reaching diagonally across the left of the picture.

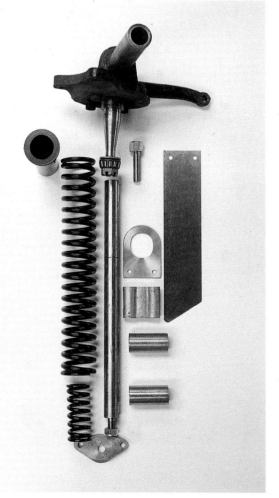

Front suspension components. The stub axle (top) has one bronze bush in place. The king pin (centre) runs through this bush and a second at its top end, and the bushes must be reamed to fit exactly Below the king pin is the king pin base plate. The rebound spring is bottom left and above it is the top spring, with its small dust cover (top left). To the right of the king pin are, from top to bottom: the king pin 'lube' bolt, which fits through the front of the crossframe into the top of the king pin and carries lubricating oil from the 'one-shot' system; the damper bronze, which swivels around the king pin between the top and rebound springs; the aluminium block which fixes between the damper blade to the damper bronze; and two new phosphor bronze bushes. The damper blade is far right.

SPECIALISTS

Morgan Motor Company Ltd, Pickersleigh Road, Malvern Link, Worcs WR14 2LL. Tel: 0684 573104. Fax: 0684 892295.

Black Phey Ltd, Raleigh Cottage, · The Street, Takeley, Bishops Stortford, Herts CM22 6QS. Tel: 0279 870698.

Harpers, The Bothy, Essex Lane, Hunton Bridge, Kings Langley, Herts WD4 8PN. Tel: 0923 260299. Fax: 0923 264813.

Heart of England Morgans, 250 Ikon Estate, Droitwich Road, Hartlebury, Worcs DY10 4EU. Tel: 0299 250141 or 250025. Fax: 0299 250012.

Melvyn Rutter Ltd, The Morgan Garage, Little Hallingbury, Bishops Stortford, Herts CM22 7RA. Tel: 0279 725725. Fax: 0279 726901.

Brands Hatch Morgans, Brands Hatch Circuit, Fawkham, Dartford, Kent DA3 8NG. Tel: 0474 874147. Fax: 0474 879727.

Holden Vintage & Classic Ltd, Unit 43B, Hartlebury Trading Estate, Kidderminster, Worcs DY10 4JB Tel: 0299 251353. Fax: 0299 251359.

Libra Motive, 2 Rosemont Road, Hampstead, London NW3 6NE. Tel: 071-435 8159 or 794 7009. Fax: 071-435 6044.

ACCESSORIES

Morgan's policy on accessories has always been that the customer can have whatever he or she wants, so long as (a) it is practical to fit, (b) he or she is willing to pay for it and (c) that it is legal!

Certain 'standard' options have always been offered. Different steering wheels and wire wheels are good examples, but the most famous option is exterior door handles, which have stubbornly remained an extra since 1936. On top of these, a number of options have been always available, so long as the customer knew to ask for them. Many of these exist to make a car more suitable for racing, while others were standard fittings or options designed for other models, but which a customer might spot in the factory and decide he or she fancied.

The most requested unofficial options are as follows (with the date from which they became available):

Trials-style number plate panel (from 1936). This was an upturned rear number plate panel for extra ground clearance.

Rear bumper (from 1950s, standard in 1977).

Aluminium body (from early 1950s, became listed from late 1970s).

Optional extras offered for other models, but only where practical (for example, the factory would not put wire wheels on a Plus 8 because they considered that the hubs were not strong enough).

Battery isolator switch for competition. Usually underneath spare wheel (which is removed for competition) or inside the car.

Underseal (wings were undersealed as standard from the late 1980s).

Re-trimmed steering wheel.